Polycyclic
Hydrocarbons

Volume 2

To

Sir Robert Robinson

Polycyclic Hydrocarbons

E. CLAR

University of Glasgow, Scotland

With a chapter on

Carcinogenesis

by

REGINA SCHOENTAL

Medical Research Council, Carshalton Surrey, England

VOLUME 2

1964

ACADEMIC PRESS *London and New York*

SPRINGER-VERLAG *Berlin-Göttingen-Heidelberg*

ACADEMIC PRESS INC. (LONDON) LTD
Berkeley Square House
Berkeley Square
London, W.1

SPRINGER-VERLAG BERLIN—GÖTTINGEN—HEIDELBERG
Berlin-Wilmersdorf
Heidelberger Platz 3

U.S. Edition published by
ACADEMIC PRESS INC.
111 Fifth Avenue
New York 3, New York

Library of Congress Catalog Card Number: 63–12392

Printed in Great Britain by
Spottiswoode, Ballantyne and Co. Ltd
London and Colchester

Preface

Polycyclic hydrocarbons are of interest in many fields of science: theoretical chemistry, physical chemistry, organic chemistry, dyestuff chemistry and biology. With regards to the latter, I am indebted to Dr. Regina Schoental of the Medical Research Council for the review in this present work of carcinogenesis by polycyclic hydrocarbons.

This book is designed to present the facts in a simple and clear order and to derive empirical rules from them, but it does not present a comprehensive theory about polycyclic hydrocarbons. An attempt is made instead to extend classical symbolism into modern structural chemistry. Thus extensive use is made of Robinson's aromatic sextet, which is applied in an uncompromising and strict way. This quasi-classical attempt is encouraged further by such completely unexpected discoveries as those of Dewar benzene and of the electronic asymmetry of formally symmetric hydrocarbons. How difficult it is to break away from any established way of thinking has been admirably expressed by Kekulé ("Organische Chemie", 1861, Part 1, page 4, translated from German):

"All our ideas are based, to an extent much greater than we ordinarily believe, on those of our predecessors. Our accumulated experience, the notions of which our training has accustomed us to, of whatever kind they have been, influence the course of our thoughts far more than we are willing to admit; only too frequently the following of our regularly used, well trodden way of thinking leads to us overlook the simplest of correlations."

Great emphasis has been given to the comparison of the physical properties of polycyclic hydrocarbons, and in this work as in future research, I have been and shall be guided by another declaration of Kekulé ("Organische Chemie", Part 1, page 158):

"Of course it must be continually kept in mind that one purpose of scientific research is to ascertain the constitution of matter and therefore the positions of atoms; this, however, cannot be achieved unambiguously by studying chemical reactions but on the contrary, only by comparing the physical properties of the existing compounds."

I am indebted to my colleagues Dr. T. H. Goodwin, Dr. J. C. Speakman and Dr. F. Schwarz for valuable advice and help and to Dr. A. McCallum and Mr. J. Stephen for checking the proofs. I also greatly appreciate the efforts of Academic Press to meet my wishes.

E. CLAR

University of Glasgow
April 1964

Contents

PART III

peri-Condensed Hydrocarbons consisting only of Six-membered Rings and derived from Fundamental Systems with Two Benzenoid Rings

CHAPTER 28. Hydrocarbons derived from Diphenyl:

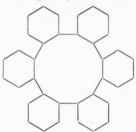
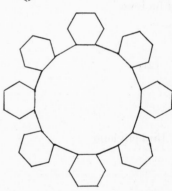
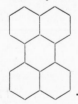

II. 1.2-Benzoperylene

III. 2.3-Benzoperylene

IV. 1.2,7.8-Dibenzoperylene

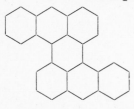

V. 1.2,10.11-Dibenzoperylene

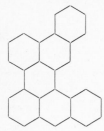

VI. 1.2,11.12-Dibenzoperylene

II—a*

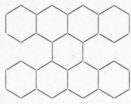
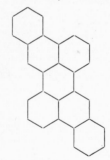

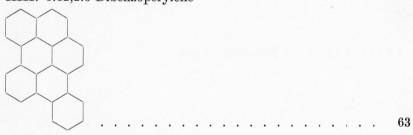

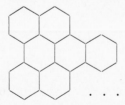

XIX. Anthraceno-(1′.4′:1.12)-perylene

XX. 1.12-*o*-Phenylene-2.3-benzoperylene

XXI. 1.12-*o*-Phenylene-2.3,10.11-dibenzoperylene

XXII. 1.2,3.4,5.6,10.11-Tetrabenzanthanthrene

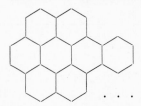

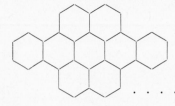

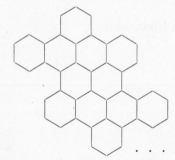

VI. Circumanthracene

CHAPTER 31. Hydrocarbons derived from Pyrene:

I. Pyrene

II. 1.2-Benzopyrene

III. 3.4-Benzopyrene

IV. 1.2,3.4-Dibenzopyrene

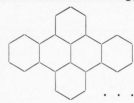

IX. 1.2,4.5,8.9-Tribenzopyrene

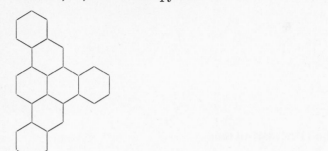

X. 1.2,3.4,9.10-Tribenzopyrene

XI. 1.2,3.4,6.7,8.9-Tetrabenzopyrene

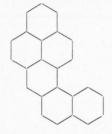

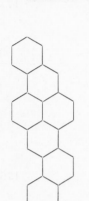 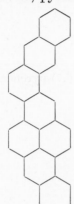

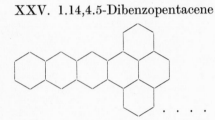

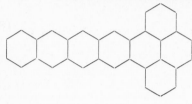
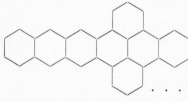
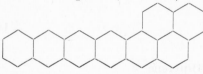
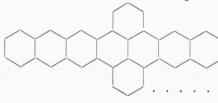
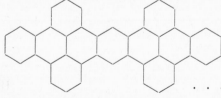

XXXV. 1.18,4.5,9.10,13.14-Tetrabenzoheptacene

XXXVI. Dinaphtho-(1′.7′:2.18);(7″.1″:9.11)-heptacene

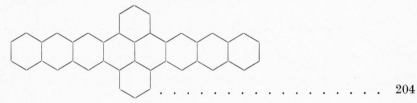

XXXVII. 7.8,17.18-Dibenzoctacene

CHAPTER 32. Hydrocarbons derived from Anthanthrene:

I. Anthanthrene

II. 1.2,7.8-Dibenzanthanthrene

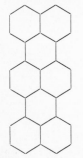

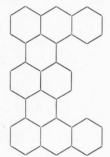
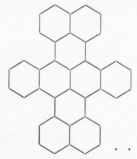

CHAPTER 35. Hydrocarbons derived from 2.3-*peri*-Naphthylenepyrene:

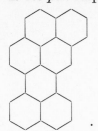

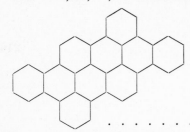
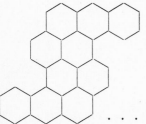

CHAPTER 36. Hydrocarbons derived from Peropyrene:

II—b

VII. 5.6,12.13-Dibenzoperopyrene

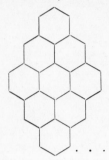

VIII. 2.3,5.6,8.9-Tribenzoperopyrene

IX. 1.14,7.8-Dibenzoperopyrene

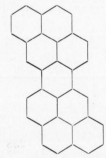

X. 1.14,10.11-Dibenzoperopyrene

XI. 3.4,5.6,7.8-Tribenzoperopyrene

XII. 3.4,5.6,10.11,12.13-Tetrabenzoperopyrene

CONTENTS

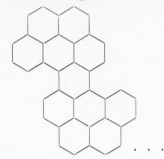

XVI. Dinaphthoperopyrenes

PART V

peri-Condensed Hydrocarbons consisting only of Six-membered Rings and Derived from Fundamental Systems with Four Benzenoid Rings

CHAPTER 37. Hydrocarbons derived from Quaterphenyl:

Quaterphenyl

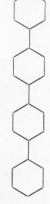

II. Dipyreno-(1′3′:10.2);(1″.3″:5.7)-pyrene

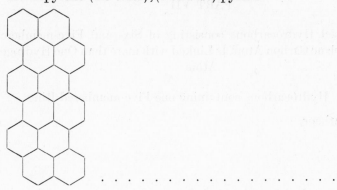

PART VI

peri-Condensed Hydrocarbons consisting only of Six-membered Rings and Derived from Fundamental Systems with Five and Six Benzenoid Rings

CHAPTER 40:

Quinquiphenyl and Sexiphenyl

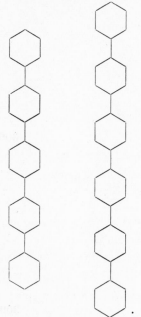

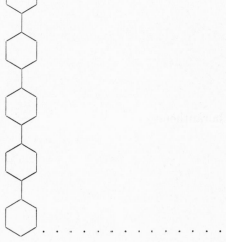

PART VII

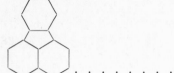

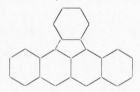

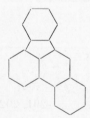

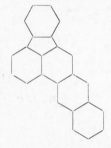
 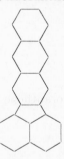

XIV. 2.3-Benzonaphthofluoranthenes

XV. 2.3-*o*-Phenylenepyrene

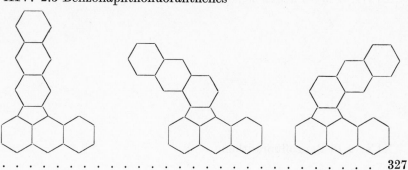

XVI. 2.3-*o*-Phenylene-4.5-benzopyrene

XVII. 2.3-*o*-Phenylenenaphtho-(2″.3″:4.5)-pyrene

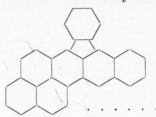
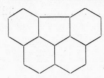

CHAPTER 42. Hydrocarbons containing Two Five-membered Rings:

II. Isorubicene

III. 5.6,11.12-Di-*o*-phenylenetetracene

IV. Rubicene

V. 2.3-Benzorubicene

VI. Dibenzorubicenes

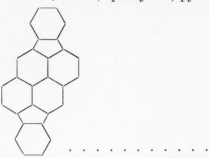
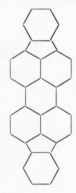
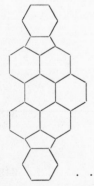

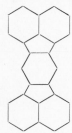

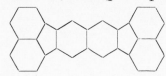

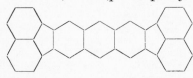

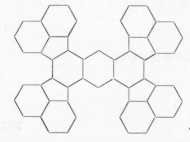

PART VIII

peri-Condensed Hydrocarbons consisting of Six-membered Rings in which One Carbon Atom Is Linked with Two Hydrogen Atoms

CHAPTER 45:

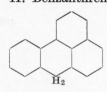
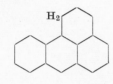 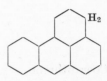
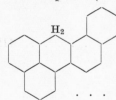

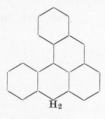

PART IX

peri-Condensed Hydrocarbons consisting of Six-membered Rings in which Two Carbon Atoms Are Linked with Two Hydrogen Atoms

CHAPTER 46:

II. 5.6-Dihydro-1.12,10.11-dibenzotetracene

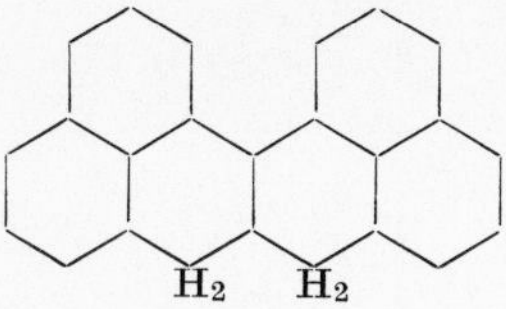

III. 3.11-Dihydro-1.2,4.5,6.7-tribenzotetracene

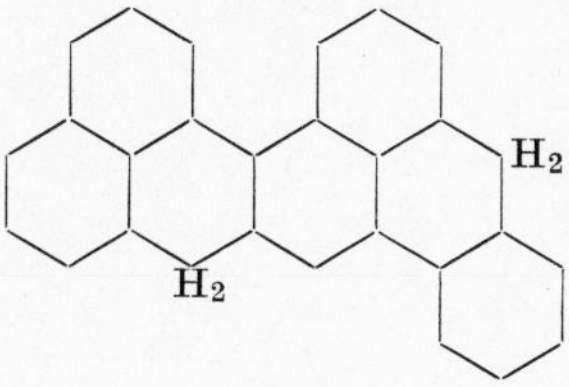

IV. 5.7-Dihydro-1.14,11.12-dibenzopentacene

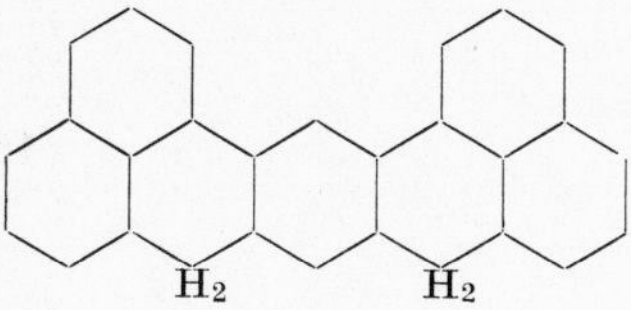

PART X

Hydrocarbons consisting of Six-membered Rings which have Formally
Fixed Double Bonds

CHAPTER 47:

I. Zethrene

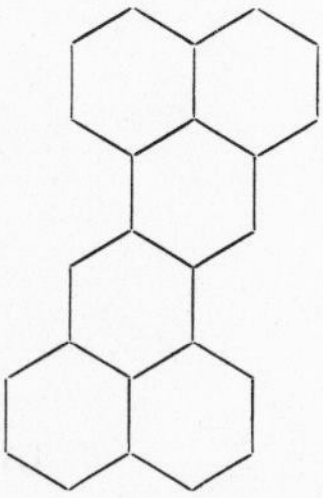

II. 5.6-Benzozethrene

III. 4.5,11.12-Dibenzozethrene

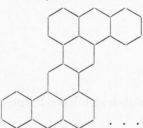

IV. 5.6,12.13-Dibenzozethrene

V. Heptazethrene

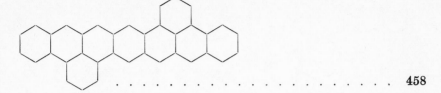
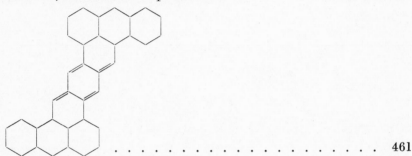
PART XI

Hydrocarbons consisting of Five- and Six-membered Rings which Have
Formally Fixed Double Bonds

III. Dianthraceno-(1′.9′:1.3);(1″.9″:4.6)-pentalene

Contents of Volume I

PART I

General

PART II

kata-Annellated Hydrocarbons

PART III

peri-Condensed Hydrocarbons consisting only of Six-membered Rings and derived from Fundamental Systems with Two Benzenoid Rings

CHAPTER 28

Hydrocarbons derived from Diphenyl

I. DIPHENYL

Diphenyl is formed in numerous pyrolyses using benzene or benzene derivatives, acetylene and other unsaturated hydrocarbons. It is therefore a main constituent of coal tar.[1]

The most important synthesis of diphenyl is the pyrolysis of benzene which can be carried out in many ways using catalysts or oxidizing agents like lead dioxide, antimony trisulphide, antimony trichloride, arsenic trichloride, tin tetrachloride and others. A very convenient application of the pyrolysis is the use of an electrically heated glowing wire in benzene vapour.[2]

There are also numerous syntheses of diphenyl known, but only a few are recommended for practical application, e.g. the condensation of iodobenzene with copper powder,[3] the reduction of phenyl magnesium bromide with cuprous chloride,[4] the condensation of bromobenzene with sodium[5] and the reduction of benzene diazonium salts with copper powder or copper compounds.[6]

Diphenyl crystallizes from alcohol in large colourless leaflets (m.p. 70°, b.p. 256° of density 1·180). The absorption spectrum is given in Fig. 81. It gives adducts with antimony trichloride, antimony tribromide, antimony tri-iodide and picryl chloride.

Diphenyl adds two atoms of sodium in liquid ammonia and yields 1,4-dihydrodiphenyl on hydrolysis.[7] Lithium forms a paramagnetic monoadduct.[8] Hydrogenation with hydrogen and nickel gives phenylcyclohexane (I).[9] Hydrogenation under pressure yields dicyclohexyl

(I)   (II)

(II).[10] Hydrogenation with sodium in amyl alcohol leads to phenylcyclo-hexane.[11] Hydrogen and platinum oxide give dicyclohexyl and phenyl-cyclohexane.[12] Ozone reacts with the formation of diphenyltetra-ozonide.[13]

Diphenyl and chlorine in the presence of antimonium pentachloride give 2-chlorodiphenyl, 4-chlorodiphenyl and 4,4'-dichlorodiphenyl.[14] Iodine as catalyst gives also 4,4'-dichlorodiphenyl.[15] Chlorination at

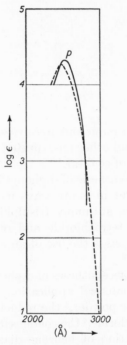

FIG. 81. Absorption spectrum of diphenyl in methanol–ethanol: at +18°, 2500 (4·15); at −180°, 2530 (4·23) (E. Clar, *Spectrochimica Acta* **4**, 116 (1950)).

higher temperatures leads to perchlorodiphenyl.[16] 4-Bromodiphenyl is obtained by bromination in carbon disulphide.[17] 4,4'-Dibromodiphenyl is formed with an excess of bromine in water.[18] The iodination of diphenyl can be carried out with iodine in nitric acid or iodine sulphide in nitric acid and results in the formation of 4,4'-di-iododiphenyl.[19] Nitration in acetic acid gives 2- and 4-nitrodiphenyl.[20] 2,4-Dinitrodiphenyl, 4,4'-di-nitrodiphenyl and 2,2'-dinitrodiphenyl can be prepared with fuming nitric acid or a mixture of nitric acid and sulphuric acid.[21] 2,4,4'-trinitro-diphenyl is formed with ethyl nitrate in sulphuric acid.[22] 2,4,2',4'-Tetra-nitrodiphenyl results from an excess of nitric acid and sulphuric acid.[23]

Sulphonation yields diphenyl-4-sulphonic acid and diphenyl-4,4'-disulphonic acid.[24]

Several Friedel–Crafts reactions with diphenyl have been reported. Oxalyl chloride and aluminium chloride give diphenyl-4-carboxylic acid.[25] Acetyl chloride yields 4-acetyl- and 4,4'-diacetyl-diphenyl.[26] Cyclohexene and aluminium chloride give 4-cyclohexenyl and 4,4'-dicyclohexenyldiphenyl.[27] Terephthalyl chloride forms 1,4-di-(4'-phenyl-benzoyl)-benzene.[28] Phthalyl chloride gives 3,3-bi-diphenylyl-phthalide.[29] Phthalic anhydride yields the 4-keto acid or the 4,4'-diketo acid according to the conditions applied.[30]

Diphenyl forms benzoic acid when oxidized with chromic acid in acetic acid.[31] Among the numerous homologues of diphenyl those with substituents in o-positions are of particular interest, as in these the rotation of the two phenyl rings is prevented. Their absorption spectra show the complexes of the two independent moieties (see p. 128). Deuterodiphenyls have also been prepared.[32]

REFERENCES

1. Fittig, R. and Büchner, E., Ber. dtsch. chem. Ges. 8, 22 (1875); Schulze, K. E., Ber. dtsch. chem. Ges. 17, 1203 (1884); Meyer, H. and Hoffmann, A., Mh. Chem. 39, 121 (1918).
2. Löb, W., Z. electr. Chem. 7, 903 (1902); Ber. dtsch. chem. Ges. 34, 917 (1901); Meyer, H. and Hoffmann, A., Mh. Chem. 37, 681 (1916).
3. Ullmann, F. and Meyer, G. M., Liebigs Ann. 332, 40 (1904).
4. Sakellarios, E. and Kyrimis, T., Ber. dtsch. chem. Ges. 57, 324 (1924); Krizewski, J. and Turner, E. E., J. chem. Soc. 115, 560 (1919).
5. Fittig, R., Liebigs Ann. 121, 363 (1862); 132, 201 (1864).
6. Gattermann, L. and Ehrhart, R., Ber. dtsch. chem. Ges. 23, 1226 (1890); Gerngross, O. and Dunkel, M., Ber. dtsch. chem. Ges. 57, 742 (1924).
7. Hückel, W. and Schwen, R., Chem. Ber. 89, 150 (1956).
8. Eisch, J. J. and Kaska, W. C., J. org. Chem. 27, 3745 (1962).
9. Eijkman, J. F., C. 1903 II, 989.
10. Ipatjew, W., Ber. dtsch. chem. Ges. 40, 1286 (1907).
11. Bamberger, E. and Lodter, W., Ber. dtsch. chem. Ges. 20, 3077 (1887).
12. Hückel, W., Liebigs Ann. 477, 118 (1930).
13. Harries, C. and Weiss, V., Liebigs Ann. 343, 374 (1905).
14. Kramers, J. G., Liebigs Ann. 189, 142 (1877).
15. Ruoff, G., Ber. dtsch. chem. Ges. 9, 1491 (1876).
16. Weber, A. and Söllscher, C., Ber. dtsch. chem. Ges. 16, 883 (1883); Merz, V. and Weith, W. Ber. dtsch. chem. Ges. 16, 2882 (1883).
17. Schultz, G., Liebigs Ann. 174, 207 (1874).
18. Fittig, R., Liebigs Ann. 132, 204 (1864).
19. Willgerodt, C. and Hilgenberg, G., Ber. dtsch. chem. Ges. 42, 3832 (1909); Novikov, A. N., J. gen. Chem. U.S.S.R. 29, 60 (1959).
20. Hübner, H. and Lüddens, H., Ber. dtsch. chem. Ges. 8, 871 (1875); Liebigs Ann. 209, 341 (1881); Schultz, G., Liebigs Ann. 174, 210 (1874); Schultz, G., Schmidt, H. and Strasser, H., Liebigs Ann. 207, 352 (1881); van Hove, T., Bull. Acad. Belg. (5) 8, 507, 527 (1923); Dewar, M. J. S., Mole, T., Urch, D. S. and Warford, E. W. T., J. chem. Soc. 3572 (1956).

21. Schultz, G., *Liebigs Ann.* **174**, 221 (1874); Fittig, R., *Liebigs Ann.* **124**, 276, 285 (1862); Bell, F. and Kenyon, J., *J. chem. Soc.* 2707 (1926).
22. Raudnitz, H., *Ber. dtsch. chem. Ges.* **60**, 740 (1927).
23. Losanitsch, S. M., *Ber. dtsch. chem. Ges.* **4**, 405 (1872); Ullmann, F. and Bielecki, J., *Ber. dtsch. chem. Ges.* **34**, 2178 (1901).
24. Engelhardt, A. and Latschinow, P., *C.* 548 (1871); Fittig, R., *Liebigs Ann.* **132**, 209 (1864).
25. Liebermann, C. and Zuffa, M., *Ber. dtsch. chem. Ges.* **44**, 857 (1911).
26. Ferris, C. V. and Turner, E. E., *J. chem. Soc.* **117**, 1147 (1920); Dilthey, W., *J. prakt. Chem.* (2) **101**, 194, 195 (1920).
27. Bodroux, D., *Ann. chim. Fr.* (10) **11**, 527 (1928); Basford, F. R., *J. chem. Soc.* 1593 (1936).
28. Schlenk, W. and Brauns, M., *Ber. dtsch. chem. Ges.* **46**, 4063 (1913).
29. Elbs, K., *J. prakt. Chem.* (2) **41**, 147 (1890); Kaiser, J., *Liebigs Ann.* **257**, 95 (1890).
30. Scholl, R. and Neovius, W., *Ber. dtsch. chem. Ges.* **44**, 1078 (1911).
31. Schultz, G., *Liebigs Ann.* **174**, 206 (1874).
32. Akawie, R. I., *J. org. Chem.* **26**, 243 (1961).

II. FLUORENE

Fluorene must be considered to be a homologue of diphenyl, and it reacts accordingly. It is best prepared from coal-tar, where it is abundantly present.[1] It has also been obtained by pyrolysis of acetylene.[2] It is formed by pyrolysis of diphenylmethane (I).[3]

(I)   (II)   (III)   (IV)   (V)

A similar pyrolysis starts from 2-methyldiphenyl (III).[4] Catalytic cyclodehydrogenation with platinum–charcoal at 300° also yields fluorene from dicyclohexylmethane (IV), diphenylmethane and dicyclohexylketone.[5] 2,2′-Dibromodiphenyl and methylene bromide in ether react with sodium to give fluorene.[6]

Fluorene crystallizes from alcohol in colourless leaflets (m.p. 116°). It distils at 293–295° and is easily sublimable. It forms molecular compounds with dinitrobenzene, dinitrotoluene, trinitroxylene, trinitrocresol, picric acid, picryl chloride and tetranitronaphthalene. The absorption spectrum is given in Fig. 82.

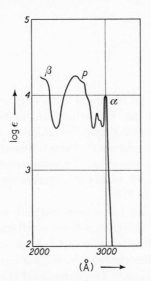

FIG. 82. Absorption spectrum of fluorene in alcohol: α, 3005 (3·99), 2890 (3·75); p, 2610 (4·23); β, 2080 (4·55).

Fluorene can be hydrogenated with hydriodic acid and red phosphorus and yields decahydrofluorene and perhydrofluorene.[7] The same compounds are obtained by catalytic hydrogenation under pressure.[8]

Fluorene forms a hydroperoxide (VI) with oxygen.[9] Maleic anhydride is added in an analogous way to form (VII).[10]

(VI)

(VII)

(VIII)

Fluorene forms the potassium compound (V) when melted with potassium hydroxide,[11] and with sodium the corresponding sodium compound.[11] Lithium gives the mono-Li compound.[12] These metal compounds can be used for many syntheses.

The hydrogen atoms in the methylene group of fluorene show considerable reactivity. Dehydrogenation leads first to the colourless compound (VIII) and then to the orange-red bisdiphenylene ethylene (IX).[13]

(IX)   (X)

2-Chlorofluorene can be obtained with sulphuryl chloride,[14] or with chlorine in cold chloroform.[15] Further chlorination yields 2,7-dichlorofluorene and 2,4,7-trichlorofluorene.[15, 16] 9-Bromofluorene is formed from fluorene and tetrabromophenol.[17] Direct bromination gives 2-bromofluorene, 2,7-dibromofluorene[15] and a tribromofluorene.[18]

Nitration in acetic acid yields 2-nitrofluorene,[19] 2,7-dinitrofluorene and 2,5-dinitrofluorene.[15, 18, 20]

Friedel–Crafts reactions have been carried out to form 2-benzoylfluorene[21] with benzoyl chloride, o-fluorenoylbenzoic acid with phthalic anhydride and 2-fluorenylacrylic acid with maleic anhydride and aluminium chloride.[22] Fluorene can be sulphonated with chlorosulphonic acid in chloroform solution.[23] The same acid is obtained in acetic acid with sulphuric acid.[24] Fluorene-2,7-disulphonic acid is formed besides isomers with sulphuric acid at 100°.[25] Fluorene with ^{14}C in position 9 has been synthesized.[26]

Fluorene can be readily oxidized to fluorenone (X) with sodium dichromate in acetic acid.[27] Fluorenone forms yellow crystals from alcohol (m.p. 84–86°), which give a deep red-violet solution with concentrated sulphuric acid.

There are numerous benzologues of fluorene known. Some of them are of interest in connection with their carcinogenic activity. 1.2-Benzofluorene and 2.3-benzofluorene can be prepared on a commercial scale from coal-tar.[28]

(1)   (2)   (3)

(1) Graebe, *Ber. dtsch. chem. Ges.* **27**, 954 (1904); **29**, 826 (1896).
(2) Thiele and Wanscheidt, *Liebigs Ann.* **376**, 276 (1910).
(3) Cook *et al., J. chem. Soc.* 1322 (1935).

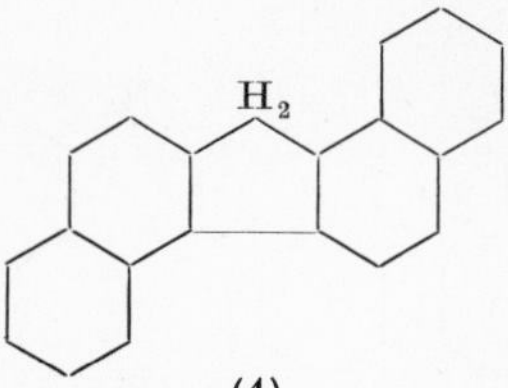

(4)

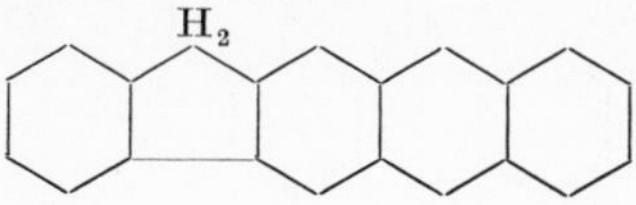

(5)

(4) Swain and Todd, *J. chem. Soc.* 674 (1941); Bergmann and Szmuszkovicz, *J. Amer. chem. Soc.* **75**, 353 (1953).
(5) de Barry Barnett, Goodway and Watson, *Ber. dtsch. chem. Ges.* **66**, 1880 (1933).

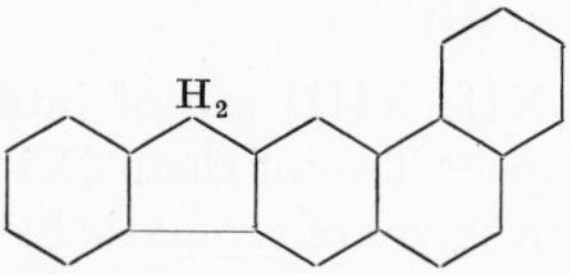

(6)

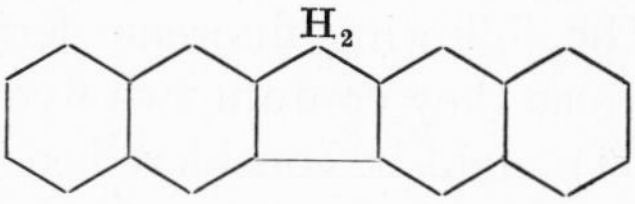

(7)

(6) Cook *et al.*, *J. chem. Soc.* 1323 (1935).
(7) Martin, *J. chem. Soc.* 679 (1941).

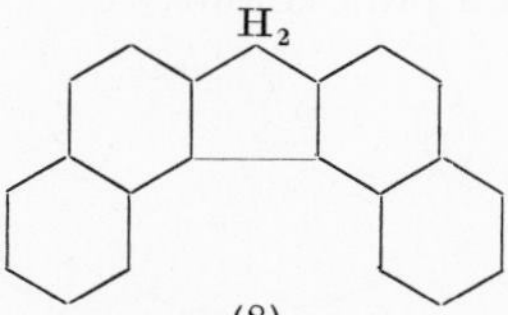

(8)

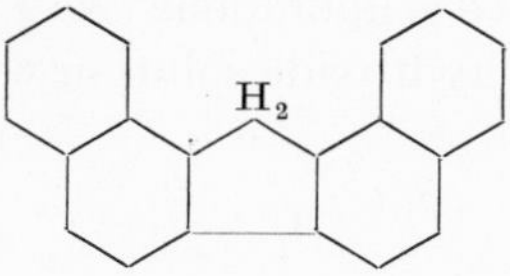

(9)

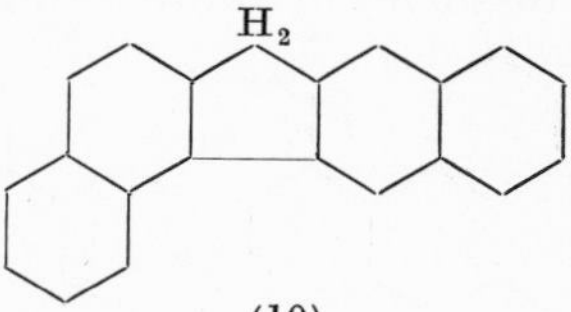

(10)

(8) Martin, *J. chem. Soc.* 679 (1941).
(9) Schmidlin and Massini, *Ber. dtsch. chem. Ges.* **42**, 2387 (1909).
(10) Martin, *J. chem. Soc.* 671 (1941).

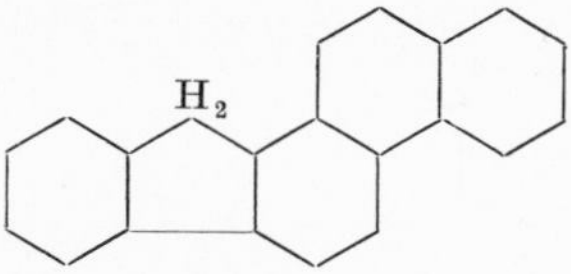

(11)

(11) Bamberger and Chattaway, *Liebigs Ann.* **284**, 70 (1895); Cook, *J. chem. Soc.* 685 (1941).

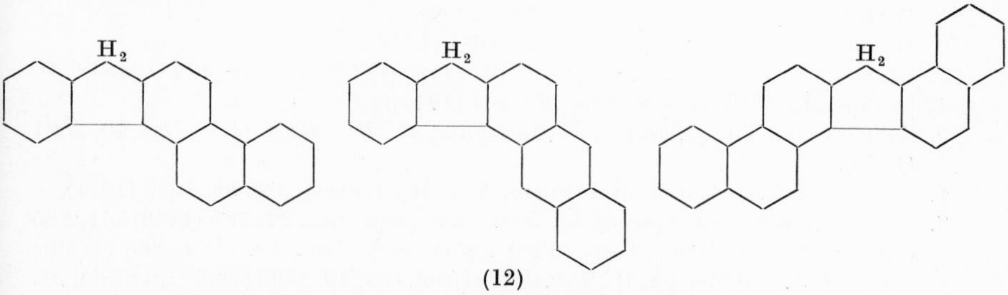

(12)

(12) Buu-Hoï and Cagniant, *Rev. sci. Instrum.* **80**, 319 (1942).
II—1*

(13) (14) (15)

(13) Martin and Vassart, *Bull. Soc. chim. Belg.* **60**, 325 (1951).
(14) DeRidder, Matzner and Martin, *Bull. Soc. chim. Belg.* **69**, 534 (1960); Martin and Vassart, *Bull. Soc. chim. Belg.* **60**, 325 (1951).
(15) DeRidder, Glazei-Tarasiejska and Martin, *Bull. Soc. chim. Belg.* **69**, 551 (1960); Martin and Vassart, *Bull. Soc. chim. Belg.* **60**, 325 (1951).

The following fluorene derivatives (XI, XII, XIII) are of interest because they contain two five-membered rings.[29] Two of them (XI and XIII) might be considered to be dihydro derivatives of aromatic hydrocarbons with fixed double bonds. The double fluorenone (XIV) gives a blue vat with alkaline sodium dithionite solution. The formation of a vat indicates that the parent hydrocarbon is capable of existence. An interesting fluorene derivative is fluoradene (XV) which is so acidic that it dissolves in dilute sodium hydroxide solution with a pink colour.[30]

(XI) (XII) (XIII)

(XIV) (XV)

REFERENCES

1. Berthelot, M., *Ann. chim. Fr.* (4) **12**, 222 (1876).
2. Meyer, R., *Ber. dtsch. chem. Ges.* **45**, 1631 (1912).
3. Graebe, C., *Ber. dtsch. chem. Ges.* **7**, 1624 (1874); *Liebigs Ann.* **174**, 194 (1874).
4. Orchin, M., *J. Amer. chem. Soc.* **67**, 504 (1945).
5. Zelinsky, N., Titz, I. and Gawerdowskaja, M., *Ber. dtsch. chem. Ges.* **59**, 2591 (1926).
6. Dobbie, J. J., Fox, J. J. and Gauge, A. J. H., *J. chem. Soc.* **99**, 1620 (1911).
7. Liebermann, C. and Spiegel, L., *Ber. dtsch. chem. Ges.* **22**, 781 (1889); **41**, 885 (1908); **42**, 919 (1909); Guye, P. A., *Bull. Soc. chim. Fr.* (3) 4, 266 (1890); Schmidt, J. and Mezger, R., *Ber. dtsch. chem. Ges.* **40**, 4566 (1907); Schmidt, J. and Fischer, E., *Ber. dtsch. chem. Ges.* **41**, 4228 (1908).

8. Ipatjew, W., *Ber. dtsch. chem. Ges.* **42**, 2093 (1909); Ssadikow, W. S. and Michailow, A. K., *Ber. dtsch. chem. Ges.* **61**, 1792 (1928).

9. Hock, H., Lang, S. and Knauel, G., *Ber. dtsch. chem. Ges.* **83**, 229 (1950).

10. I.G. Farbinindustrie AG, German Patent 607380 (1933); *Chem. Zbl.* **1935 I**, 2087; Alder, K., Pascher, F. and Vagt, H., *Ber. dtsch. chem. Ges.* **75**, 1501 (1942).

11. Weissgerber, R., *Ber. dtsch. chem. Ges.* **34**, 1659 (1901); *Ber. dtsch. chem. Ges.* **41**, 2914 (1908).

12. Eisch, J. J. and Kaska, W. C. *J. org. Chem.* **27**, 3745 (1962).

13. de la Harpe, C. and van Dorp, W. A., *Ber. dtsch. chem. Ges.* **8**, 1049 (1875); Graebe, C., *Ber. dtsch. chem. Ges.* **25**, 3146 (1892); Graebe, C. and von Mantz, B., *Liebigs Ann.* **290**, 241 (1896).

14. Streitwieser, A., *J. Amer. chem. Soc.* **66**, 2127 (1944).

15. Courtot, C. and Vignati, C., *C. R. Acad. Sci., Paris* **184**, 608, 1179; *Ann. chim. Fr.* (10) **14**, 52, 55, 58, 59, 83, 98 (1930); *Bl.* (4) **41**, 59, 60 (1927).

16. Sieglitz, A. and Schatzkes, J., *Ber. dtsch. chem. Ges.* **54**, 2073 (1921); **53**, 1236 (1920).

17. Wittig, G. and Vidal, F., *Ber. dtsch. chem. Ges.* **81**, 368 (1948).

18. Courtot, C. and Moreaux, J., *C. R. Acad. Sci., Paris* **217**, 453, 506 (1943).

19. Strasburger, J., *Ber. dtsch. chem. Ges.* **17**, 107 (1884); Diels, O., *Ber. dtsch. chem. Ges.* **34**, 1759 (1901).

20. Fittig, R. and Schmitz, A., *Liebigs Ann.* **193**, 140 (1878); Morgan, G. T. and Thomason, R. W., *J. chem. Soc.* 2693 (1926).

21. Fortner, M., *Mh. Chem.* **23**, 922 (1902); Perrier, G., *Mh. Chem.* **24**, 591 (1903).

22. Goldschmiedt, G. and Lipschitz, A., *Ber. dtsch. chem. Ges.* **36**, 4035 (1903); de Barry Barnett, E., Goodway, N. F. and Watson, J. W., *Ber. dtsch. chem. Ges.* **66**, 1880 (1933); Kretov, A. E. and Lutvinov, V. V., *J. gen. Chem. U.S.S.R.* **31**, 2682 (1961).

23. Hodgkinson, W. R. and Matthews, F. E., *J. chem. Soc.* **43**, 166 (1883); Courtot, C. and Geoffroy, R., *C. R. Acad. Sci., Paris* **178**, 2261 (1924).

24. Wedekind, E. and Stüsser, R., *Ber. dtsch. chem. Ges.* **56**, 1561 (1923).

25. Schmidt, J., Retzlaff, F. and Haid, A., *Liebigs Ann.* **390**, 217 (1912).

26. Harris, A. S., White, E. N. and McNeil, C., *J. chem. Soc.* 4216 (1955).

27. Graebe, C. and Rateanu, A. S., *Liebigs Ann.* **279**, 258 (1894).

28. Kruber, O., *Ber. dtsch. chem. Ges.* **70**, 1556 (1937).

29. Deuschel, W., *Helv. chim. Acta* **35**, 1774 (1952); Chardonnes, L., Schmitz, M. and Ritter, R., *Helv. chim. Acta* **38**, 393 (1955); **39**, 1981 (1956); Ebel, F. and Deuschel, W., *Ber. dtsch. chem. Ges.* **89**, 2794 (1957); Behr, O. M., Eglinton, J., Galbraith, A. R. and Raphael, R. A., *J. chem. Soc.* 3614 (1960).

30. Rapoport, H. and Smolinsky, G., *J. Amer. chem. Soc.* **80**, 2910 (1958).

III. BIPHENYLENE

(*Diphenylene*)

Biphenylene was first synthesized from *o,o'*-dibromodiphenyl (I) or *o,o'*-diphenyliodonium iodide (II) by distillation with cuprous oxide.

The yield, however, is only 5%.[1] It can be obtained from the Grignard compound of (I) with cupric chloride.[2]

o,o'-Di-iododiphenyl gives a di-lithium compound (IV) from which the mercury compound (V) can be obtained. The latter yields biphenylene by sublimation with silver powder.[3] o-Bromoiodobenzene gives biphenylene with magnesium.[4]

Biphenylene is formed by pyrolysis or irradiation of phthalyl peroxide (VI).[5] The cyclic acetylene compound (VII) gives biphenylene when treated with potassium butoxide.[6]

Biphenylene crystallizes in straw-yellow needles from alcohol (m.p. 110°). They form an orange-yellow picrate which crystallizes in needles (m.p. 122°). The absorption spectrum is given in Fig. 83. The aromatic (resonance) energy of biphenylene amounts to 17·4 kcal which is 64 kcal less than the aromatic energy of diphenyl (81·4 kcal).[7] The X-ray structure of diphenylene has also been determined.[8] There is apparently a high degree of bond fixation in biphenylene in favour of the Kekulé-structure (III).[9]

The most striking reaction of biphenylene is its fission to diphenyl by hydrogenation with hydrogen and nickel or copper. Oxidation with chromic anhydride or dilute nitric acid yields phthalic acid. The structure of biphenylene was proved by the synthesis of 2,7-dimethylbiphenylene by three different methods. 4,4′-Dimethyldiphenyl-2,2′-di-iodonium iodide (VIII) or 4,4′-dimethyl-2,2′-dibromodiphenyl both gave 2,7-di-

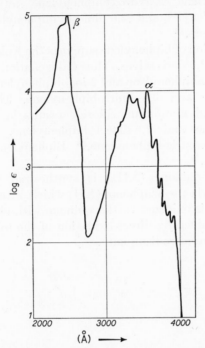

FIG. 83. Absorption spectrum of biphenylene in hexane: α, 3920 (2·34), 3850 (2·40), 3790 (2·52), 3740 (2·84), 3680 (3·35), 3560 (4·00), 3430 (3·90), 3330 (3·95); β, 2490 (5·00) (Carr, E. P., Pickett, L. W. and Voris, D., *J. Amer. chem. Soc.* **63**, 3230 (1941)).

methylbiphenylene (IX) when distilled with cuprous oxide. The latter has also been obtained from 3,3′-dimethyldiphenyl-2,2′-iodonium iodide (X).

(VIII)   Cu₂O   (X)

(IX)

Several derivatives of biphenylene were prepared from diphenyl derivatives: 1-methylbiphenylene, 2-methylbiphenylene, 2-methoxy-biphenylene, 1-methoxybiphenylene, 1,8-dimethoxybiphenylene, 2,7-dimethoxybiphenylene, 2-hydroxybiphenylene, tetramethylbiphenyl-ene, 2,2'-biphenylenyl[10] and 2,6-dimethylbiphenylene[11] and 2,3-di-methoxybiphenylene.[12]

Direct substitution of biphenylene supports the Kekulé structure (III) and gives 2- and 2,6-derivatives. Thus halogenation yields 2-chlorobi-phenylene, 2-bromobiphenylene and 2-iodobiphenylene. Nitration gives 2-nitrobiphenylene and 2,6-dinitrobiphenylene. The reaction with acetyl chloride and aluminium chloride results in the formation of 2-acetylbiphenylene and 2,6-diacetylbiphenylene. Mercuric acetate gives 2-acetoxymercuric-biphenylene.[13] Biphenylene-2-aldehyde has also been prepared.[14]

Biphenylene-2,3-quinone (XIII) is synthesized from 2-hydroxy-biphenylene (XI) via the azophenol (XII) which, after reduction to the amino compound, is oxidized to the quinone with chromium trioxide. It can also be obtained by direct oxidation of the hydroxy-compound (XI) with potassium nitrodisulphate.

(XI)   (XII)   (XIII)

(XIV)

2.3-Biphenylene-2,3-quinone (XIII) crystallizes from ethanol in orange needles which melt at 216–217°. It has remarkable stability and gives an azine with o-phenylenediamine. Treatment with acetic anhydride and sulphuric acid leads to the unusual tetra-acetate (XIV).[15]

REFERENCES

1. Lothrop, W. C., *J. Amer. chem. Soc.* **63**, 1187 (1941); Baker, W., Boarland, M. P. V. and McOmie, J. F. W., *J. chem. Soc.* 1476 (1954).
2. Rapson, W. S., Shuttleworth, R. G. and van Niekerk, J. N., *J. chem. Soc.* 326 (1943).
3. Wittig, G. and Herwig, W., *Ber. dtsch. chem. Ges.* **87**, 1511 (1954).

4. Heaney, H. F., Mann, G. and Millar, I. T., *J. chem. Soc.* 3930 (1957).
5. Wittig, G. and Ebel, H. F., *Liebigs Ann.* **650**, 20 (1961).
6. Wolovsky, R. and Sondheimer, F., *J. Amer. chem. Soc.* **84**, 2844 (1962).
7. Cass, R. C., Springall, H. D. and Quincey, P. G., *J. chem. Soc.* 1188 (1955); Bedford, A. F., Carey, J. G., Millar, I. T., Mortimer, C. T. and Springall, H. D., *J. chem. Soc.* 3895 (1962).
8. Mak, T. C. W. and Trotter, J., *J. chem. Soc.* 3 (1962); Waser, J. and Chia-Si Lu, *J. Amer. chem. Soc.* **66**, 2035 (1944).
9. Longuet-Higgins, H. C., *Proc. chem. Soc.* 157 (1957); Baker, W., McOmie, J. F. W., Preston, D. R. and Rogers, V., *J. chem. Soc.* 414 (1960).
10. Baker, W., Barton, J. W. and McOmie, J. F. W., *J. chem. Soc.* 2658 (1958).
11. Hart, F. A. and Mann, F. G., *J. chem. Soc.* 3943 (1957).
12. Blatchly, J. M., McOmie, J. F. W. and Watts, M. L., *J. chem. Soc.* 5085 (1962).
13. Baker, W., Boarland, M. P. V. and McOmie, J. F. W., *J. chem. Soc.* 1476 (1954); Baker, W., Barton, J. W. and McOmie, J. F. W., *J. chem. Soc.* 2666 (1958).
14. McOmie, J. F. W. and Thatte, S. D., *J. chem. Soc.* 5298 (1962).
15. Blatchly, J. M., McOmie, J. F. W. and Thatte, S. C., *J. chem. Soc.* 5090 (1962).

IV. 1.2-BENZOBIPHENYLENE

ω-Tetrabromo-o-xylene (I) can be reduced to the cyclobutene derivative (II) with iodide solution. Further reduction with zinc yields the obviously unstable benzocyclobutadiene (III), which dimerizes to the dihydro derivative (IV). The latter can be dehydrogenated to 1.2-benzobiphenylene (V) with bromosuccinimide.[1]

Another synthesis starts from o,o-diamino-1-phenylnaphthalene (VI). Diazotization and treatment with iodide gives the di-iodo compound

(VII). Cyclization with cuprous oxide yields 1.2-benzobiphenylene (V). The iodo compound can be transformed into the di-lithium compound (VIII) which gives the mercury derivative (IX). Sublimation with silver powder at 360° also yields 1.2-benzobiphenylene (V).[2]

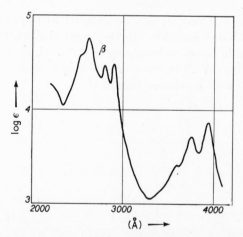

1.2-Benzobiphenylene forms yellow needles (m.p. 72°) which sublime *in vacuo* at about 100°. Its solutions are unstable under the influence of

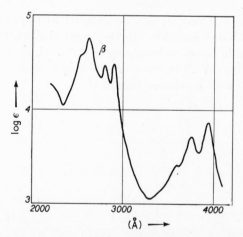

FIG. 84. Absorption spectrum of 1.2-benzobiphenylene in ethanol: 3930 (3·87), 3750 (3·71), 3590 (3·41); β, 2910 (4·48), 2790 (4·47); 2620 (4·77); 2540 (4·58).[1]

light. It forms a molecular compound with trinitrobenzene. The absorption spectrum is given in Fig. 84. Hydrogenation of 1.2-benzobiphenylene with hydrogen and nickel leads to a mixture of 1-phenylnaphthalene and 2-phenylnaphthalene. Oxidation with chromic acid gives benzophenone-o,o'-dicarboxylic anhydride (X).

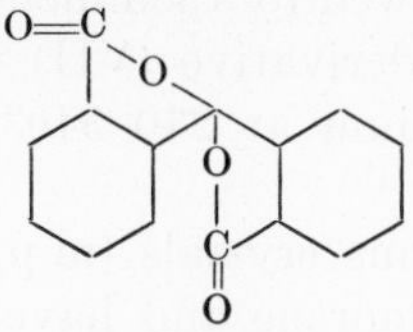

(X)

REFERENCES

1. Cava, M. P. and Napier, D. R., *J. Amer. chem. Soc.* **79**, 1701 (1956); **80**, 2255 (1958).
2. Cava, M. P. and Stucker, J. F., *J. Amer. chem. Soc.* **77**, 6022 (1955).

V. 2.3-BENZOBIPHENYLENE

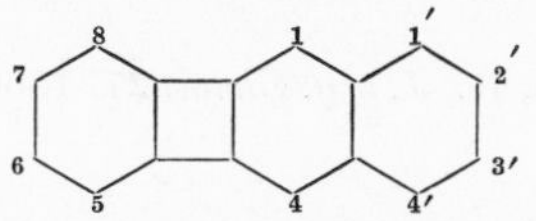

Treatment of the bromo compound (I) with potassium butoxide gives dibromobenzobiphenylene (II) and the tetrabromo compound (III). Addition of lithium to (II) followed by treatment with methanol yields 2.3-benzobiphenylene (IV).[1]

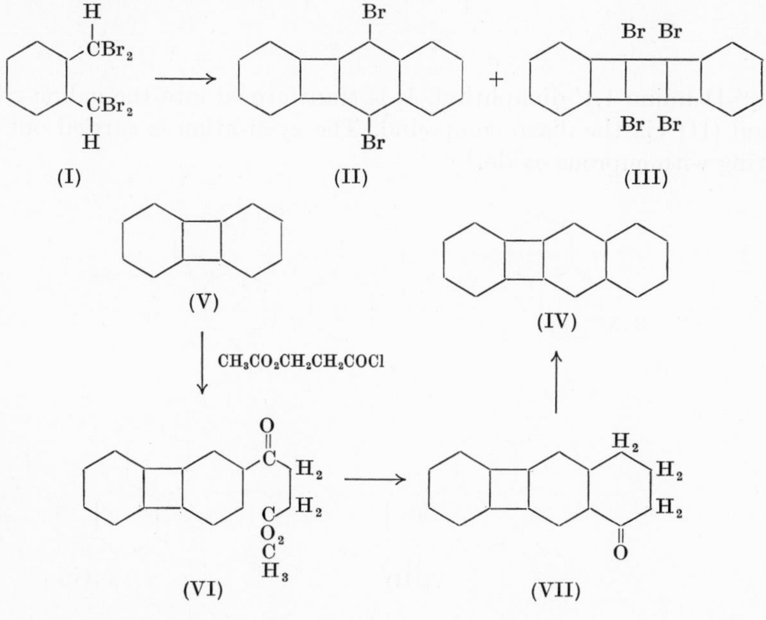

(I)   (II)   (III)

(V)   (IV)

$CH_3CO_2CH_2CH_2COCl$

(VI)   (VII)

Another synthesis starts from biphenylene (V), which reacts with carbomethoxypropionyl chloride and aluminium chloride to give the ester (VI). Hydrolysis, followed by Clemmensen reduction and cyclization, yield the tetrahydro-derivative (VII) which, after reduction, is dehydrogenated with selenium at 270–340° to 2.3-benzobiphenylene (IV).[2]

2.3-Benzobiphenylene forms crystals (m.p. 242–243°) which form a red complex with trinitrofluorene and have the following absorption bands: 3860 (3·78), 3670 (3·83), 3410 (3·71), 3310 (3·68), 2960 (4·55), 2850 (4·40), 2640 (4·89), 2550 (4·87). Catalytic hydrogenation gives 2-phenylnaphthalene. 1,4-Diphenyl-2.3-benzobiphenylene has also been synthesized.[3]

REFERENCES

1. Jensen, F. A. and Coleman, W. E., *Tetrahedron Letters* **20**, 7 (1959).
2. Baker, W., Barton, J. W., McOmie, J. F. W. and Searle, R. J. G., *J. chem. Soc.* 2633 (1962).
3. Cava, M. P. and Pohlke, R., *J. org. Chem.* **27**, 1564 (1962).

VI. 1.2,7.8-DIBENZOBIPHENYLENE

2,2'-Diamino-1,1'-dinaphthyl (I) is transformed into the iodine compound (II) via the diazo compound. The cyclization is carried out by heating with cuprous oxide.[1]

(I)   (II)

(III)   (IV)

1.2,7.8-Dibenzobiphenylene (III) crystallizes as deep red needles (m.p. 136·8–138·9°). The absorption spectrum is given in Fig. 85. It is less stable than 1.2-benzobiphenylene and decomposes during sublimation at 160°. Hydrogenation with hydrogen and nickel gives 2,2′-dinaphthyl (IV).

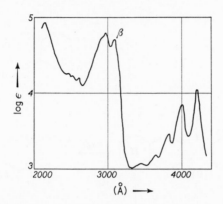

FIG. 85. Absorption spectrum of 1.2,7.8-dibenzobiphenylene in ethanol: 4200 (4·05), 4000 (3·86), 3820 (3·47), 3650 (3·20), 3500 (3·08); β, 3080 (4·72), 2980 (4·79); 2610 (4·10), 2570 (4·17), 2470 (4·26); 2160 (4.94).[1]

REFERENCE

1. Cava, M. P. and Stucker, J. F., *J. Amer. chem. Soc.* **77**, 6022 (1955).

VII. 2.3,6.7-DIBENZOBIPHENYLENE

2-Amino-3-nitronaphthalene (I) can be transformed into the iodine compound (II) which is condensed to (III). Catalytic reduction of the nitro groups, diazotization and substitution by iodine give the dinaphthyl-iodonium iodide (IV). The cyclization is achieved using cuprous oxide and yields dibenzobiphenylene (V).[1] The latter can also be obtained from the hydrogenated iodonium iodide (VI) in the same way involving a simultaneous dehydrogenation.[2]

2,3-Dibromonaphthalene (VII) gives dibenzobiphenylene with lithium amalgam. It is also formed from 2-bromo-3-iodonaphthalene with copper powder in dimethylformamide.[3]

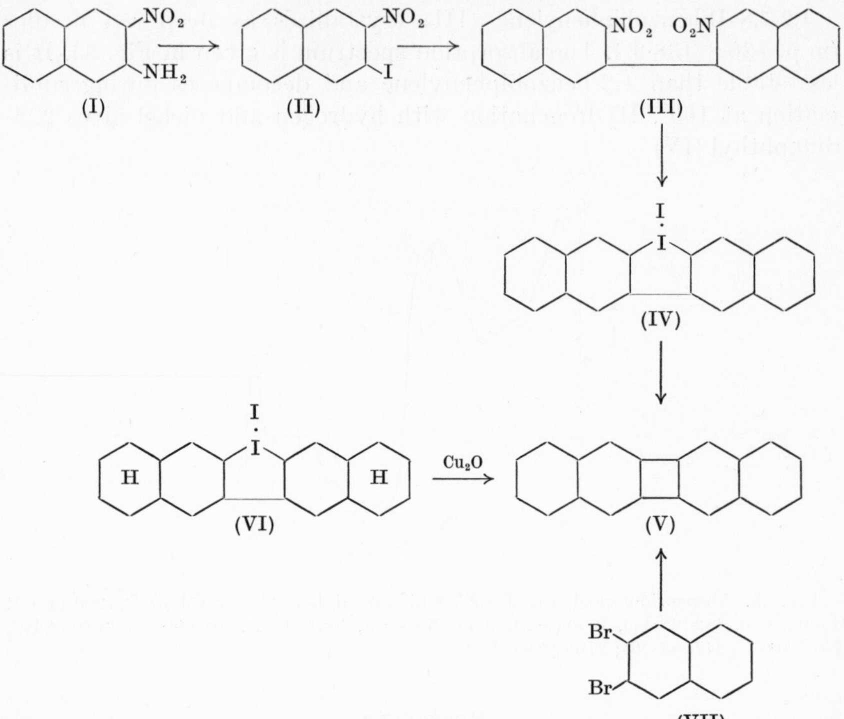

(I) (II) (III)

(IV)

(VI) Cu$_2$O (V)

(VII)

2.3,6.7-Dibenzobiphenylene (V) forms yellow plates (m.p. 376° (corr)). The absorption spectrum is given in Fig. 86. Hydrogenation yields 2,2'-dinaphthyl (VI).

The irradiation of 1,4-naphthoquinone (VIII) with a mercury lamp gives the dimeride (IX), which yields the tetrasodium salt of tetrahydroxydibenzobiphenylene (X) when treated with 10% sodium

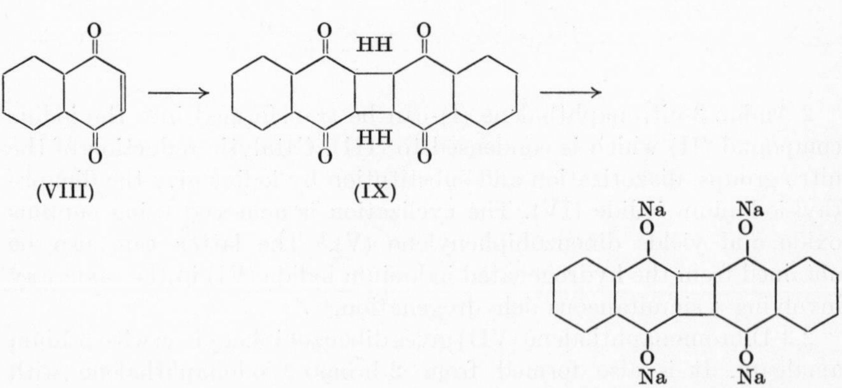

(VIII) (IX)

(X)

hydroxide solution. A tetra-acetate and a tetramethyl ether have been obtained. The spectra of these compounds are closely related to the parent hydrocarbon.[4]

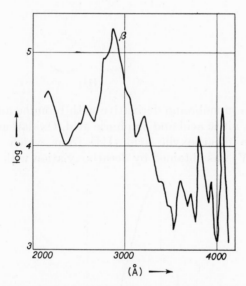

(XI)

1,2,5,8-Tetraphenyl-2.3,6.7-dibenzobiphenylene (XI) has been synthesized.[5]

FIG. 86. Absorption spectrum of 2.3,6.7-dibenzobiphenylene in ethanol: 4060 (4·43), 3940 (3·63), 3800 (4·15), 3700 (3·57), 3620 (3·63), 3490 (3·56), 3410 (3·61); 3220 (4·31); 3010 (4·47); 2880 (5·23), 2780 (4·93), 2570 (4·41); 2500 (4·23); 2170 (4·56).[1]

REFERENCES

1. Curtis, R. F. and Viswanath, G., *J. chem. Soc.* 1670 (1959).
2. Ward, E. R. and Pearson, B. D., *J. chem. Soc.* 1676 (1959).
3. Ward, E. R. and Pearson, B. D., *J. chem. Soc.* 515 (1961).
4. Schönberg, A., Mustafa, M. Z., Barakat, M. Z., Latif, N., Mousbasher, R. and Moustafa, A., *J. chem. Soc.* 2126 (1948); Bruce, J. M., *J. chem. Soc.* 2782 (1962).
5. Nenitzescu, C. D., Avram, M., Dinŭlescu, I. G. and Mateescu, G., *Liebigs Ann.* **653**, 79 (1962).

VIII. TETRAPHENYLENE, HEXAPHENYLENE AND OCTAPHENYLENE

Tetraphenylene (II) can be obtained in 16% yield from the Grignard compound (I) and cupric chloride. It forms colourless crystals (m.p.

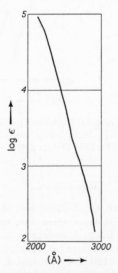

233°). It gives a monobromo derivative with bromine and a tetranitro compound with nitric acid and sulphuric acid. Oxidation with chromic acid yields the dicarboxylic acid (III) from which tribenzocyclo-octatetraene (IV) was obtained by decarboxylation with barium oxide.

FIG. 87. Absorption spectrum of tetraphenylene in cyclohexane Rapson, W. S., Schwartz, H. M. and Theal Stewart, E., *J. chem. Soc.* 73 (1944).

Tetraphenylene does not react with alkaline potassium permanganate solution and does not give a molecular compound with trinitrobenzene, picric acid or styphnic acid.[1]

The absorption spectrum of tetraphenylene is given in Fig. 87. This is more related to diphenyl than to diphenylene, thus indicating that there can be only very little electronic interchange between the phenylene complexes.[1]

(V)   (II)   (VI)

(VII)

Tetraphenylene can also be prepared from the di-lithium compound (V) with cobaltic chloride or nickel chloride. Hexaphenylene (VI) and octaphenylene (VII) are also formed in this reaction. Both hydrocarbons are colourless (m.p. 334° and 424° respectively). They can be sublimed. Their absorption spectra are diffuse and shifted to shorter wavelengths in comparison with triphenylene.[2]

REFERENCES

1. Rapson, W. S., Shuttleworth, R. G. and van Niekerk, J. N., J. chem. Soc. 326 (1943); 71 (1944).
2. Wittig, G. and Lehmann, G., Ber. dtsch. chem. Ges. 90, 875 (1957).

CHAPTER 29

Hydrocarbons derived from Perylene

I. PERYLENE

Perylene (II) was first prepared by heating 1,1'-dinaphthyl (I) or naphthalene with aluminium chloride. However, the yield was poor.[1] The constitution was proved by its formation from 1,8-di-iodonaphthalene (III) and copper powder.[1] It is also formed in 4% yield from 1-bromonaphthalene and aluminium chloride.[2] A yield of 3% is obtained from 1-bromonaphthalene and lithium.[3] A small yield of perylene is formed by pyrolysis of naphthalene at 650°, the main product being 2,2'-dinaphthyl.[4]

(I)	(II)	(III)

Better yields are obtained by heating 2,2'-dinaphthol (IV) with phosphorus pentachloride and phosphoric acid to 400–500°, when perylene and dinaphthylene oxide distil off. These can be separated by their different solubilities.[5] In a similar process phosphorus oxychloride and zinc dust were used.[6]

The cyclization of dinaphthyl can be more successfully used with derivatives of dinaphthyl. Thus β,β'-dinaphthol (IV) and α,α'-dinaphthol (V) cyclize when heated with aluminium chloride to 1,12-dihydroxyperylene (VI) and 3,10-dihydroxyperylene (VII). Both compounds give perylene (II) when distilled with zinc dust.[7] Perylene was accidentally discovered by the reaction of naphthalene and tetrachloroethane with aluminium chloride which was thought to give 1.2,5.6-dibenzanthracene.[8] The real nature of this reaction was established later.[9]

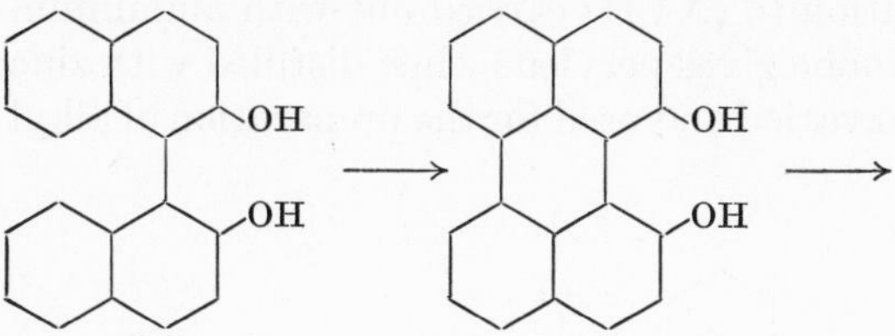

(IV)   (VI)

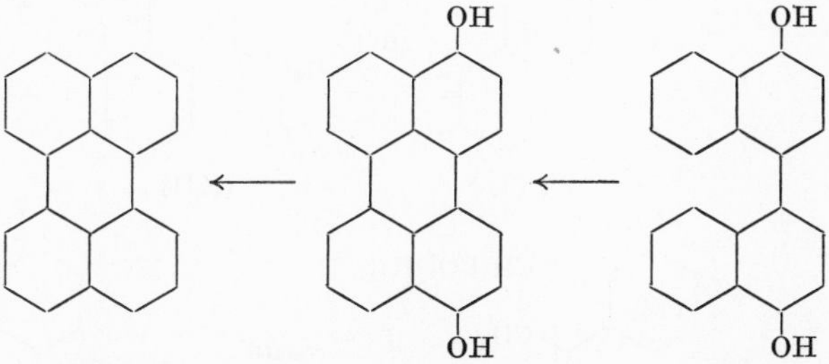

(II)   (VII)   (V)

Another synthesis of perylene starts from phenanthrene (VIII) which condenses twice with acrolein under the influence of anhydrous hydrofluoric acid. The crude product which consists of hydrogenated perylenes can be dehydrogenated by distillation with mercury or fusion with sulphur.[10] 1,10-Trimethylene-9-hydroxyphenanthrene (IX) which is readily obtainable from benzanthrone[11] condenses in the same way with acrolein and anhydrous hydrofluoric acid.[10]

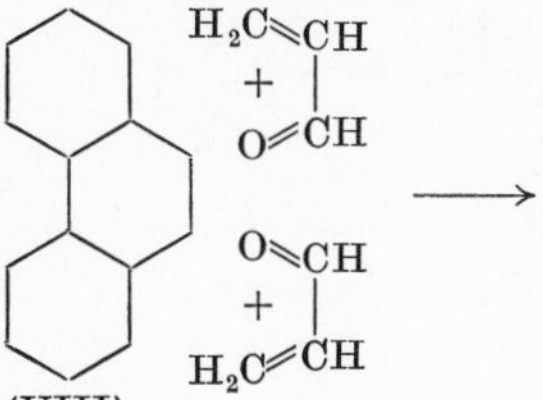

(VIII)

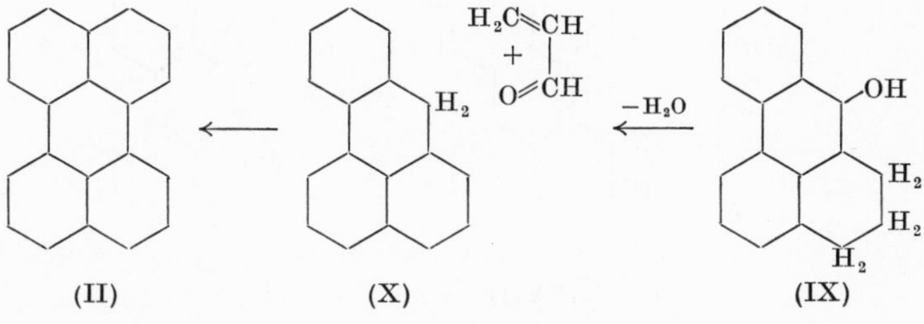

(II)   (X)   (IX)

Perylene has also been synthesized from anthracene (XI). Chloromethylation gives (XII). The chlorine atoms react with sodio-malonic ester to form (XIII). Saponification gives (XIV) and decarboxylation yields the dicarboxylic acid (XV). The chloride (XVI) is prepared with thionyl chloride and cyclization to (XVII) carried out with aluminium chloride. The tetrahydroquinone gives perylene when distilled with zinc dust.[12] This method has been varied and used for the preparation of alkyl perylenes.[13]

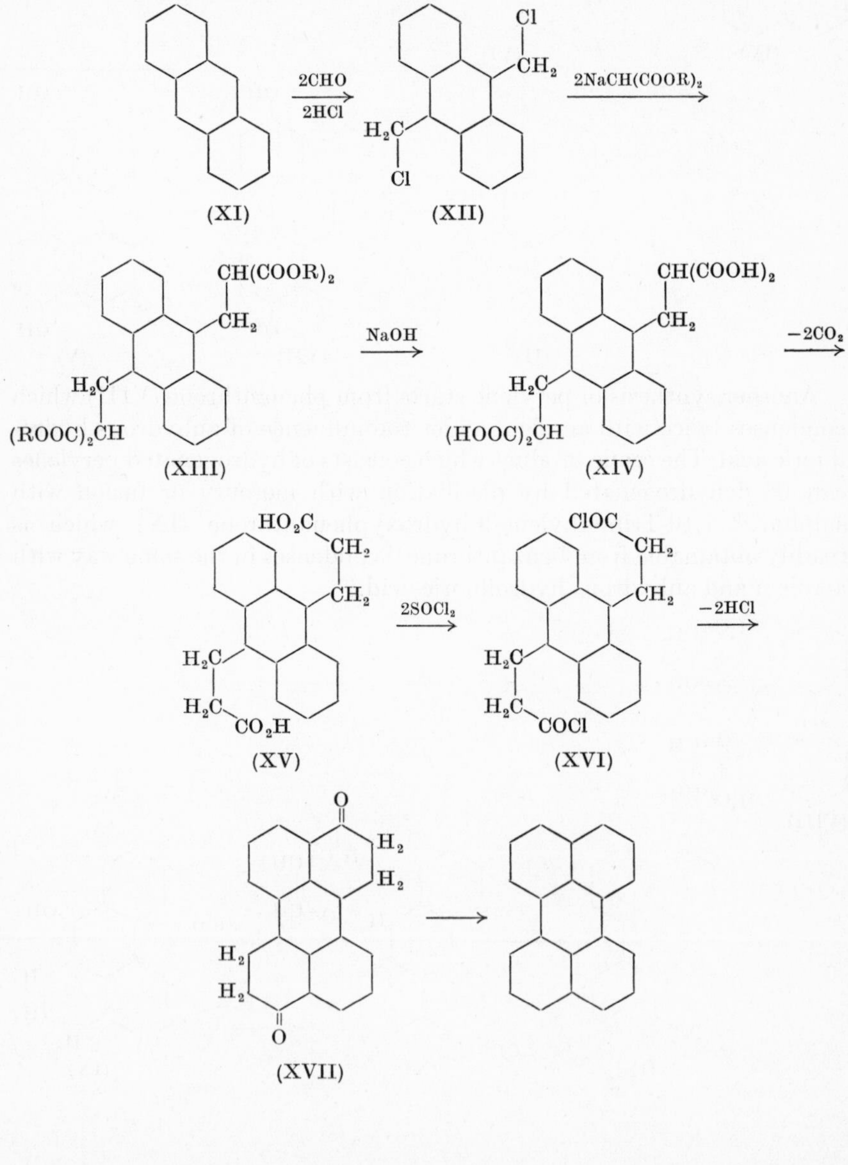

$$\text{(XI)} \xrightarrow[\text{2HCl}]{\text{2CHO}} \text{(XII)} \xrightarrow{\text{2NaCH(COOR)}_2}$$

(XI)   (XII)

$$\text{(XIII)} \xrightarrow{\text{NaOH}} \text{(XIV)} \xrightarrow{-2\text{CO}_2}$$

(XIII)   (XIV)

$$\text{(XV)} \xrightarrow{\text{2SOCl}_2} \text{(XVI)} \xrightarrow{-2\text{HCl}}$$

(XV)   (XVI)

(XVII)

Perylene has been isolated from coal-tar[14] and can now be obtained commercially. It was also separated from the sulphur dioxide extracts of petroleum.[15]

Perylene crystallizes from xylene in large golden yellow plates (m.p. 273–274°). The solutions show a strong blue fluorescence. They are

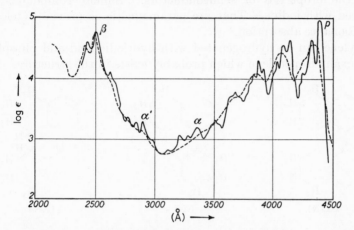

FIG. 88. Absorption spectrum of perylene in methanol–ethanol at +18° (broken line) and at −170° (full line) (Clar, E., *Spectrochimica Acta* **4**, 116 (1950)).

	+18°	−170°		+18°	−170°
p-Bands	4340 (4·56)	4395 (4·98)	α-Bands		3375 (3·19)
		4330 (4·63)			3305 (3·04)
		4260 (4·08)			3235 (3·04)
	4060 (4·42)	4145 (4·64)			
		4095 (4·56)	α'-Bands		2915 (3·29)
		4045 (4·30)			2865 (3·26)
	3870 (4·08)	3920 (4·14)			2795 (3·35)
		3883 (4·32)			2645 (4·10)
		3845 (4·08)			
	3680 (3·68)	3698 (3·78)	β-Bands	2510 (4·70)	2530 (4·74)
		3525 (3.30)		2450 (4·44)	2460 (4·59)

photo-oxidizable in the presence of acid.[16] This causes a bronze colour of the crystals and a considerable depression of the melting point. The absorption spectrum is given in Fig. 88. The fluorescence spectrum has also been measured,[17] as well as the X-ray structure.[18]

Perylene forms a monopicrate[19] and a dipicrate.[20] It gives molecular compounds with trinitrobenzene,[21] styphnic acid,[22] antimony pentachloride, stannic chloride and ferric chloride.[23] Perylene dissolves in concentrated sulphuric acid to form a green solution which changes rapidly to brown. The solution proved to be paramagnetic when tested by electron spin resonance absorption.[23]

Perylene forms deep brown molecular compounds with halogens. It adds three atoms of bromine in benzene solution,[24] and four atoms of bromine in the solid state.[25] These compounds decompose readily and show the properties of semiconductors.[26] Similar compounds were obtained with iodine.[24] They are paramagnetic as proved by electron spin resonance absorption.[27]

Perylene can be hydrogenated with hydriodic acid and phosphorus to a hexahydroperylene which probably exists in the structures (XIX)

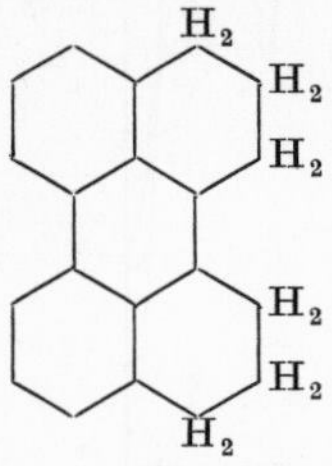

(XIX) 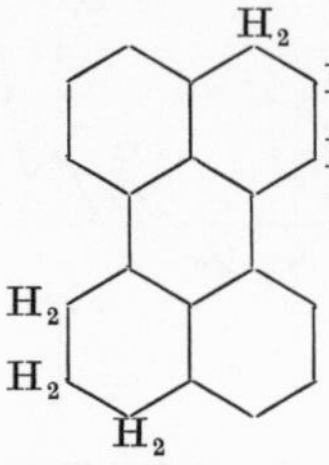   (XX) 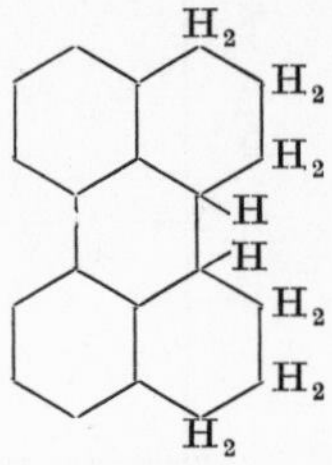   (XXI)

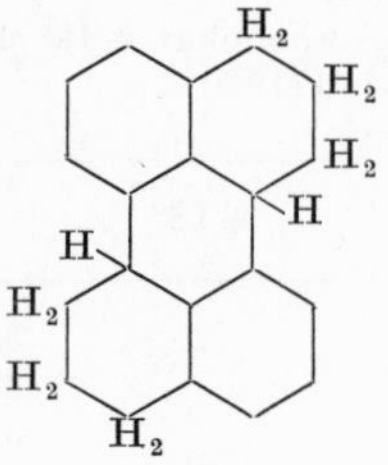

(XXII) 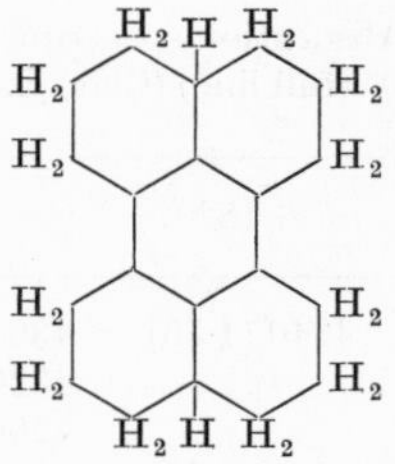   (XXIII)

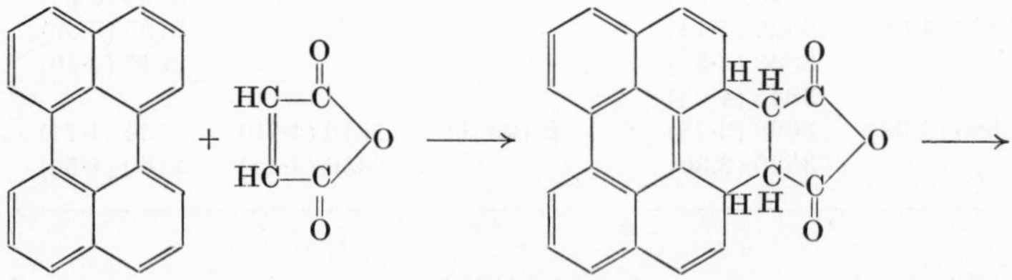

(XXIV)

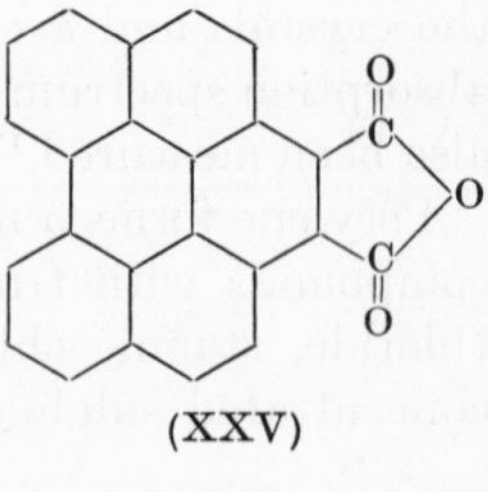

(XXV)

and (XX).[28] It is also obtained with hydrogen and palladium–charcoal[29] or with sodium in amyl alcohol.[30]

The two latter methods yield also an octahydroperylene (XXI) or (XXII). Further hydrogenation leads to a tetradecahydroperylene (XXIII). Two isomeric tetradecahydroperylenes have been obtained from perylene in decalin with hydrogen and palladium–charcoal under pressure.[31]

Disubstitution of perylene takes place in the positions 3,9- and 3,10- with the exception of the reaction with maleic anhydride.[32]

The primary adduct (XXIV) is unstable. To obtain the anhydride (XXV) the reaction must be carried out in the presence of an oxidizing agent like nitrobenzene, air, nitrogen oxides, lead dioxide or copper oxide. The best dehydrogenating agent is chloranil which gives almost quantitative yields.[33] Perylene reacts in the same way with benzoquinone. The yield is, however, poor.[34]

Perylene is very readily halogenated. A mixture of 3,9- and 3,10-dichloroperylene is obtained from perylene in nitrobenzene with hydrogen peroxide and hydrochloric acid.[35] Their constitution results from the fact that perylene-3,9-quinone and perylene-3,10-quinone respectively are formed by heating with concentrated sulphuric acid.[36] 3,9- and 3,10-Dichloroperylene can be also prepared from perylene in nitrobenzene or acetic acid with sodium dichromate and hydrochloric acid,[37] or with sulphuryl chloride in benzene.[38] Further chlorination leads to 3,4,9,10-tetrachloroperylene and a hexachloroperylene.[35, 37] Tetrachloroperylene is also obtained from perylene in nitrobenzene and aluminium chloride; phosphorus pentachloride gives hexachloroperylene. A pentachloroperylene has also been obtained.[39]

Adducts with chlorine can be prepared at low temperatures. 3,9-Dichloroperylene and perylene in tetrachloroethane give colourless adducts of the compositions $C_{20}H_9Cl_7$ and $C_{20}H_{11}Cl_9$ respectively.[40]

Bromination of perylene in sulphuric acid yields 3,9-dibromoperylene and 3,10-dibromoperylene. Their structures were established by their transformation into the corresponding perylenequinones.[41] The two dibromoperylenes can also be prepared from perylene in nitrobenzene and aluminium bromide or from perylene in nitrobenzene with sodium bromide, acetic acid and hydrogen peroxide.[37] 3,9-Dibromoperylene and 3,10-dibromoperylene yield two tetrabromoperylenes on further bromination in benzene with bromine and iodine.[42]

Perylene and formylmethylaniline give perylene-3-aldehyde (XXVI) which can be reduced to 3-methylperylene (XXVII) (m.p. 217°). The reaction can be repeated with the latter and yields the aldehyde (XXVIII), whose reduction produces 3,10-dimethylperylene (XXIX) (m.p. 202°).[43]

(XXVI) (XXVII) (XXVIII) (XXIX)

2,8-Dimethylperylene and 3,9-dimethylperylene were obtained by a modification of the perylene synthesis from anthracene (see p. 26).[44] Other alkyl derivatives of perylene have been isolated by a zinc-dust melt of erithroaphin.[45]

Perylene in acetic anhydride gives 3-nitroperylene with nitric acid.[46] Further nitration leads to 3,10-dinitroperylene[37, 47] or trinitroperylene, 3,4,9,10-tetranitroperylene[48] and pentanitroperylene.[49]

3,9-Dichloroperylene and 3,9-dibromoperylene exchange the halogen atoms for the CN-group in boiling quinoline with CuCN. Perylene-3,9-dicarboxylic acid can be obtained from the resulting perylene dinitrile by saponifiication.[50] Perylene-tetracarboxylic acid can be prepared from acenaphthene. Oxidation gives naphthalic acid from which naphthalic imide (XXX) is obtained with ammonia. A fusion with potassium hydroxide yields the di-imide (XXXI) and saponification with concentrated sulphuric acid gives perylene-tetracarboxylic acid (XXXII).[51] The latter can be obtained by a fusion of *peri*-naphthindione (XXXIV) with potassium hydroxide which leads to (XXXIII) and oxidation to (XXXII).[52] The decarboxylation of perylene-tetracarboxylic acid (XXXII) in alkaline solution under pressure gives perylene in good yield.[53]

(XXX) (XXXI) (XXXII) (XXXIII) (XXXIV)

Perylene-ketones can be obtained by the Friedel–Crafts reaction which gives a mixture of 3,9- and 3,10-diketones. The following ketones have been prepared in this way: diacetylperylene,[54] 3,9- and 3,10-dibenzoylperylene,[41] 3,4-dibenzoylperylene[55] and tribenzoylperylene,[56] and 3,9-ditoluylperylene.[54] Diketones have also been obtained from 3,9-dichloroperylene and 3,9-dibromoperylene.[57] Diketones can be prepared from perylene-3,9-dicarboxylic chloride and aromatic hydrocarbons.[58] Perylene, phthalic anhydride and aluminium chloride give a mono- and a di-ketone acid. The latter can be condensed to 2.3,8.9-diphthalylperylene.[59, 60] Succinoyl chloride condenses with perylene and aluminium chloride to form a monoketone acid.[60]

Perylene-3,10-dinitrile can be obtained from 1,1'-dinaphthyl-4,4'-dinitrile and aluminium chloride. Saponification of the former gives perylene-3,10-dicarboxylic acid.[2]

Perylene and sulphuric acid give perylene disulphonic acids.[61] The reaction is best carried out in acetic acid and yields perylene-3,9-disulphonic acid and perylene-3,10-disulphonic acid.[62]

Perylene quinones

Perylene-3,10-quinone (XXXV) is readily obtained by oxidation of perylene with aqueous chromic acid.[63] It forms yellow needles (m.p. 350°) which dissolve in concentrated sulphuric acid to form a red solution. A red vat is formed with alkaline sodium dithionite solution.

Further oxidation with chromic acid, with potassium permanganate in pyridine or with manganese dioxide in sulphuric acid gives benzanthrone-7,8-dicarboxylic anhydride (XXXVI).[64] This can be further oxidized to phenanthrene-1,8,9,10-tetracarboxylic dianhydride (XXXVII) with nitric acid in acetic acid.[65]

(XXXV)   (XXXVI)   (XXXVII)

Perylene-3,9-quinone (XXXIX) reacts with sodium hydroxide or ammonia in the presence of oxygen to form a 1-hydroxy- and a 1-amino derivative respectively.[66]

Perylene-3,9-quinone (XXXIX) can be prepared by hydrolysis of 3,9-dichloroperylene or 3,9-dibromoperylene (XXXVIII) with sulphuric acid.[36] It can be obtained by oxidation of tetrahydroperylenequinone (p. 26) with iodine in pyridine.[67] It forms violet needles from nitro-benzene which give a red solution in concentrated sulphuric acid. With alkaline sodium dithionite a red vat is formed which dyes cotton violet.

(XXXVIII)   (XXXIX)

(XL)   (XLI)

Oxidation of perylene-3,9-quinone with manganese dioxide in sul-phuric acid gives anthraquinone-1,5-dicarboxylic acid (XL) which can be obtained directly from perylene. The dicarboxylic acid (XL) is reduced to the dilactone (XLI) with sulphuric acid and copper powder.[68]

Perylene-1,12-quinone (XLIV) can be prepared from 2,2'-dihydroxy-1,1'-dinaphthyl (XLII). The cyclization to dihydroxyperylene (XLIII) is effected with aluminium chloride. The latter is easily oxidized to perylene-1,12-quinone (XLIV) in alkaline solution with air. It forms red-brown crystals (m.p. 287°) which give a brown solution with concen-trated sulphuric acid.[69]

(XLII)   (XLIII)   (XLIV)   (XLV)

Perylene-1,12-peroxide (XLV) is isomeric with perylene-1,12-quinone (XLIV). It is formed from (XLIII) by melting with zinc chloride.[70] It can be reduced neither with hydriodic acid nor with alkaline sodium dithionite. It does not melt below 340° and dissolves in concentrated sulphuric acid to form a reddish-yellow solution which shows a green fluorescence. It crystallizes in brown or orange-yellow needles and is sublimable.

4,9-Dihydroxy-3,10-perylenequinone (XLVII) is formed instead of perylene-3.4,9.10-diquinone when tetrachloroperylene, 3,9-dichloro-4,10-dinitroperylene, 3,10-dinitroperylene or 3,4,9,10-tetranitroperylene (XLVI) is hydrolysed with sulphuric acid.[71] It was thought to be perylene-3.4,9.10-diquinone.[72] The dihydroxyquinone (XLVII) crystallizes from nitrobenzene as red needles. A dark red vat is formed with alkaline sodium dithionite. It gives mellitic acid (XLVIII) when oxidized with nitric acid under pressure.[73]

(XLVI)   (XLVII)   (XLVIII)

2,11-Dihydroxyperylene-3,10-quinone (L) is obtained from the dinaphthyldiquinone (XLIX) with aluminium chloride.[74] It cannot be oxidized to a diquinone. It forms a phenanzine derivative (LI) with o-phenylenediamine.[75]

Perylene shows no carcinogenic properties.[76]

(XLIX)   (L)   (LI)

REFERENCES

1. Scholl, R. and Weitzenböck, R., *Mh. Chem.* **43**, 2202 (1910).
2. Weitzenböck, R. and Seer, C., *Ber. dtsch. chem. Ges.* **46**, 1994 (1913).
3. Gilman, H. and Brannen, C. G., *J. Amer. chem. Soc.* **71**, 657 (1949).
4. Lang, K. F., Buffleb, H. and Kalowy, J., *Ber. dtsch. chem. Ges.* **90**, 2888 (1957).
5. Hansgirg, F. and Zinke, A., *Mh. Chem.* **40**, 403, (1919); Hansgirg, F., German Patent 386040 (1918).
6. Companie National de Matiére Colorantes et de Produits Chimiques, French Patent 571739 (1922); 571738 (1922); 28528 (1923); Brit. Patent 208721 and 208722 (1923); *Chem. Zbl.* **1926 I**, 498; Marschalk, Ch., *Bull. Soc. chim. Fr.* (4), **43**, 1388 (1928).
7. Zinke, A. and Dengg, R., *Mh. Chem.* **43**, 125 (1922); Pereira, German Patent 390619; 391825 (1921); 394437 (1922); Zinke, A. and von Schlieszl, K. J., *Mh. Chem.* **67**, 196 (1936); Zinke, A., and Schöpfer, H., *Mh. Chem.* **44**, 365 (1923); Zinke, A., Stimler, F. and Reuss, E., *Mh. Chem.* **64**, 415 (1934).
8. Homer, A., *J. chem. Soc.* **97**, 1148 (1910).
9. Cook, J. W., *J. chem. Soc.* 488 (1931).
10. Weinmayr, V., Amer. Patent 2145905 (1937); *Chem. Zbl.* **1939 II**, 230; *J. Amer. chem. Soc.* **61**, 949 (1939).
11. Clar, E. and Furnari, Fr., *Ber. dtsch. chem. Ges.* **65**, 1420 (1932).
12. Postowski, I. J. and Bednjagina, N. P., *J. gen. Chem. U.S.S.R.* **7**, (69) 2919 (1937).
13. Anderson, J. M., Campbell, A. D., Emerson, G. W. and Murray, J., *J. chem. Soc.* 410 (1960).
14. Cook, J. W., Hewett, C. L. and Hieger, I., *J. chem. Soc.* 396 (1933).
15. Cook, F. W. and Carruthers, W., *J. chem. Soc.* 2047 (1954).
16. Clar, E., unpublished results.
17. Bowen, E. and Brocklehurst, B., *J. chem. Soc.* 4320 (1955).
18. Donaldson, D. M., Robertson, J. M. and White J. G., *Proc. roy. Soc.* **A220**, 311 (1953).
19. Morgan, G. T. and Mitchell, J. G., *J. chem. Soc.* 536 (1934).
20. Brass, K. and Tengler, E., *Ber. dtsch. chem. Ges.* **64**, 1650 (1931).
21. Hertel, E. and Bergk, H. W., *Z. phys. Chem.* **33**, 324 (1936).
22. Brass, K. and Fanta, K., *Ber. dtsch. chem. Ges.* **69**, 1 (1936).
23. Yokozawa, Y. and Miyoshita, I., *J. chem. Phys.* **25**, 796 (1956); Weissmann, J. I. and de Boer, E., *J. chem. Phys.* **26**, 963 (1957); Carrington, A., Dravnieks, F. and Symons, M. C. R., *J. chem. Soc.* 947 (1959).
24. Brass, K. and Clar, E., *Ber. dtsch. chem. Ges.* **65**, 1660 (1932); **69**, 1977 (1936); **72**, 604 (1939).
25. Zinke, A. and Pongratz, A., *Ber. dtsch. chem. Ges.* **69**, 1591 (1939); **70**, 214 (1937); Pestemer, M. and Treiber, E., *Ber. dtsch. chem. Ges.* **74**, 964 (1941).
26. Akamatu, H., Inokuchi, H. and Matsunaga, Y., *Nature, Lond.* **173**, 168 (1954).
27. Matsunaga, Y., *J. chem. Phys.* **30**, 855 (1955).
28. Zinke, A. and Unterkreuter, E., *Mh. Chem.* **40**, 405 (1929).
29. Zinke, A. and Schniederschitsch, N., *Mh. Chem.* **59**, 280 (1929).
30. Zinke, A. and Benndorf, O., *Mh. Chem.* **59**, 241 (1932); **64**, 87 (1934).
31. Uchida, S. and Takata, S., *J. Soc. chem. Ind. Japan (Suppl.)* **36**, 222B (1933).
32. Clar, E., *Ber. dtsch. chem. Ges.* **65**, 846 (1932); I.G. Farbinindustrie AG, German Patent 651677 (1934); *Chem. Zbl.* **1938 I**, 2447.
33. Clar, E. and Zander, M., *J. chem. Soc.* 4660 (1957); Clar, E., *Ber. dtsch. chem. Ges.* **82**, 53 (1949).

34. Hopff, H. and Schweizer, H. R., *Helv. chim. Acta* **42**, 2315.
35. Zinke, A., Pongratz, A. and Funke, K., *Ber. dtsch. chem. Ges.* **58**, 330 (1925).
36. Zinke, A., Springer, R. and Schmid, A., *Ber. dtsch. chem. Ges.* **58**, 2386; Zinke, A. and Hirsch, W., *Mh. Chem.* **52**, 13 (1929).
37. Zinke, A., Funke, K. and Lorber, N., *Ber. dtsch. chem. Ges.* **60**, 577 (1927).
38. Pongratz, A., and Eichler, E., *Ber. dtsch. chem. Ges.* **69**, 1292 (1936).
39. Felice Bensa, Österr. Patent 104133 (1924); *Chem. Zbl.* **1926 II**, 3007.
40. Zinke, A., Funke, K. and Ipavic, H., *Mh. Chem.* **48**, 741 (1927).
41. Zinke, A., Linner, F., and Wolfbauer, O., *Ber. dtsch. chem. Ges.* **58**, 323 (1925).
42. Zinke, A., Noculak, U., Skrabal, R. and Troger, H., *Ber. dtsch. chem. Ges.* **73**, 1187 (1940).
43. Buu-Hoï, N. P. and Lavit, D., *Rec. trav. chim.* **75**, 1221 (1956).
44. Anderson, J. M., Campbell, A. D., Emerson, G. W. and Murray, J., *J. chem. Soc.* 410 (1960).
45. Bromn, B. R., Johnson, A. W., Quayle, J. R. and Todd, A. R., *J. chem. Soc.* 107 (1954).
46. Dewar, M. J. S. and Mole, T., *J. chem. Soc.* 1441 (1956).
47. Funke, K., Kirchmayr, F. and Wolf, H., *Mh. Chem.* **51**, 221 (1928); Funke, K. and Wolf, H., *Mh. Chem.* **52**, 1 (1929).
48. Zinke, A. and Hirsch, W., *Mh. Chem.* **52**, 13 (1929).
49. Calderbank, A., Johnson, A. W. and Todd, A. R., *J. chem. Soc.* 1285 (1954).
50. Pongratz, A., *Mh. Chem.* **48**, 585, 639 (1927).
51. Kalle, German Patent 394794 (1921); 411217 (1922); 486491 (1926); Porai-Koshits, A. E. and Pavlushenko, I. S., *J. gen. Chem. U.S.S.R.* **17**, 1739 (1947); *Amer. Abstr.* 5892 (1948); Bradley, W. and Pexton, F. W., *J. chem. Soc.* 4432, 4436 (1954).
52. Kalle, German Patent 408513 (1922).
53. I.G. Farbinindustrie AG, French Patent 635599 (1927); *Chem. Zbl.* **1929 I**, 2472.
54. Pongratz, A., *Mh. Chem.* **48**, 585 (1927).
55. Zinke, A. and Benndorf, O., *Mh. Chem.* **56**, 153 (1930).
56. Zinke, A. and Gesell, E., *Mh. Chem.* **67**, 187 (1936).
57. Zinke, A., Funke, K. and Pongratz, A., *Ber. dtsch. chem. Ges.* **58**, 799 (1925); Zinke, A. and Funke, K., *Ber. dtsch. chem. Ges.* **58**, 2222 (1925); Pongratz, A. *Mh. Chem.* **48**, 585 (1927).
58. Pongratz, A., *Mh. Chem.* **56**, 163 (1927).
59. Zinke, A., Gorbach, G. and Schimka, O., *Mh. Chem.* **48**, 593 (1927); I.G. Farbinindustrie AG, German Patent 642650; *Chem. Zbl.* **1937 I**, 5057.
60. Zinke, A., Troger, H. and Ziegler, E., *Ber. dtsch. chem. Ges.* **73**, 1042 (1940).
61. Kalle & Co., German Patent 432178 (1923).
62. Marschalk, Ch., *Bull. Soc. chim. Fr.* (4) **41**, 74 (1927).
63. Zinke, A. and Unterkreuter, E., *Mh. Chem.* **40**, 405 (1919); Zinke, A. and Schöpfer, H., *Mh. Chem.* **44**, 365 (1923).
64. Zinke, A. and Wenger, R., *Mh. Chem.* **56**, 143 (1930); Brown, B. R. and Todd, A. R., *J. chem. Soc.* 1280 (1954).
65. Zinke, A., *Mh. Chem.* **57**, 405 (1931); Zinke, A., Herzog, O. and Skrabal, R., *Ber. dtsch. chem. Ges.* **77**, 272 (1944).
66. Brown, B. R. and Todd, A. R., *J. chem. Soc.* 1280 (1954).
67. Haslam, E., *Tetrahedron* **5**, 99 (1959).
68. Zinke, A. and Wenger, R., *Mh. Chem.* **55**, 52 (1930).
69. Zinke, A. and Dengg, R., *Mh. Chem.* **43**, 125 (1922); Zinke, A. and Haselmayer, F., *Mh. Chem.* **45**, 231 (1924).
70. Zinke, A. and von Schlieszl, K. J., *Mh. Chem.* **67**, 196 (1936).

71. Calderbank, A., Johnson, A. W. and Todd, A. R., *J. chem. Soc.* 1285 (1954).
72. Zinke, A., Hirsch, W. and Brozek, E., *Mh. Chem.* **51**, 205; **52**, 13 (1929).
73. Zinke, A., *Mh. Chem.* **57**, 105 (1931).
74. Badische Anilin und Soda Fabrik, German Patent 412120 (1922).
75. Zinke, A., Stimler, F. and Reuss, E., *Mh. Chem.* **64**, 415 (1934).
76. Cook, J. W., Hieger, I., Kennaway, E. L. and Mayneord, W. V., *Proc. roy. Soc.* **B111**, 455 (1932); Rondoni, P., *Z. Krebsforsch.* **47**, 59 (1937).

II. 1.2-BENZOPERYLENE

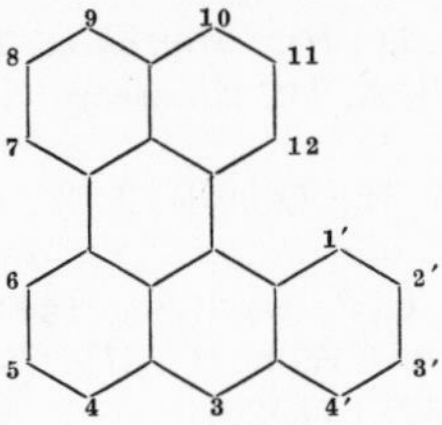

1.2-Benzoperylene (III) can be prepared as a fission product from dinaphthylanthracene (I) in a sodium chloride–aluminium chloride melt. The other products of the reaction are 7.8-benzoterrylene (II) (see p. 230), anthracene and naphthalene.[1]

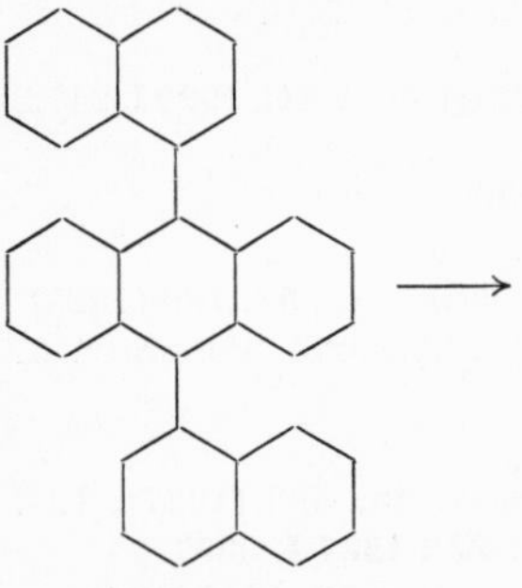

(I)

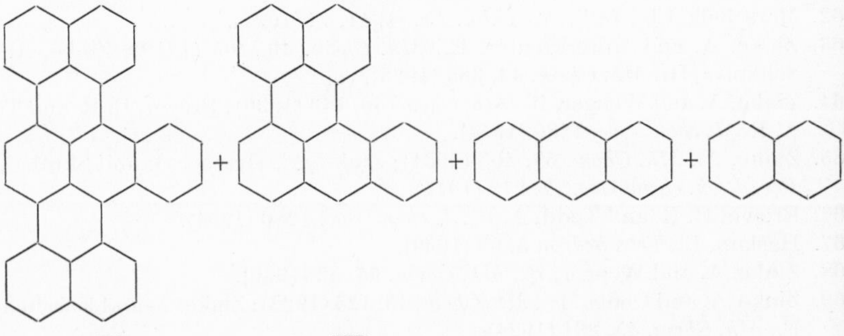

(II)   (III)

1.2-Benzoperylene is obtained by a zinc-dust melt from 1.2-benzo-perylene-3,10-quinone.[2] It is also observed as a dehydrogenation product of the hydrogenated dioxido compound.[1]

2-Naphthyl-1.2-benzoperylene (V) is formed from the compound (IV) by treatment with potassium hydroxide in boiling quinoline.[1] The same

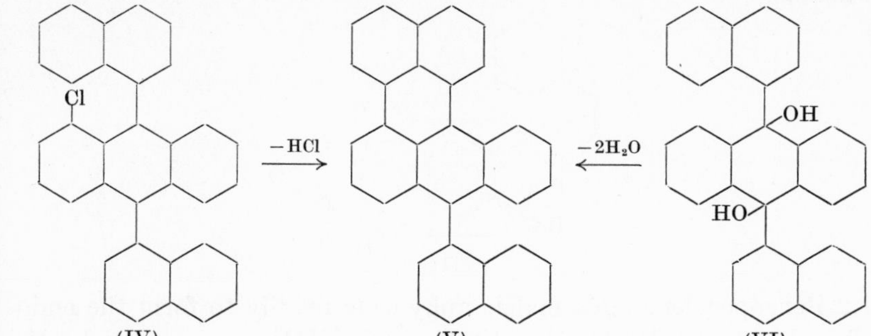

(IV)   (V)   (VI)

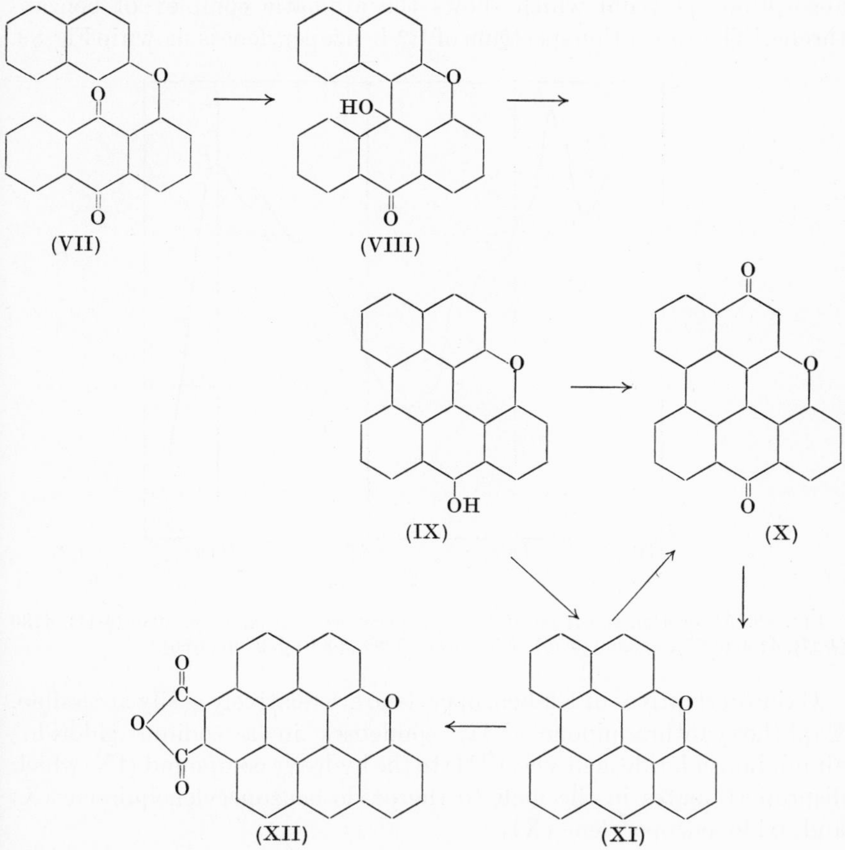

(VII)   (VIII)

(IX)   (X)

(XII)   (XI)

hydrocarbon results from the cyclization of the diol (VI) in benzene solution with aluminium chloride.[1]

1.2-Benzoperylene (III) crystallizes from petroleum ether or alcohol in orange-red needles (m.p. 115–116°), which dissolve in concentrated sulphuric acid to form a green solution. The solutions are rather photo-oxidizable.

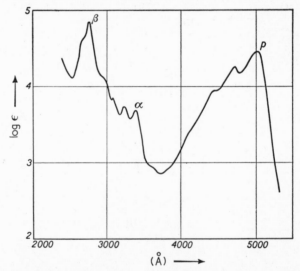

(XIII)

1.2-Benzoperylene adds maleic anhydride readily to form the endocyclic adduct (XIII). The constitution of (XIII) is confirmed by the absorption spectrum which shows the aromatic complex of benzanthrene.[1] The absorption spectrum of 1.2-benzoperylene is shown in Fig. 89.

Fig. 89. Absorption spectrum of 1.2-benzoperylene in ethanol: p, 5030 (4·47), 4730 (4·27), 4450 (3·95); α, 3390 (3·70), 3230 (3·74), 3080 (3·85); β, 2760 (4·86).

Oxido derivatives of 1.2-benzoperylene are relatively easily accessible. Naphthoxyanthraquinone (VII) condenses in a sodium chloride-aluminium chloride melt via (VIII) to the hydroxy compound (IX) which disproportionates in the melt to the oxido-benzoperylenequinone (X) and oxidobenzoperylene (XI).[3]

12,1'-Oxido-1.2-benzoperylene (XI) crystallizes from xylene in violet-blue, coppery shining leaflets (m.p. 280–281°), which dissolve in concentrated sulphuric acid to give an orange-yellow solution with a yellow fluorescence. It is sublimable. Its red solutions are photo-oxidizable. It reacts in nitrobenzene with maleic anhydride to form the anhydride (XII).

12,1'-Oxido-1.2-benzoperylene-3,10-quinone (X) crystallizes from nitrobenzene in brown needles which give a violet-red solution with concentrated sulphuric acid. It forms a green vat with alkaline sodium dithionite solution which dyes cotton in brown shades. It can be sublimed. It is the sole product of the sodium chloride–aluminium chloride melt if oxygen is stirred into the melt.

(XIV)   (XV)   (XVI)

1. Hydrogenation | 2. Dehydrogenation

(XVII)   (III)

Dinaphthoxyanthraquinone (XIV) cyclizes in a sodium chloride–aluminium chloride melt first to the red compound (XV) and then to the blue benzoperylene derivative (XVI). The condensation ends with the formation of the green dioxido-diperinaphthylene-anthracene (XVII). The constitution of the 1.2-benzoperylene derivative (XVI) was proved by the hydrogenation of (XVI), followed by dehydrogenation which led to 1.2-benzoperylene (III).[1]

1.2-Benzoperylene-3,10-quinone (XX) can be prepared by a condensation of dichloroanthrone (XVIII) with naphthalene and aluminium chloride in benzene solution. The resulting 3-hydroxy-1.2-benzoperylene (XIX) is oxidizable to benzoperylenequinone (XX). This crystallizes from xylene in brownish-yellow needles (m.p. 302–304°) which dissolve in concentrated sulphuric acid to form a red solution with a strong orange-red fluorescence. Alkaline sodium dithionite solution produces a blue vat.[2]

(XVIII)   (XIX)   (XX)

REFERENCES

1. Clar, E., Kelly, W. and Wright, J. W., J. chem. Soc. 2656 (1956).
2. Clar, E. and Frömmel, H., Chem. Ber. 82, 52 (1949).
3. Clar, E., Ber. dtsch. chem. Ges. 73, 351 (1940); Amer. Patent 2179920 (1938).

III. 2.3-BENZOPERYLENE

1-Naphthylpropiolic acid (I) dimerizes in boiling acetic anhydride to form the phenanthrene derivative (II).[1] Decarboxylation with soda-lime and copper powder results in partial cyclization to 2.3-benzoperylene (III) and naphthylphenanthrene (IV). Both compounds can be separated through their adducts with trinitrobenzene.[2]

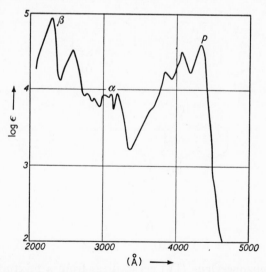

HO₂C

+

HO₂C

(I)

⟶

(II)

⟶

(III)

+

(IV)

2.3-Benzoperylene (III) forms yellow plates from benzene or alcohol (m.p. 200–201°). The solutions show a blue fluorescence. The absorption spectrum is shown in Fig. 90. The adduct with trinitrobenzene forms reddish-brown needles (m.p. 208–209°).

Fig. 90. Absorption spectrum of 2.3-benzoperylene in ethanol: p, 4350 (4·59), 4080 (4·51), 3850 (4·24); α, 3200 (3·95), 3110 (3·94), 3030 (3·92), 2880 (3·90), 2790 (3·94); β, 2600 (4·52); 2300 (4·94).[1]

II—2*

REFERENCES

1. West, B. L., *J. Amer. chem. Soc.* **42**, 1656 (1920); Woyak, G., Glupe, S. and Jatzkewitz, H. I., *Ber. dtsch. chem. Ges.* **71**, 1372 (1938).
2. Campbell, A. D., *J. chem. Soc.* 3659 (1954).

IV. 1.2,7.8-DIBENZOPERYLENE

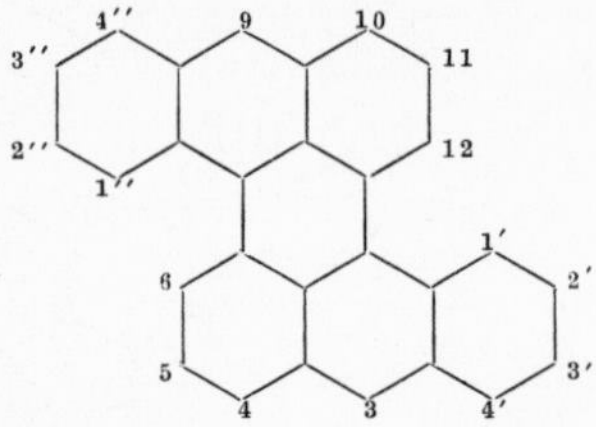

1-Chloroanthrone-(10) (I)[1] condenses in a melt of zinc chloride and pyridine at 245°. The initially formed hydroquinol (II) is readily oxidized to dibenzoperylenequinone (III). This is reduced to 1.2,7.8-dibenzo-perylene (IV) by a reduction in pyridine with zinc dust and acetic acid, followed by sublimation.[2]

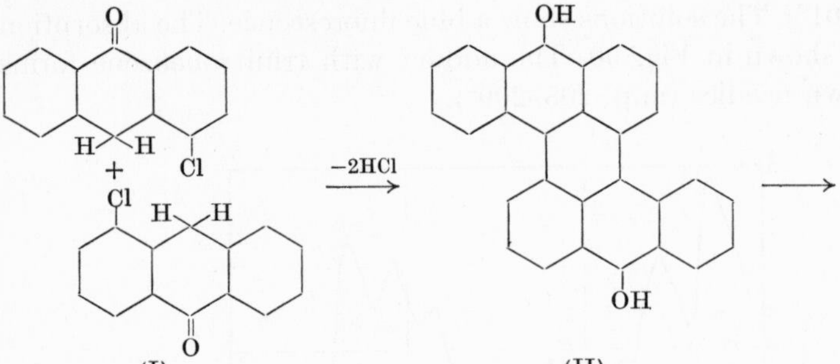

(I)

(II)

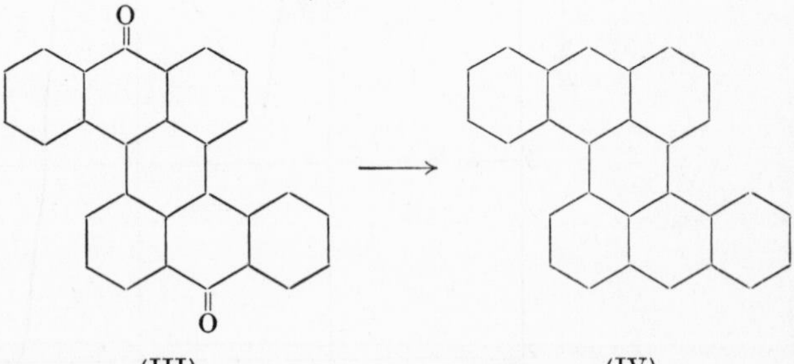

(III)

(IV)

1.2,7.8-Dibenzoperylene (IV) crystallizes from a mixture of benzene and alcohol in deep violet leaflets which have a shining coppery surface. They melt at 246°, and dissolve in concentrated sulphuric acid to form

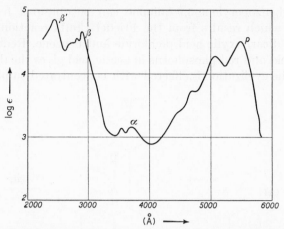

FIG. 91. Absorption spectrum of 1.2,7.8-dibenzoperylene in methanol: p, 5460 (4·50), 5050 (4·28), 4680 (3·72); α, 3710 (3·14), 3530 (3·12); β, 2900 (4·65), 2820 (4·54); β', 2450 (4·86).

a green solution which soon changes to violet. The red solutions show a red fluorescence and are readily photo-oxidizable. It also reacts rapidly with maleic anhydride and forms an endocyclic adduct. The absorption spectrum is given in Fig. 91. The deep green picrate melts at 197–198°.[2]

(V)   (VI)

(III)   (VII)

1.2,7.8-Dibenzoperylene-3,9-quinone can be obtained from the dilactone (V) which results from the Friedel–Crafts reaction of anthra-
quinone-1,5-dicarboxylic acid dichloride and benzene. Reduction with
hydriodic acid and red phosphorus in acetic acid gives the dicarboxylic
acid (VI). The cyclization is effected with concentrated sulphuric acid.[3]

(VIII)   (IX)

(III)   (XIII)

The quinone (III) can be oxidized to the diol (VII) with chromic acid.
Another synthesis of the quinone (III) consists in a condensation of
methyleneanthrone (VIII) in a melt with aluminium chloride. The

(X)   (III)

endocyclic compound (IX) splits out ethylene on heating and gives the quinone (III).[4]

A melt of 1,5-dibenzoylanthracene (X) with aluminium chloride and manganese dioxide gives also dibenzoperylenequinone (III).[5] Oxido- and sulpho-derivatives of the quinone (III) have also been prepared.[6] Other hydroxy derivatives can be obtained from the oxidation of certain hydroxyanthrones with iodine in pyridine, e.g. (XI) →(XII).[7]

(XI)   (XII)

1.2,7.8-Dibenzoperylene-3,9-quinone (III, hetero-coerdianthrone) crystallizes from acetic anhydride or pyridine in violet-bronze shining needles which dissolve in concentrated sulphuric acid to form a green solution. It gives a green vat with alkaline sodium dithionite which dyes cotton violet. Its solutions in organic solvents are violet with a strong red fluorescence. The solutions are photo-oxidizable to the endo- cyclic photo-oxide (XIII).[8]

REFERENCES

1. deBarry Barnett, E. and Matthews, M. A., *J. chem. Soc.* **123**, 2549 (1923).
2. Clar, E., *Ber. dtsch. chem. Ges.* **82**, 46 (1949).
3. Scholl, R., Meyer, K. and Winkler, W., *Liebigs Ann.* **494**, 201 (1932).
4. I.G. Farbenindustrie AG, German Patent 566518 (1930); 571523, 568034, 577560, 580010; *Chem. Zbl.* **1932 II**, 1526, 3790; **1933 II**, 620.
5. E. I. du Pont de Nemours & Co., Amer. Patent 1991687 (1933); *Chem. Zbl.* **1935 II**, 2454.
6. Scholl, R., Böttger, O. and Wanka, L., *Ber. dtsch. chem. Ges.* **67**, 599 (1934).
7. Perkin, A. G. and Haddock, N. H., *J. chem. Soc.* 1512 (1933).
8. Dufraisse, Ch. and Mellier, M. T., *C. R. Acad. Sci., Paris* **215**, 541 (1942).

V. 1.2,10.11-Dibenzoperylene

Dichloroanthrone (I) reacts with phenanthrene and aluminium chloride in benzene solution to form the brownish-yellow keto-form (II) of the red 3-hydroxy-1.2,10.11-dibenzoperylene (III). Reduction with zinc dust and acetic acid in pyridine gives the colourless compound (IV). Sublimation of the latter yields 1.2,10.11-dibenzoperylene (V).[1]

1,2,10,11-Dibenzoperylene (V) crystallizes from xylene in brick-red needles (m.p. 177–178°) which dissolve in concentrated sulphuric acid to form an olive-green solution. The solutions in organic solvents are yellow and show a yellow-green fluorescence. The absorption spectrum

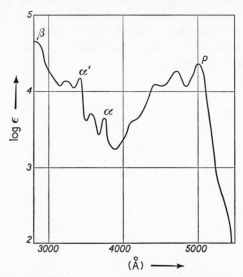

FIG. 92. Absorption spectrum of 1.2,10.11-dibenzoperylene in benzene: p, 5025 (4·36), 4710 (4·26), 4460 (4·08); α, 3760 (3·66), 3570 (3·70); 3410 (4·16), 3230 (4·13); β, 2850 (4·66).

is shown in Fig. 92. The hydrocarbon gives a violet quinone with selenium dioxide in acetic acid. The quinone which can have structure (VI) or (VII) forms a blue-green vat with sodium dithionite solution.[1]

REFERENCE

1. Clar, E. and Frömmel, H., *Ber. dtsch. chem. Ges.* **82**, 50 (1949).

VI. 1.2,11.12-DIBENZOPERYLENE

1.2,11.12-Dibenzoperylene-3,10-quinone (II, helianthrone) can be prepared from 1,1'-dianthraquinonyl (I) by reduction with copper powder in sulphuric acid or with a number of other reducing agents like zinc dust in acetic acid, stannous chloride in alcoholic hydrochloric acid, zinc in fused zinc chloride or zinc in alcoholic potassium hydroxide.[1]

Several derivatives of helianthrone (II) have been prepared in this way: carboxylic acids,[2] chloro-[3] and hydroxy derivatives.[4] 5,8-Dihydroxy-1.2,11.12-dibenzoperylene-3,10-quinone was obtained from 2-hydroxyanthraquinone,[5] other derivatives were prepared from hydroxyanthrones by oxidation.[6]

(I)   (II)   (III)

(IV)   (V)

Attempts to reduce helianthrone were at first unsuccessful.[7]

However, the zinc-dust melt yields a mixture of 1.2,11.12-dibenzoperylene (IV) and its dihydro derivative (III). The latter can be obtained in a pure state by a short treatment of its solution in xylene with maleic anhydride. Dibenzoperylene reacts immediately. The adduct (V) can be removed with sodium hydroxide solution. 1.2,11.12-Dibenzoperylene (IV) is best prepared by a reduction of helianthrone (II) in pyridine with zinc dust and acetic acid, followed by sublimation of the almost colourless reduction product.[8] It can be reduced also by a zinc-dust distillation. Its purification, particularly by chromatography, is complicated by its great reactivity.[9]

1.2,11.12-Dibenzoperylene (IV) forms dark red needles. Its solutions are very rapidly photo-oxidized to the endocyclic photo-oxide. The structure is supported by the fact that its absorption spectrum shows a close relation to 1.2,7.8-dibenzoperinaphthene. The absorption spectrum is shown in Fig. 93.

3,10-Dihydro-1.2,11.12-dibenzoperylene (III) crystallizes in pale yellow needles (m.p. 269–270°) from xylene and dissolves in concentrated sulphuric acid to form a green solution with a blue fluorescence. It forms bisanthene when dehydrogenated with copper.[8]

FIG. 93. Absorption spectrum of 1.2,11.12-dibenzoperylene in benzene: p, 5580 (4·08), 5160 (3·85), 4780 (3·54), 4460 (3·26); α, 3710 (3·88), 3530 (3·86); β, 3130 (4·36), 3000 (4·43).

6,7-Dimethyl-1.2,11.12-dibenzoperylene can be prepared from dimethylhelianthrone.[9] 3,10-Diphenyl-1.2,11.12-dibenzoperylene was obtained from the Grignard reaction of helianthrone with phenyl magnesium bromide and reduction of the resulting diol. Its photo-oxide

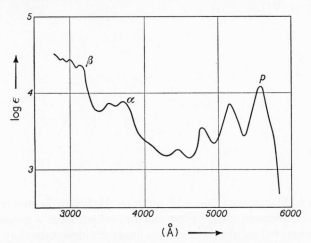

(VI)   (VII)   (VIII)

was given the structure (VI). However, the distribution of double bonds does not indicate the highest degree of aromaticity possible.[10]

Interesting results were obtained by an investigation of the photocyclization of dianthrone (VII). In the absence of air dihydrohelianthrone (VIII) is formed while aerial oxidation gives helianthrone (II).[11] The red acetyl derivative also gives a photo-oxide which has been formulated analogous to (VI).

(IX)

1.2,11.12-Dibenzoperylene-3,10-quinone (II, helianthrone) crystallizes from nitrobenzene in dark yellow needles which form a green solution with concentrated sulphuric acid. In a finely divided state they give with sodium dithionite solution a green vat which dyes cotton yellow. Helianthrone and dimethylhelianthrone (IX) can be separated into optically active isomers.[12]

REFERENCES

1. Scholl, German Patent 190799 (1906); Scholl, R. and Mansfeld, J., Ber. dtsch. chem. Ges. **43**, 1734 (1910).
2. Ullmann, F. and Minajew, W., Ber. dtsch. chem. Ges. **55**, 689 (1912); Scholl, R. and Tänzer, C., Liebigs Ann. **433**, 172 (1923).
3. Eckert, A. and Tomaschek, R., Mh. Chem. **39**, 839 (1918).
4. Scholl, R. and Seer, C., Ber. dtsch. chem. Ges. **44**, 1091 (1911).
5. Perkin, A. G. and Bradshaw, G. G., J. chem. Soc. **121**, 911 (1922); Perkin, A. G. and Whattam, T. W., J. chem. Soc. **121**, 297 (1922); Perkin, A. G. and Haller, J. W. E., J. chem. Soc. **125**, 231 (1924).
6. Perkin, A. G. and Yoda, G., J. chem. Soc. **127**, 1884 (1925); Attree, G. F. and Perkin, A. G., J. chem. Soc. 144 (1931); Perkin, A. G. and Haddock, N. H., J. chem. Soc. 1512 (1933).
7. Scholl, R. and Mansfeld, J., Ber. dtsch. chem. Ges. **43**, 1734, 1746 (1910).
8. Clar, E., Ber. dtsch. chem. Ges. **82**, 48 (1949).
9. Brockmann, H., Pohl, F., Mair, K. and Haschad, M. N., Liebigs Ann. **553**, 11 (1942).
10. Dufraisse, C. and Sauvage, G., C. R. Acad. Sci., Paris **225**, 126 (1947).
11. Brockmann, H. and Mühlmann, R., Ber. dtsch. chem. Ges. **82**, 348 (1949).
12. Theilacker, W. and Thomas, W., Liebigs Ann. **632**, 115 (1960).

VII. 1.2,5.6-DIBENZOPERYLENE

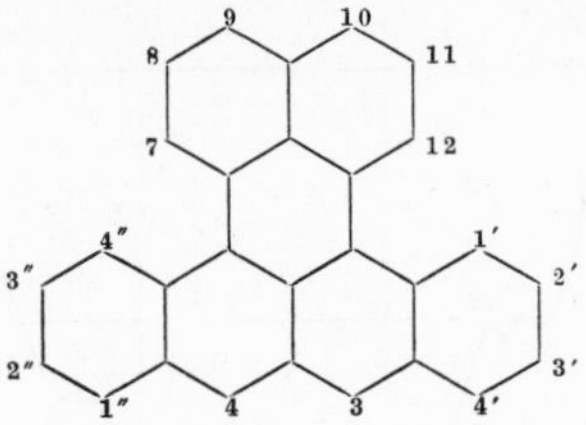

Tetracenone (I) reacts with naphthyl lithium to form naphthyltetra-cene (II). If this is submitted to a sodium chloride–aluminium chloride melt, cyclization is achieved with the formation of 1.2,5.6-dibenzo-perylene (III) and 2.3,6.7,10.11-tribenzofluoranthene (IV). Both hydro-carbons can be separated by chromatography.

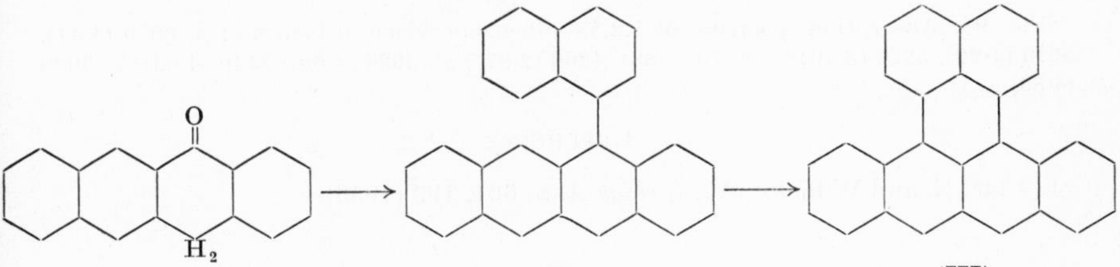

(I)   (II)   (III)

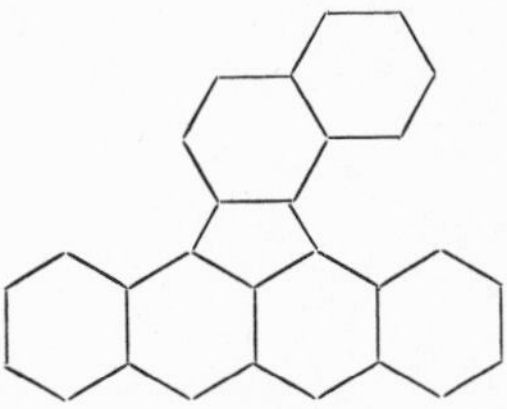

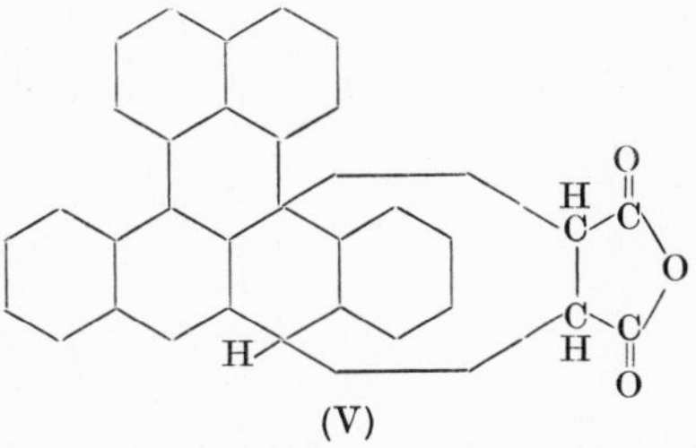

(IV)   (V)

1.2,5.6-Dibenzoperylene (III) forms red-violet needles (m.p. 238°) from xylene. The solutions in organic solvents are blue with a red fluorescence and are very photo-oxidizable. Dibenzoperylene (III) can be sublimed and dissolves in concentrated sulphuric acid to form a yellow solution which changes to emerald green. With maleic anhydride in xylene solu-tion an adduct is formed. This has the structure (V) as shown by the close relationship of its absorption spectrum to naphtho-(1'.2':7.8)-perinaphthene (see p. 402). The absorption spectrum of 1.2,5.6-dibenzo-perylene is shown in Fig. 94.[1]

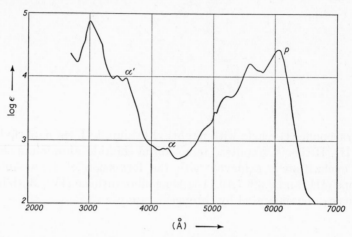

FIG. 94. Absorption spectrum of 1.2,5.6-dibenzoperylene in benzene: p, 6070 (4·44), 5610 (4·22), 5220 (3·70); α, 4270 (2·88), 4200 (2·87); α', 3620 (4·00), 3440 (4·03); β, 3020 (4·89).

REFERENCE

1. Clar, E. and Willicks, W., *Liebigs Ann.* **601**, 193 (1956).

VIII. 1.2,5.6,7.8,11.12-TETRABENZOPERYLENE

Only the quinone of this hydrocarbon has been described. 1-Hydroxy-2-naphthoyl-*o*-benzoic acid (I) gives the chloro compound (II) with phosphorus pentachloride and this is cyclized to (III). Ullmann reaction with copper powder in boiling nitrobenzene yields the ditetracene-quinone derivative (IV). The second cyclization to (V) is carried out with copper powder in concentrated sulphuric acid.

1.2,5.6,7.8,11.12-Tetrabenzoperylenequinone (V) crystallizes from dichlorobenzene in orange needles (m.p. > 350°) which give a green solution in concentrated sulphuric acid.[1]

REFERENCE

1. Waldmann, H. and Pollak, G., *J. prakt. Chem.* N.F. **150**, 113 (1938).

IX. 2.3,8.9-DIBENZOPERYLENE

If phenanthrene or phenanthrenedibromide is condensed with aluminium chloride in benzene a dibenzoperylene is formed which was thought to be 2.3,10.11-dibenzoperylene (I).[1] However, the later synthesis of the hydrocarbon (I) showed that it was not identical with the condensation product of phenanthrene which then must have the structure of 2.3,8.9-dibenzoperylene (II).[2]

(I)   (II)

2.3,8.9-Dibenzoperylene (II) was also prepared by a diene synthesis from benzoquinone and o-tolylbutadiene (III). The resulting anthraquinone derivative (IV) was brominated with bromosuccinimide to form (V). Replacement of the bromine atoms by nitrile groups gave (VI), involving a double cyclization.

(III)   (IV)   (V)

(VI)   (VII)   (II)

Saponification of the two nitrile groups with potassium hydroxide yielded the dicarboxylic acid (VII) and then 2.3,8.9-dibenzoperylene.[3] This is also one of the pyrolysis products of phenanthrene.[4]

2.3,8.9-Dibenzoperylene (II) crystallizes from nitrobenzene or xylene in long golden yellow needles (m.p. 343°), which are sublimable *in vacuo*. They dissolve in concentrated sulphuric acid to form a violet solution. Solutions in organic solvents show a strong blue fluorescence. Molecular compounds are obtained with picric acid, styphnic acid, antimony pentachloride and stannic chloride.[5] The absorption spectrum is given in Fig. 95.

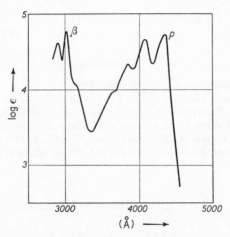

FIG. 95. Absorption spectrum of 2.3,8.9-dibenzoperylene in benzene: p, 4335 (4·71), 4080 (4·66), 3860 (4·32), 3655 (3·96); β, 3035 (4·77), 2910 (4·60).

2.3,8.9-Dibenzoperylenequinone (VIII or IX) is prepared from dibenzoperylene by oxidation with chromic anhydride in acetic acid. It can have the structure (VIII) or (IX). It crystallizes in deep brown needles (m.p. 377–378°), which dissolve in concentrated sulphuric acid to form a violet-brown solution. An orange-red vat is produced with alkaline sodium dithionite. The quinone can be oxidized to the pentacene

(VIII)   (IX)

56   POLYCYCLIC HYDROCARBONS

derivative (X) which could originate from the structures (VIII) or (IX).
Zinc-dust distillation of this compound (X) yields 2.3-benzonaphtho-
$(2''.3'':7.8)$-perinaphthene (XI) (see p. 423).[6]

(X)   (XI)

REFERENCES

1. Clar, E., *Ber. dtsch. chem. Ges.* **65**, 846 (1932).
2. Ioffe, I. S., *J. gen. Chem. U.S.S.R.* **3** (65), 524 (1933).
3. Braude, E. A., Fawcett, J. S. and Webb, A. A., *J. chem. Soc.* 1049 (1954).
4. Lang, K. F., Buffleb, H. and Kalowy, J., *Chem. Ber.* **93**, 303 (1960).
5. Brass, K. and Fanta, K., *Ber. dtsch. chem. Ges.* **69**, 1 (1936).
6. Zinke, A., Holzer, K. and Ziegler, E., *Mh. Chem.* **82**, 645 (1951).

X. 2.3,10.11-DIBENZOPERYLENE

2-Hydroxyphenanthrene (I) can be oxidized to 2,2'-dihydroxy-1,1'-
diphenanthrenyl (II) in acetic acid with ferric chloride. Zinc-dust distillation gives oxido-1,1'-diphenanthryl (III) together with oxidodibenzo-
perylene (IV). (V) can also be obtained from (II) via dihydroxydibenzo-
perylene by a condensation with aluminium chloride and sodium chloride
followed by a zinc-dust distillation.[1]

9.9'-Diphenanthryl (VIII) is prepared from the Grignard compound
of 9-bromophenanthrene (VII) and cupric chloride[2] or in low yield by
heating (VII) with copper powder.[3] The cyclization can be achieved in a
sodium chloride–aluminium chloride melt[3,4] or better in 50% yield

in benzene solution with aluminium chloride and stannic chloride.[5]
Dibenzoperylene (V) is one of the products of the pyrolysis of phenanthrene.[6]

2.3,10.11-Dibenzoperylene (V) can be synthesized from tetraphenyl-
thiophene (IX) which gives flavophene (X) when condensed with
aluminium chloride. This is desulphurized with Raney nickel in mesi-
tylene to dibenzoperylene (V).[7]

(I)   (II)   (III)   (IV)

(VII)   (VIII)   (V)   (VI)

(IX)   (X)   (XI)   (XII)

2.3,10.11-Dibenzoperylene (V) crystallizes from xylene in yellow needles which melt at 330–332° and dissolve in concentrated sulphuric acid to form a violet solution. Its solutions in organic solvents show a blue fluorescence and are photo-oxidizable. The absorption spectrum is given in Fig. 96. Dibenzoperylene (V) reacts very readily with maleic anhydride in boiling xylene with the formation of the colourless adduct (XII).[8]

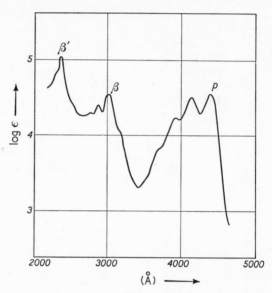

Fig. 96. Absorption spectrum of 2.3,10.11-dibenzoperylene in benzene: p, 4400 (4·54), 4140 (4·51), 3920 (4·22); in ethanol: β, 3020 (4·54), 2881 (4·41); β', 2380 (5·05).

2.3,10.11-Dibenzoperylene-1,12-quinone (VI) is obtained from the hydrocarbon by oxidation with chromic acid. It forms deep brown needles which are sublimable and dissolve in concentrated sulphuric acid to give a dark green solution. Alkaline sodium dithionite produces a yellow vat. In accordance with its constitution (VI) it forms the azine (XI) with hydrazine hydrate in pyridine solution. This is a yellow compound that gives a blue-violet solution in concentrated sulphuric acid.[9]

REFERENCES

1. Ioffe, I. S., *J. Gen. Chem. U.S.S.R.* **3** (65), 524 (1933); Crawford, M. and Supanekar, V. R., *J. chem. Soc.* 675 (1962).
2. Bachmann, W. E., *J. Amer. chem. Soc.* **56**, 1363 (1934).
3. Zinke, A. and Ziegler, E., *Ber. dtsch. chem. Ges.* **74**, 115 (1941).
4. Schauenstein, E. and Bürgermeister, E., *Ber. dtsch. chem. Ges.* **76**, 205 (1943).

5. Clar, E. and Zander, M., *J. chem. Soc.* 1861 (1958).
6. Lang, K. F., Buffleb, H. and Kalowy, J., *Chem. Ber.* **93**, 303 (1960).
7. Badger, G. M., Christie, B. J., Pryke, J. M. and Sasse, W. H., *J. chem. Soc.* 4417 (1957).
8. Clar, E. and Zander, M., *J. chem. Soc.* 1861 (1958).
9. Zinke, A., *Mh. Chem.* **80**, 202 (1949).

XI. DINAPHTHO-(2′.3′:2.3);(2″.3″:8.9)-PERYLENE

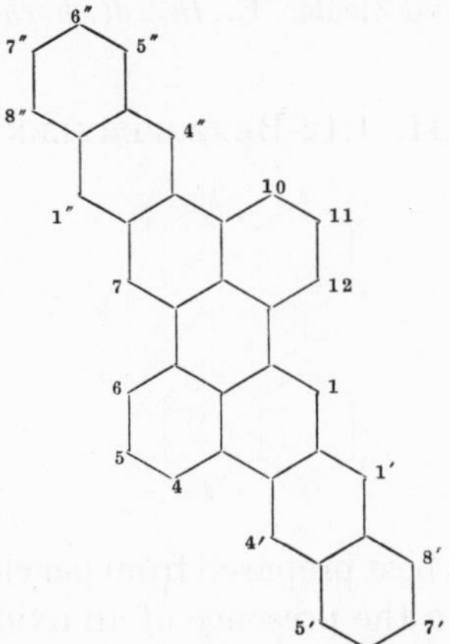

This hydrocarbon has not yet been described. Only a diquinone is known. This is obtained from a sodium chloride–aluminium chloride melt of perylene with excess phthalic anhydride.[1] An analogous reaction was carried out using chloro substituted phthalic anhydrides. Since the Friedel–Crafts reaction with perylene yields at least two isomers it is likely that the above condensation product consists of the two isomers (I) and (II).[2]

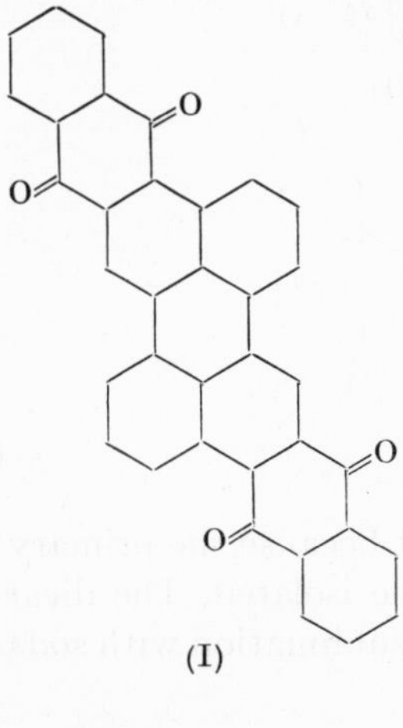

(I)

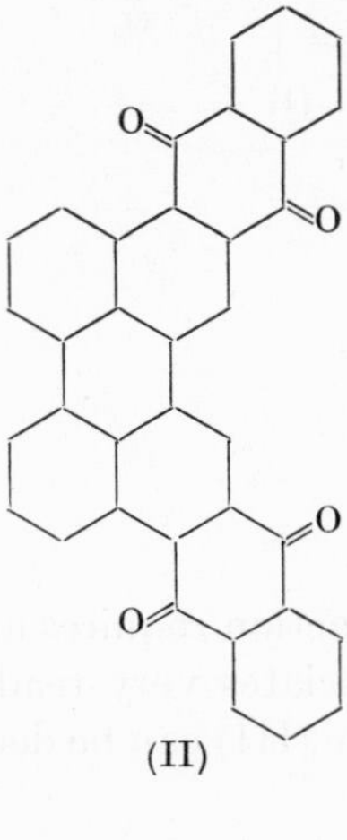

(II)

The condensation product forms dark green crystals from nitrobenzene and gives a blue-green solution with concentrated sulphuric acid. Alkaline sodium dithionite solution forms a blue vat which dyes cotton wine-red.

REFERENCES

1. Zinke, A., Gorbach, G. and Schimka, O., *Mh. Chem.* **48**, 593 (1927); I.G. Farbenindustrie AG, German Patent 642650 (1934).
2. Zinke, A., Troger, H. and Ziegler, E., *Ber. dtsch. chem. Ges.* **73**, 1042 (1940).

XII. 1.12-BENZOPERYLENE

1.12-Benzoperylene is best prepared from perylene (I) which condenses with maleic anhydride in the presence of an oxidizing agent, like nitrobenzene,[1] air, nitrogen oxides, lead dioxide and copper oxide.[2] However, a quantitative yield is obtained in boiling maleic anhydride with chloranil as an oxidizing agent.[3]

(I)   (II)

(III)   (IV)

The reaction requires an oxidizing agent because the primary adduct (II) dissociates very readily and cannot be isolated. The dicarboxylic anhydride (III) can be decarboxylated by sublimation with soda-lime.

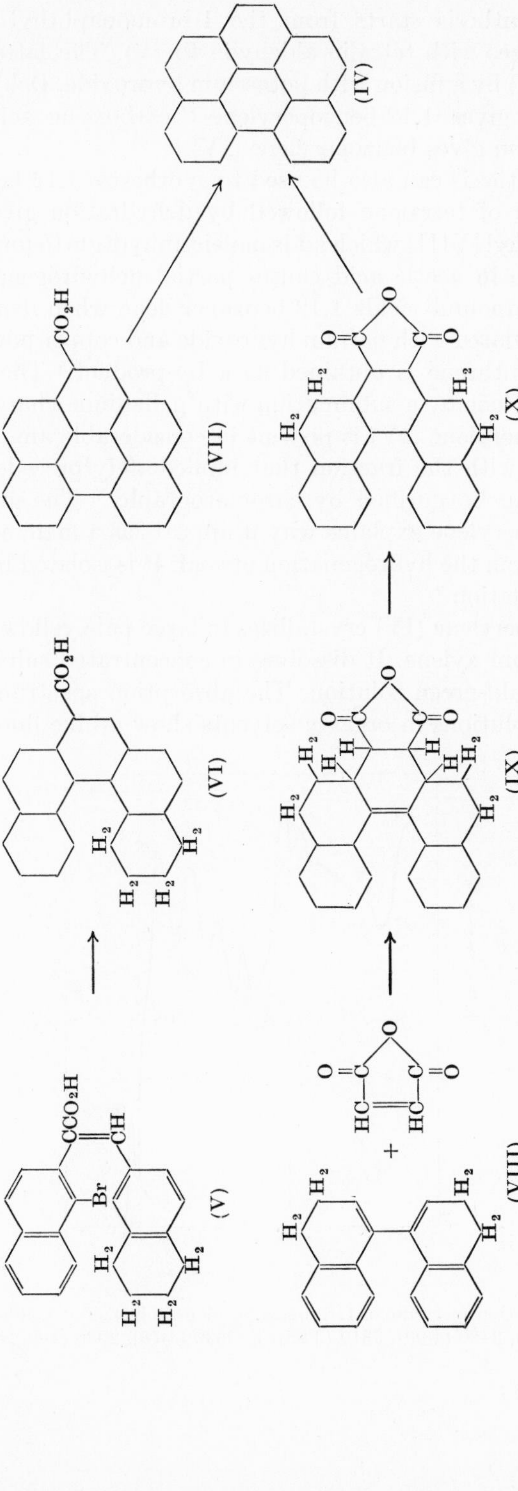
(IV)
(VII)
(X)
(VI)
(IX)
(V)
(VIII)

Another synthesis starts from the 1-bromonaphthyl-2-acetic acid which condenses with tetralin aldehyde to (V). The latter compound cyclizes to (VI) by a fusion with potassium hydroxide. Dehydrogenation with sulphur gives 1.12-benzoperylene-1'-carboxylic acid (VII) and decarboxylation gives benzoperylene (IV).[4]

A diene synthesis can also be used to synthesize 1.12-benzoperylene. The reduction of tetralone followed by dehydration gives the tetrahydrodinaphthyl (VIII) which adds maleic anhydride to form the adduct (IX). Bromine in acetic acid causes partial dehydrogenation to (X). The latter compound yields 1.12-benzoperylene when dehydrogenated and decarboxylated with barium hydroxide and copper powder. 3.4,5.6-Dibenzophenanthrene is obtained as a by-product.[5] The latter gives also benzoperylene by a sublimation with palladium–charcoal.

1.12-Benzoperylene (IV) is present in considerable amounts in coal-tar. It distils with the fraction that immediately precedes the picene fraction. It can be purified by chromatography.[6] The great stability of 1.12-benzoperylene explains why it appears as a main constituent in the residues from the hydrogenation of coal. It is isolated by a dehydrogenating distillation.[7]

1.12-Benzoperylene (IV) crystallizes in large pale yellow-green plates (m.p. 273°) from xylene. It dissolves in concentrated sulphuric acid to form an emerald-green solution. The absorption spectrum is given in Fig. 97. The solutions in organic solvents show a blue fluorescence. Its

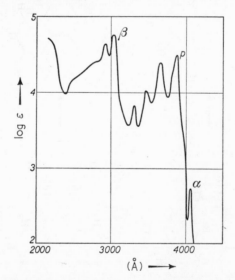

FIG. 97. Absorption spectrum of 1.12-benzoperylene in benzene: α, 4065 (2·70); p, 3875 (4·50), 3670 (4·40), 3480 (4·00), 3310 (3·82); β, 3030 (4·76), 2920 (4·65), from 2800 Å in ethanol.

fluorescence spectrum has been recorded.[8] The crystal structure has been determined and the C—C distances measured.[9] Benzoperylene forms a picrate (m.p. 267°) and other molecular compounds with styphnic acid, antimony pentachloride and stannic chloride.[10] An alkyl-benzoperylene was isolated from fossil sea-lilies embedded in sedimentary rocks.[11] Alkyl-benzoperylenes were also obtained by a zinc-dust melt of erythroaphin.[12]

A dibromo-1.12-benzoperylene is formed as a by-product when bromomaleic anhydride reacts with 1.12-benzoperylene to form coronene-dicarboxylic anhydride.[13] A number of other derivatives can be prepared from perylene derivatives by the maleic anhydride method. 3,9-Dichloro-, 3,9-dibenzoyl-, tribenzoyl- and a diphenylace-1.12-benzoperylene were obtained from the corresponding perylene derivatives.[14]

REFERENCES

1. Clar, E., Ber. dtsch. chem. Ges. **65**, 846 (1932).
2. I.G. Farbenindustrie AG, German Patent 651677 (1934); Chem. Zbl. **1938** I, 2448.
3. Clar, E. and Zander, M., J. chem. Soc. 4616 (1957).
4. Hewett, C. L., J. chem. Soc. 1286 (1938).
5. Weidlich, H. A., Ber. dtsch. chem. Ges. **71**, 1203 (1938); Altman, Y. and Ginzburg, D., J. chem. Soc. 466 (1959).
6. Cook, J. W. and Percy, N., J. Soc. chem. Ind. **64**, 27 (1945).
7. I.G. Farbenindustrie AG, Brit. Patent 470338 (1936); 497089 (1937); French Patent 816162 (1937); Chem. Zbl. **1937** II, 3846; French Patent 49332 (1938); Belg. Patent 427268 (1938); Chem. Zbl. **1939** I, 3832; Brit. Patent 510736 (1938).
8. Brown, E. J. and Brocklehurst, B., J. chem. Soc. 3875 (1954); 4320 (1955).
9. White, J. G., J. chem. Soc. 1398 (1948).
10. Brass, K. and Fanta, K., Ber. dtsch. chem. Ges. **69**, 3 (1936).
11. Blumer, M., Mikrochemie 1048 (1951); Geochimica et Cosmochimica Acta **26**, 225 (1962); Science **134**, 3477 (1961).
12. Brown, B. R., Johnson, A. W., Quayle, J. R. and Todd, A. R., J. chem. Soc. 107 (1954).
13. Clar, E. and Zander, M., J. chem. Soc. 4616 (1957).
14. Zinke, A., Noculak, U., Skrabal, R. and Troger, H., Ber. dtsch. chem. Ges. **73**, 1187 (1940).

XIII. 1.12,2.3-DIBENZOPERYLENE

3.4-Benzonaphthanthrene, which can have the two structures (I) and (II), adds maleic anhydride to form the succinic anhydride (III) or (IV). When fused with sodium chloride and zinc chloride the cyclization of both compounds should give 1.12,2.3-dibenzoperylene (V).

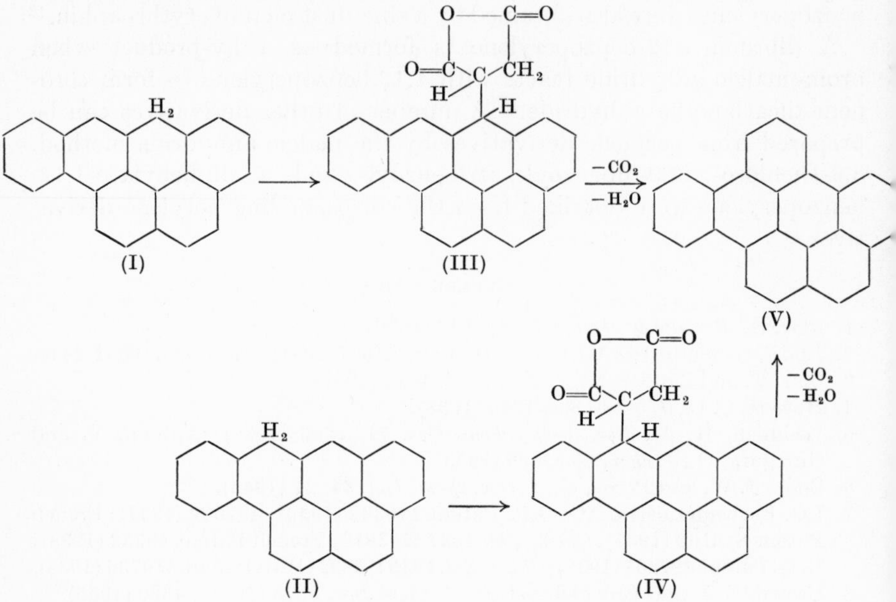

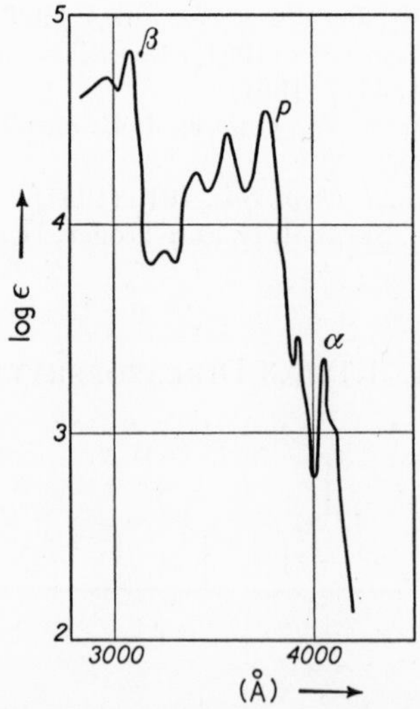

Fig. 98. Absorption spectrum of 1.12,2.3-dibenzoperylene in benzene: α, 4050 (3·36), 3920 (3·44); p, 3775 (4·55), 3585 (4·45), 3430 (4·24), 3270 (3·88); β, 3095 (4·84), 2970 (4·73).

1.12,2.3-Dibenzoperylene (V) crystallizes from xylene in pale yellow leaflets or flat needles (m.p. 288°), which dissolve in concentrated sulphuric acid to give a red solution which soon changes to yellow-green. The solution in xylene shows a strong blue fluorescence. The absorption spectrum is given in Fig. 98.[1]

REFERENCE

1. Clar, E., *Chem. Ber.* **81**, 520 (1948).

XIV. 1.12,2.3,8.9-TRIBENZOPERYLENE

2.3,8.9-Dibenzoperylene (I) reacts with maleic anhydride in boiling nitrobenzene[1] or better with boiling maleic anhydride and chloranil[1] or with bromomaleic anhydride alone[2] to form the dicarboxylic anhydride (II). The decarboxylation to 1.12,2.3,8.9-tribenzoperylene (III) is effected by a sublimation *in vacuo* with soda-lime.

(I)   (II)   (III)

1.12,2.3,8.9-Tribenzoperylene (III) crystallizes from 1-methylnaphthalene or sublimes *in vacuo* as long yellow needles (m.p. 391°), which

II—3

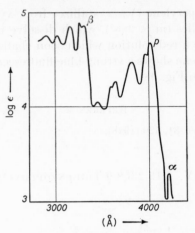

FIG. 99. Absorption spectrum of 1.12,2.3,8.9-tribenzoperylene in benzene: α, 4210 (3·27); p, 4020 (4·66), 3920 (4·46), 3630 (4·27), 3440 (4·04); β, 3290 (4·86), 3155 (4·84), 3030 (4·74), 2910 (4·74).

dissolve in concentrated sulphuric acid to form a violet solution which changes to brown. The solutions in benzene or xylene show a strong blue fluorescence. The absorption spectrum is given in Fig. 99.

REFERENCES

1. Clar, E., *Ber. dtsch. chem. Ges.* **65**, 846 (1932); *Chem. Ber.* **82**, 53 (1949).
2. Clar, E. and Zander, M., *J. chem. Soc.* 4616 (1957).

XV. 1.12,2.3,10.11-TRIBENZOPERYLENE

2.3,10.11-Dibenzoperylene (I) very readily adds maleic anhydride in boiling xylene to form the adduct (II). This can be directly dehydrogenated to the anhydride (III) if the reaction is carried out in boiling xylene with chloranil as dehydrogenating agent. Decarboxylation of the anhydride (III) by sublimation *in vacuo* with soda-lime gives tribenzo-perylene (IV).

The dehydrogenation of the adduct (II) can be achieved in stages. An alkaline solution of the dicarboxylic acid derived from the adduct (II) is dehydrogenated by atmospheric oxygen to a yellow acid, derived from (V). The absorption spectrum shows that it contains the aromatic complex of dibenzoperylene (I). If the solution of (V) is boiled in trichloro-benzene the spectrum changes to a type closely related to the adduct (II), indicating isomerization to the form (VI). The high reactivity of

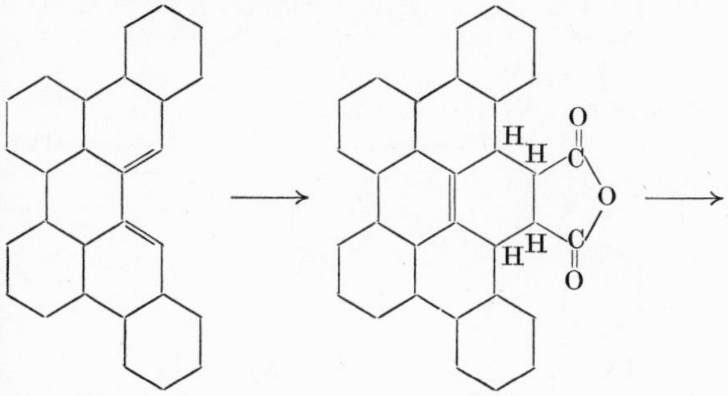

(I)   (II)

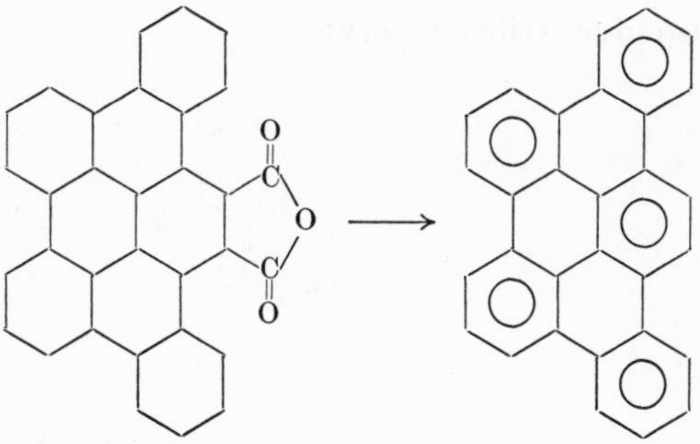

(III)   (IV)

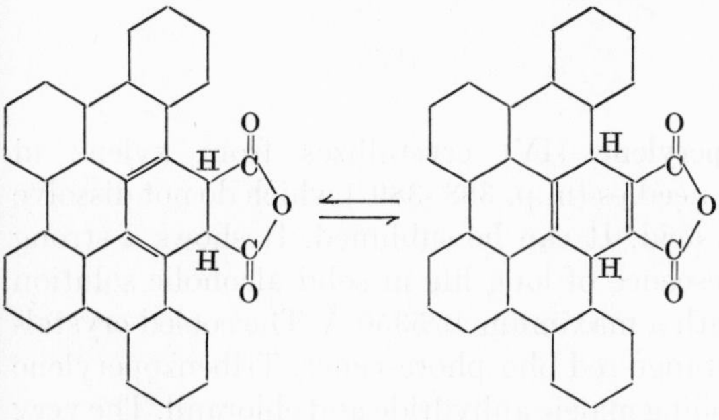

(V)   (VI) 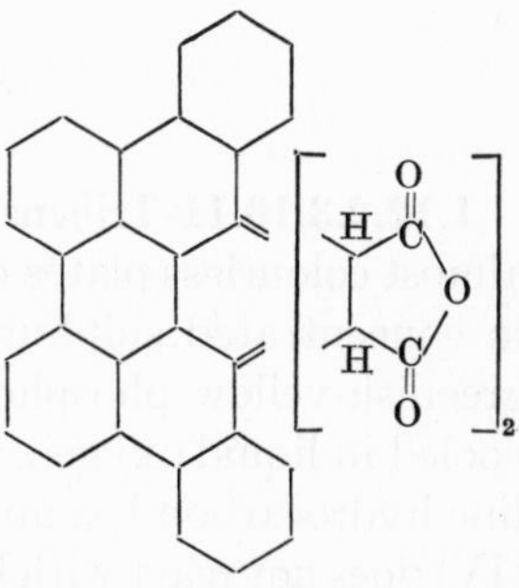   (VII)

dibenzoperylene (I) is retained in its derivative (V) which adds another
molecule of maleic anhydride to form the adduct (VII).[1]

Tribenzoperylene (IV) was also synthesized from phencyclone (VIII).[2]
This reacted with maleic anhydride in boiling nitrobenzene to yield the
anhydride (IX). Its decarboxylation to (X) was carried out with copper
carbonate in boiling quinoline. The diphenyl-triphenylene (X) was
cyclized in a sodium chloride–aluminium chloride melt.[3]

(VIII)   (IX)   (X)

Cyclization of the dibenzopicene (XI) with palladium–charcoal
also gives tribenzoperylene.[4]

(XI)   (IV)

1.12,2.3,10.11-Tribenzoperylene (IV) crystallizes from xylene in
almost colourless plates or needles (m.p. 388–389°) which do not dissolve
in concentrated sulphuric acid. It can be sublimed. It shows a strong
greenish-yellow phosphorescence of long life in solid alcoholic solution
cooled in liquid oxygen, with a maximum at 5350 Å. The cooled crystalline hydrocarbon has an orange-red phosphorescence. Tribenzoperylene
(IV) does not react with boiling maleic anhydride and chloranil. The very
low reactivity and the stability of tribenzoperylene is explained by the

structure (IV) which presents a condensed polyphenyl containing five benzenoid rings marked with circles.[1] For the absorption spectrum see Fig. 100.

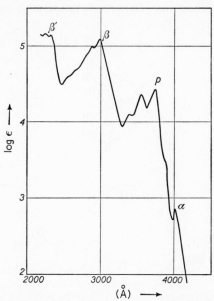

FIG. 100. Absorption spectrum of 1.12,2.3,10.11-tribenzoperylene in 1,2,4-trichloro-benzene: α, 4010 (2·86); p, 3740 (4·45), 3540 (4·37), 3380 (4·11); in ethanol: β, 3000 (5·09), 2880 (5·00); β', 2340 (5·14).

REFERENCES

1. Clar, E. and Zander, M., *J. chem. Soc.* 1861 (1958).
2. Dilthey, W., Horst, I., and Schaefer, A., *J. prakt. Chem.* **148**, 53 (1937).
3. Reimlinger, H. and van Overstraeten, A., *Chem. Ber.* **91**, 2053.
4. Jenard-De Koninck, A., Defay, N. and de Ridder, R., *Bull. Soc. chim. Belg.* **69**, 558 (1960).

XVI. 1.12,4.5,8.9-TRIBENZOPERYLENE

1.2,3.4-Tetrahydro-1-keto-phenanthrene (IV) gives the pinacol (II) with amalgamated aluminium. Dehydration leads to (III). This adds maleic anhydride to form the adduct (IV) which can be partially dehydrogenated to (V) with bromine. Decarboxylation with copper carbonate in

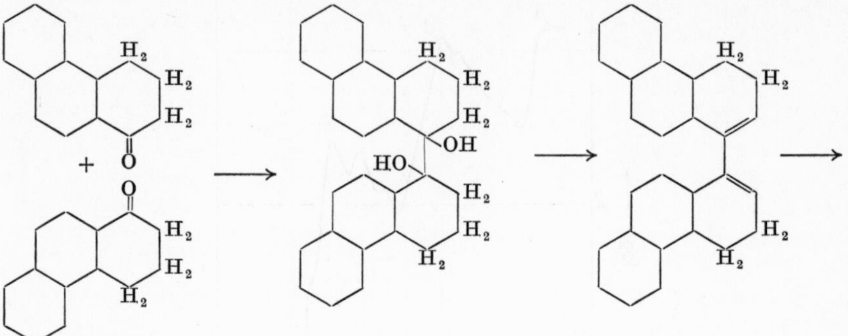

(I)   (II)   (III)

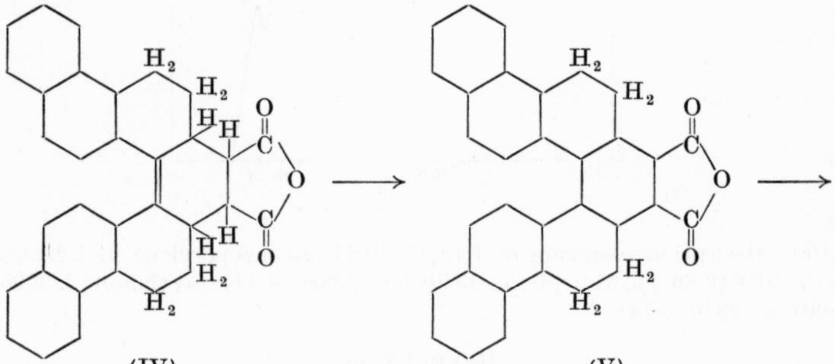

(IV)   (V)

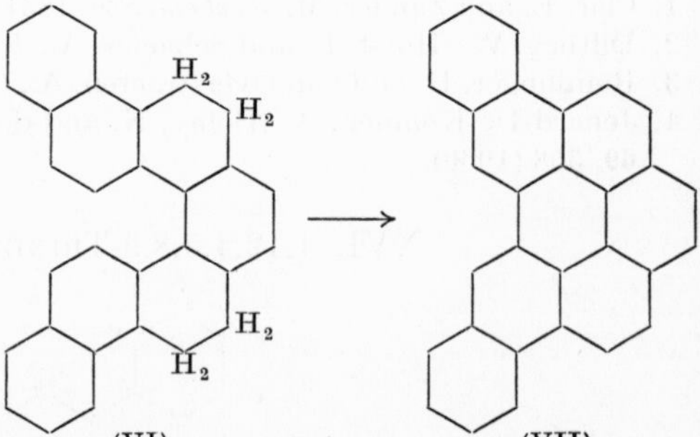

(VI)   (VII)

boiling quinoline yields (VI) which cyclizes with aluminium chloride to tribenzoperylene (VII). Dehydrogenation of the anhydride (V) with palladium–charcoal at 300° gives tribenzoperylene directly.

1.12,4.5,8.9-Tribenzoperylene (VII) crystallizes in yellow needles (m.p. 371–372°) from benzene. The fluorescence of the solution is blue.[1]

REFERENCE

1. Renninger, H. and van Overstraeten, A., *Chem. Ber.* **91**, 2053 (1958).

XVII. 1.12,5.6,7.8-TRIBENZOPERYLENE

The reduction of 2,2′-dimethyl-1,1′-dianthraquinonyl (I) in concentrated sulphuric acid with copper powder gives 6,7-dimethyl-1.2,11.12-dibenzoperylene-3,10-quinone (II). Cyclization of the methyl groups can be achieved by oxidation in boiling nitrobenzene with barium oxide or a melt with alcoholic potassium hydroxide or with potassium hydroxide and aniline. The resulting 1.12,5.6,7.8-tribenzoperylene-4,9-quinone (III) is a vat dye which dyes cotton orange.[1] Reduction with zinc dust and acetic acid in pyridine followed by sublimation *in vacuo* gives the hydrocarbon (IV).

(I)   (II)

(III)   (IV)   (V)

1.12,5.6,7.8-Tribenzoperylene (IV) has not been obtained in a pure state because it goes readily over into 1.14-benzobisanthene (V). It forms yellow crystals which show the following absorption bands in benzene solution: 4650, 4370, 4140 Å.[2]

REFERENCES

1. I.G. Farbenindustrie AG, German Patent 456583 (1926); C. **1928** I, 2011.
2. Clar, E., *Chem. Ber.* **82**, 54 (1949).

XVIII. 1.12-*o*-PHENYLENEPERYLENE

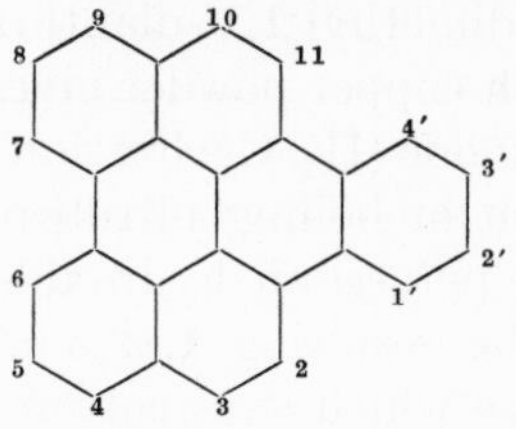

Tetrahydrodinaphthyl (I), which can be obtained by reduction of tetralone, reacts with benzoquinone to form the quinone (II).[1] This can be reduced in a zinc-dust melt to phenyleneperylene (III), cyclization taking place simultaneously.[2]

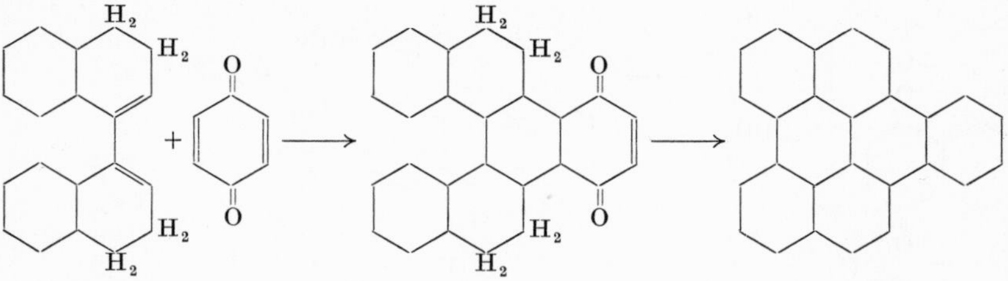

(I)   (II)   (III)

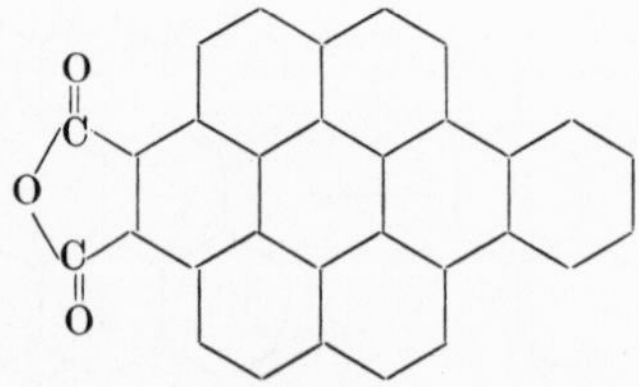

(IV) 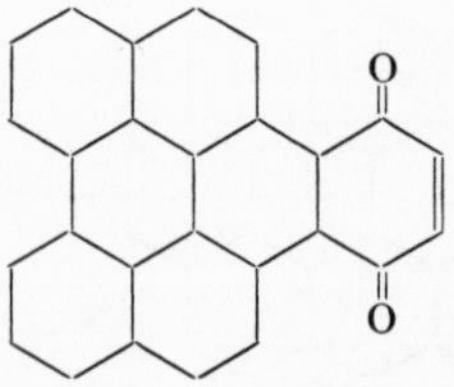   (V)

1.12-*o*-Phenyleneperylene (III) crystallizes in long yellow needles (m.p. 268–270°) from benzene, which dissolve in concentrated sulphuric acid to form a green, violet and then brown solution. The absorption spectrum is given in Fig. 101. It reacts readily with boiling maleic anhydride and chloranil to give benzocoronene-dicarboxylic anhydride (IV).[2]

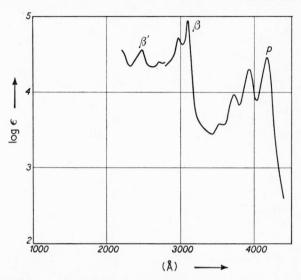

FIG. 101. Absorption spectrum of 1,12-o-phenyleneperylene in benzene: p, 4180 (4·47), 3940 (4·31), 3730 (3·98), 3530 (3·58); β, 3105 (4·96), 2975 (4·74); in cyclohexane: 2720 (4·40): β', 2490 (4·56).

1.12-o-Phenyleneperylene-1',4'-quinone (V) can be obtained in poor yield from perylene and benzoquinone in nitrobenzene. It forms dark violet needles (m.p. > 360°), which dissolve in concentrated sulphuric acid with a green colour.[3]

REFERENCES

1. Bergmann, F., Eschinazi, H. E. and Neeman, M., J. org. Chem. 8, 179 (1943).
2. Clar, E., Ironside, C. T. and Zander, M., Tetrahedron 6, 358 (1959).
3. Hopff, H. and Schweizer, H. R., Helv. chim. Acta 42, 2315 (1959).

XIX. ANTHRACENO-(1'.4':1.12)-PERYLENE

Tetrahydrodinaphthyl (I) condenses with *p*-naphthoquinone to yield the quinone (II). Reduction and simultaneous cyclization can be achieved in a zinc-dust melt.

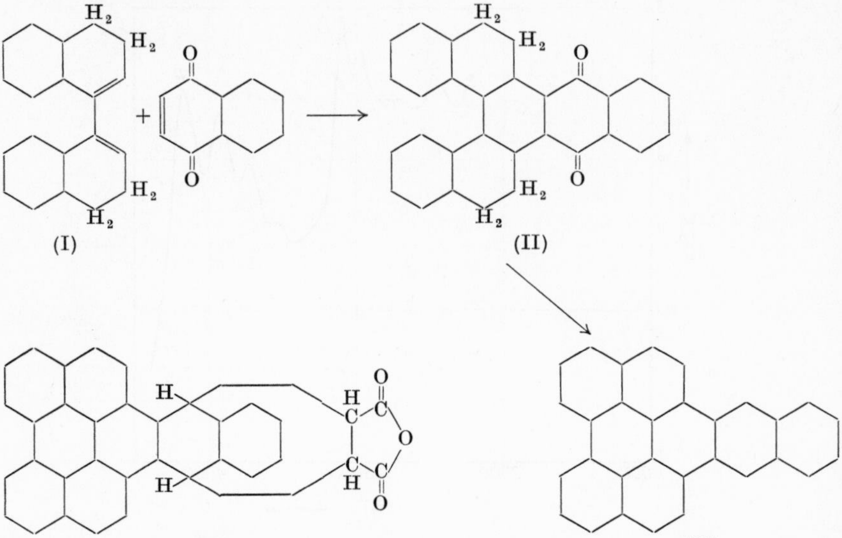

(I) (II) (IV) (III)

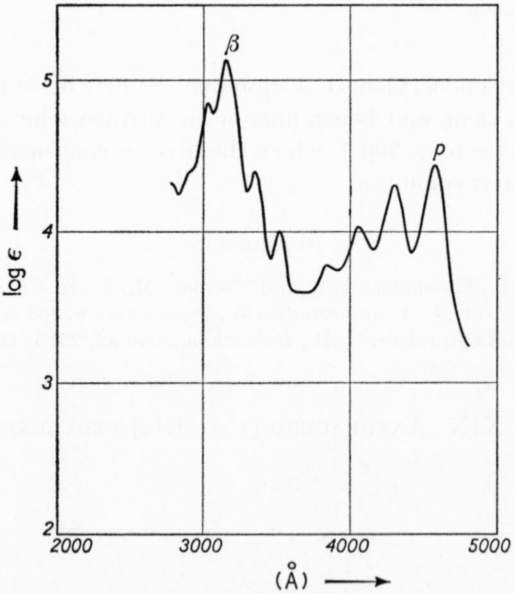

FIG. 102. Absorption spectrum of anthraceno-(1′.4′:1.12)-perylene in benzene: *p*, 4575 (4·44), 4300 (4·30), 4055 (4·03), 3845 (3·78); 3520 (4·00), 3345 (4·40); β, 3153 (5·14), 3023 (4·86).

Anthraceno-(1′.4′:1.12)-perylene (III) crystallizes from xylene in yellow needles (m.p. 356°), which dissolve in concentrated sulphuric acid to give an olive green solution. It adds maleic anhydride to form the adduct (IV) whose absorption spectrum shows the aromatic complex of 1.12-benzoperylene. The absorption spectrum of anthracenoperylene is given in Fig. 102.[1]

REFERENCE

1. Ironside, C. T., Thesis, Glasgow (1959), p. 39.

XX. 1.12-o-PHENYLENE-2.3-BENZOPERYLENE

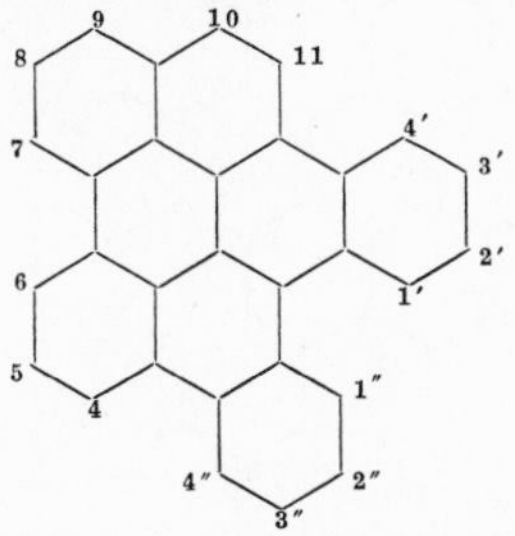

Chrysenequinone (I) reacts with two molecules of phenyl magnesium bromide to give the diol (II). This can be reduced to 1,2-diphenyl-

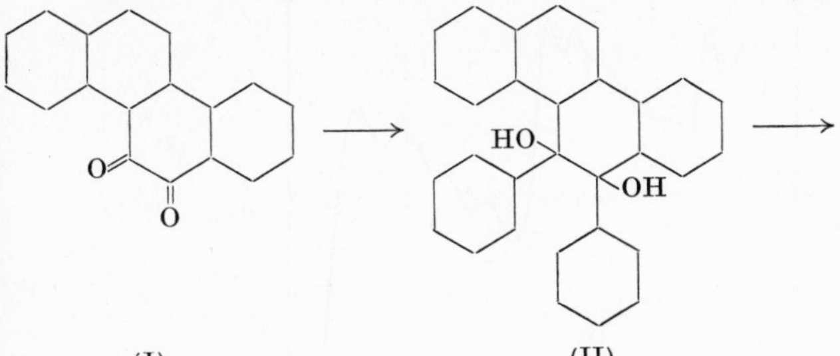

(I) (II)

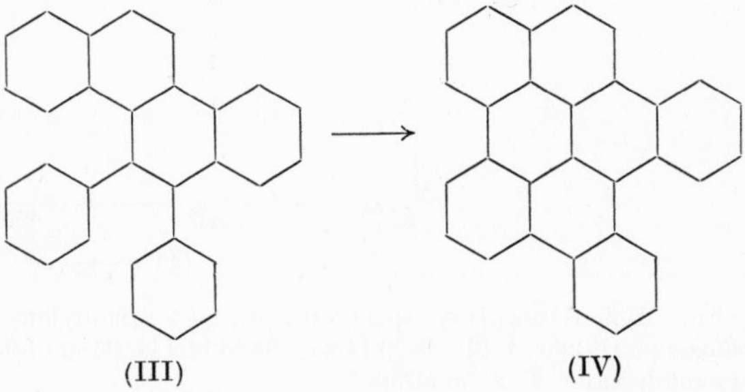

(III) (IV)

chrysene (III) via a retropinacol re-arrangement. Cyclization in a sodium chloride–aluminium chloride melt yields smoothly phenylene-benzoperylene (IV).[1]

1.12-o-Phenylene-2.3-benzoperylene forms crystals of m.p. 243–244°.

REFERENCE

1. Adriaensen, P. and Martin, R. H., Private communication.

XXI. 1.12-o-PHENYLENE-2.3,10.11-DIBENZOPERYLENE

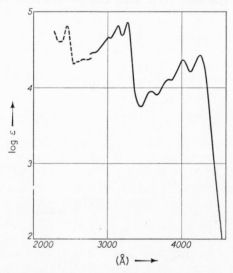

The keto-acid (I) is obtained by a condensation of octahydrophenanthrene with phthalic anhydride and aluminium chloride. Cyclization

FIG. 103. Absorption spectrum of 1.12-o-phenylene-2.3,10.11-dibenzoperylene in benzene: p, 4260 (4·43), 4020 (4·37), 3820 (4·11), 3580 (3·95); β, 3260 (4·87), 3130 (4·82); in cyclohexane: β', 2450 (4·80).

with hydrofluoric acid gives the quinone (II) and reaction with phenyl lithium the diol (III). If this is treated with hydrochloric acid in acetic acid, water is eliminated and a hydrocarbon formed which probably has the structure (IV). Dehydrogenation with copper powder at 400° gives the hydrocarbon (V).

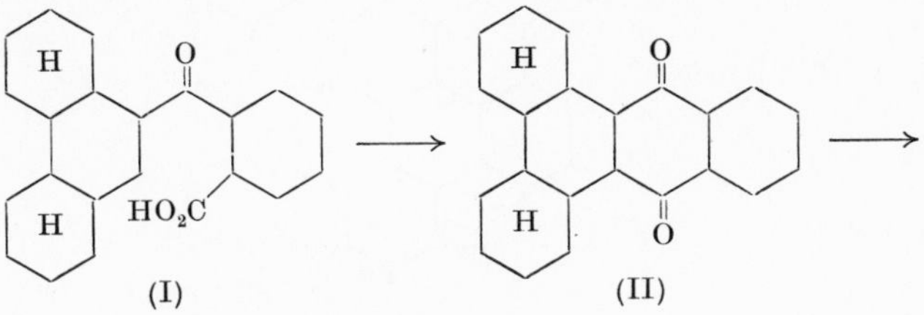

(I)   (II)

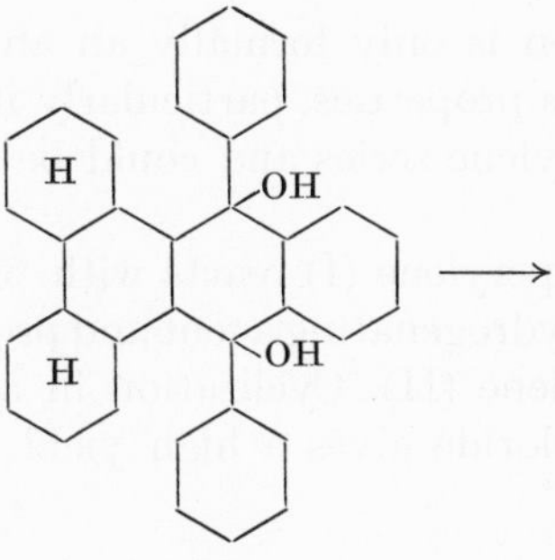

(III)

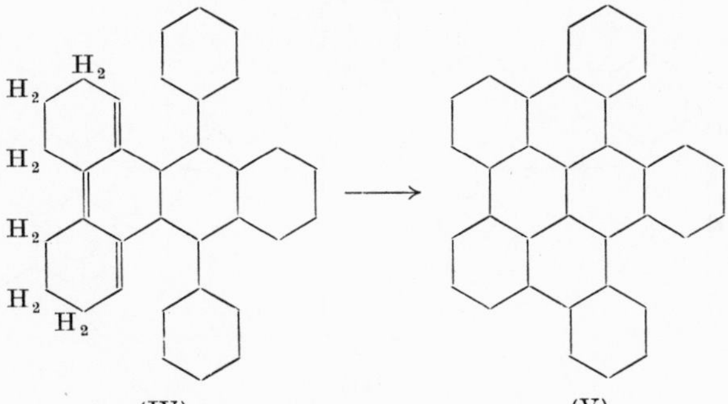

(IV)   (V)

1.12-o-Phenylene-2.3,10.11-dibenzoperylene (V) forms yellow fern-like crystals (m.p. 324–324·5°) which dissolve slowly in concentrated sulphuric acid to give a blue solution. The hydrocarbon does not react with maleic anhydride and chloranil. The absorption spectrum is shown in Fig. 103.[1]

REFERENCE

1. Clar, E. and McCallum, A., Tetrahedron, in press.

XXII. 1.2,3.4,5.6,10.11-Tetrabenzanthanthrene

This hydrocarbon is only formally an anthanthrene derivative. In accordance with its properties, particularly its absorption spectrum, it belongs to the perylene series and could be called an o-phenylene-tri-benzoperylene.

2.3,9.10-Dibenzoperylene (I) reacts with phenylacetylene, the latter acting also as a dehydrogenating agent and producing 1'-phenyl-1.12,2.3, 10.11-tribenzoperylene (II). Cyclization in a melt of sodium chloride and aluminium chloride gives a high yield of tetrabenzanthanthrene (III).

(I)   (II)   (III)

1.2,3.4,5.6,10.11-Tetrabenzanthanthrene (III) crystallizes from trichlorobenzene in long flat greenish-yellow needles (m.p. 434–436°) which do not dissolve in concentrated sulphuric acid. It shows a strong yellow phosphorescence (band at 5440 Å) of long life in solid solution in dioxane cooled in liquid nitrogen. These properties are in accordance with the structure of a fully benzenoid hydrocarbon as indicated by the aromatic sextets (marked with circles) in formula (III). The absorption spectrum is given by Fig 104.[1]

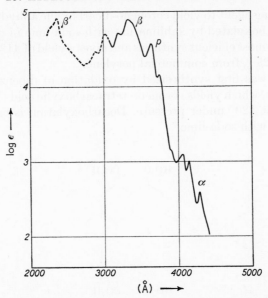

FIG. 104. Absorption spectrum of 1.2,3.4,5.6,10.11-tetrabenzanthanthrene in 1,2,4-trichlorobenzene: α, 4300 (2·60), 4150 (3·01), 4050 (3·09), 3750 (4·15); p, 3650 (4·57); β, 3340 (4·89), 3200 (4·70); in dioxane: 3020 (4·70), 2900 (4·47); β', 2380 (4·91).

REFERENCE

1. Clar, E., Ironside, C. T. and Zander, M., *J. chem. Soc.* 142 (1959).

XXIII. CORONENE

The simplest synthesis of coronene starts from 1.12-benzoperylene (I) which condenses readily with boiling maleic anhydride and chloranil as an oxidizing agent to yield coronene-dicarboxylic anhydride (II). This can be decarboxylated by sublimation with soda-lime *in vacuo*.

This is the most efficient synthesis and gives a yield of 41% from benzo-perylene or 25% from commercial perylene.[1]

Coronene was first synthesized by oxidation of dibenzoperopyrene-quinone (IV), which yields coronene-tetracarboxylic acid (V) with dilute nitric acid at 220° under pressure. Decarboxylation is carried out by sublimation with soda-lime.[2]

(IV)　　　　　　　　　(V)　　　　　　　　(III)

Another synthesis of coronene starts from methyltetralone (VI) which gives the pinacol (VII) with amalgamated aluminium. Dehydration leads to the diene (VIII), which reacts with maleic anhydride to form the adduct (IX). Partial dehydrogenation with lead tetra-acetate in acetic acid gives the anhydride (X), and dehydrogenation with palladium–charcoal at 320–350° gives the anhydride (XI) and the acid (XII). Both compounds can be cyclized and decarboxylated to coronene (III) with molten potassium hydroxide at 320°. The yield is 5·5%.[3]

Xylylene-dibromide (XIII) gives the cyclic system (XIV) with sodium. Its dehydrogenation with palladium oxide effects cyclization to coro-nene in 1·9% yield.[4] A related synthesis starts with 2,7-dimethyl-naphthalene (XV) which can be brominated to (XVI) with bromosucci-nimide in 49% yield. Sodium in dioxane leads to the ring system (XVII) and its dehydrogenation with palladium gives coronene (III) in 49% yield. If the cyclization of (XVII) is carried out with aluminium chloride in carbon disulphide, 1,2-dihydrocoronene (XVIII) is obtained besides coronene. The former is easily dehydrogenated with palladium.[5]

An almost unlimited supply of coronene could be obtained by hydro-genation of coal or coal extracts.[6] The mechanism of its formation has been reviewed.[7]

Coronene has been isolated from the highest boiling fraction of coal-tar by chromatography.[8] It has also been isolated from soil and fossils.[9]

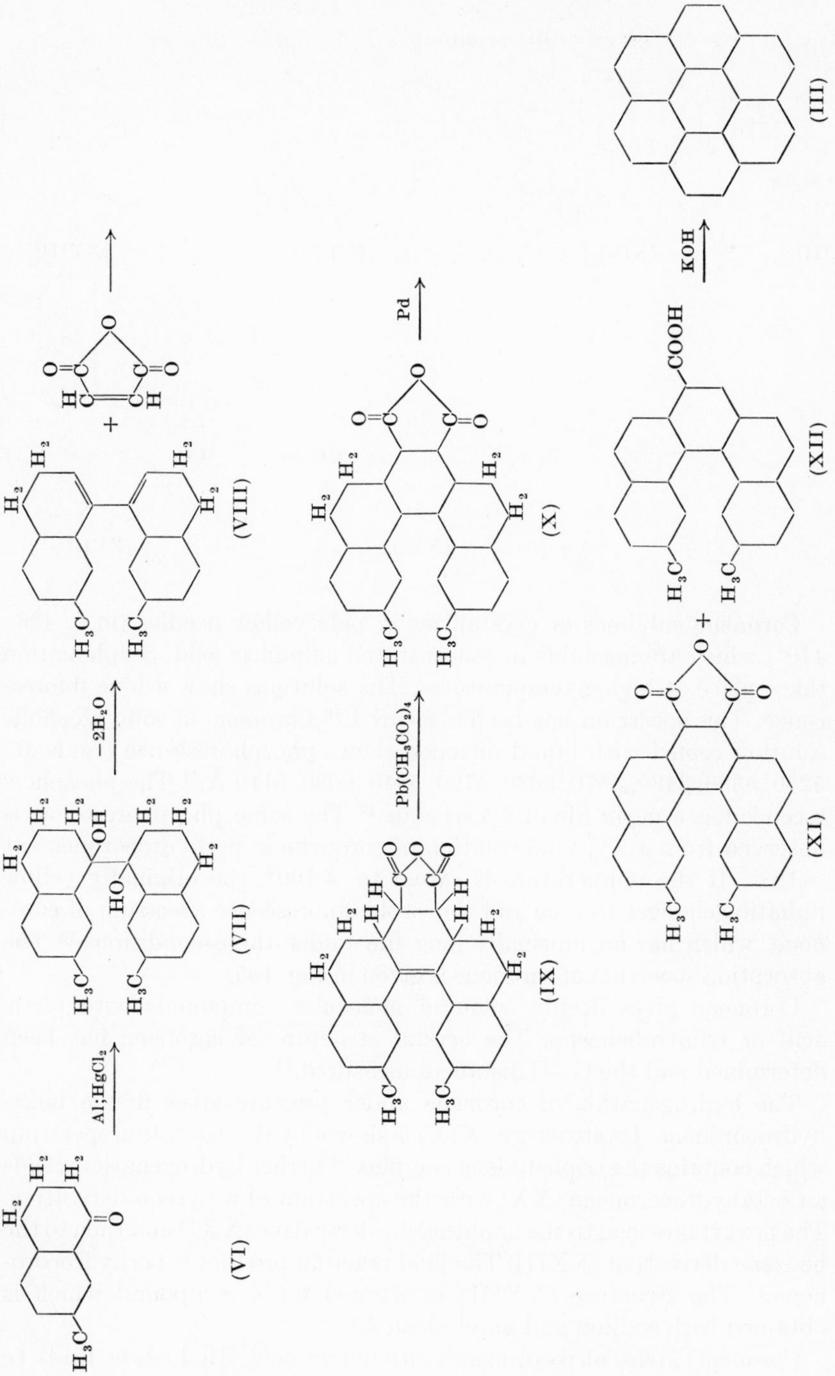
(VI)
Al;HgCl2
(VII)
−2H2O
(VIII)
Pb(CH3CO2)4
(IX)
Pd
(X)
(XI)
KOH
(XII)
(III)

CH$_2$Br

Na →

(XIII)   (XIV)   (III)   (XVIII)

H

H

H$_3$C   CH$_3$ BrH$_2$C   CH$_2$Br   Na →   H$_2$C   CH

(XV)   (XVI)   (XVII)

Coronene sublimes or crystallizes in pale yellow needles (m.p. 438–440°) which are insoluble in concentrated sulphuric acid. Sulphonation takes place at higher temperatures. The solutions show a blue fluorescence. This spectrum has been measured.[10] Coronene in solid alcoholic solution cooled with liquid nitrogen shows phosphorescence bands at: 5250, 5390, 5480, 5570, 5630, 5790, 5940, 6030, 6110 Å.[11] The phosphorescence has a mean life of 9·4 seconds.[12] The same phosphorescence is observed from a 2% solid solution of coronene in perhydrocoronene at −198°. If the temperature is raised to +100°, the originally yellow radiation changes to blue and shows the fluorescence spectrum of coronene, which has an unusually long life under these conditions.[13] The absorption spectrum of coronene is given in Fig. 105.

Coronene gives deeply coloured molecular compounds with picric acid or trinitrobenzene. The crystal structure of coronene has been determined and the C—C distances measured.[14]

The hydrogenation of coronene under pressure gives first a hexahydrocoronene. Its structure (XIX) is shown by its absorption spectrum which contains the triphenylene complex. Further hydrogenation yields an octahydrocoronene (XX) with the spectrum of a pyrene derivative. The next stages lead to the naphthalene derivative (XXI) and then to the benzene derivative (XXII). The final reaction product is perhydrocoronene.[15] The structure (XXIII) is claimed for a compound which is obtained with sodium and amyl alcohol.[16]

Coronene gives nitrocoronene with nitric acid. Reduction leads to aminocoronene. Fuming nitric acid forms dinitrocoronene.[16] Trinitro-coronene and hexanitrocoronene can also be obtained.[17] Chlorination in trichlorobenzene gives pentachlorocoronene.[17] Bromine in acetic acid

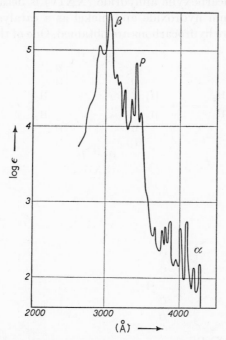

FIG. 105. Absorption spectrum of coronene in benzene: α, 4280 (2·15), 4200 (2·12), 4100 (2·75), 4020 (2·65), 3965 (2·23), 3880 (2·75), 3815 (2·67) 3780 (2·63), 3685 (2·67); 3475 (4·15); p, 3415 (4·85), 3360 (4·35), 3255 (4·45), 3195 (4·60), 3165 (4·70); β, 3050 (5·50), in ethanol: 2900 (5·10), 2520 (3·88), 2280 (4·08).

gives dibromocoronene.[16,17] Sulphur dyes can be prepared from coronene.[17]

Coronene gives benzoylcoronene with benzoyl chloride and aluminium chloride in carbon disulphide.[16] It also reacts with one molecule of succinic anhydride or phthalic anhydride to form mono substitution

(XIX)   (XX)

products.[18] Coronene-carboxylic acid and a mixture of di- and tricarboxylic acids are obtained with carbaminic chloride and aluminium
chlorides.[19]

If coronene-dicarboxylic anhydride (XXIV) is decarboxylated with
aqueous potassium hydroxide and nickel as a catalyst at 350° under
pressure two more hydrocarbons are obtained. One of them can easily be

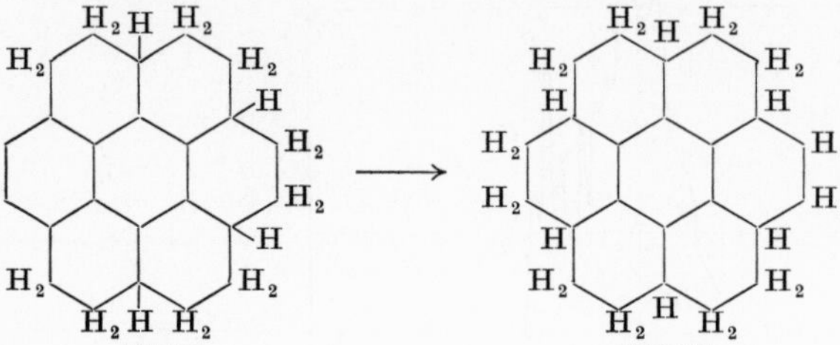

(XXI)   (XXII) 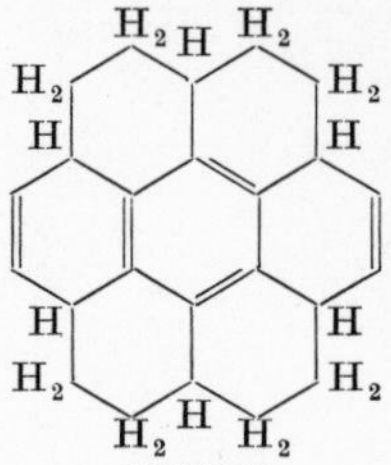   (XXIII)

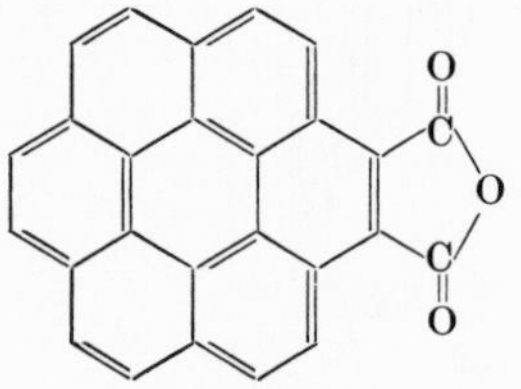

(XXIV)

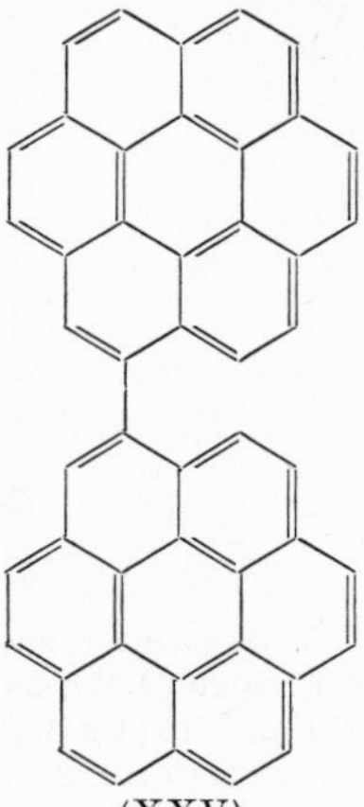

(XXV)

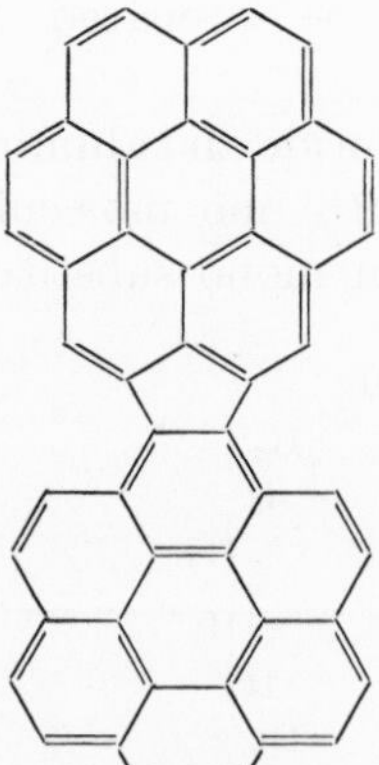

(XXVIa)   (XXVIb)   (XXVII)

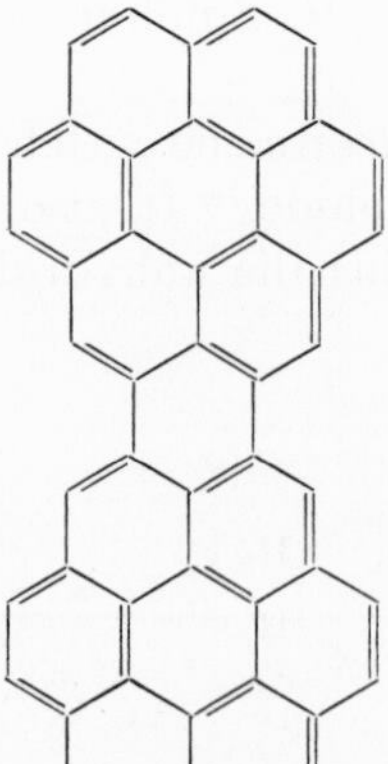

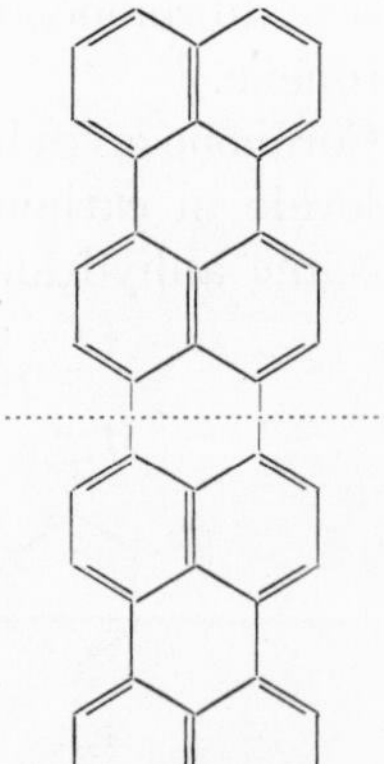

identified by its absorption spectrum as dicoronenyl (XXV). Another red hydrocarbon which is also formed in small yields is better obtained from a sodium chloride–aluminium chloride melt of coronene. This could produce a dicoronylene (XXVIb) analogous to the formation of quaterrylene (XXVII) from two molecules of perylene (see p. 283) or a fluoranthene type (XXVIa). Spectroscopic evidence appears to support the latter possibility.[20]

An alkyl derivative of coronene was obtained from erythroaphin.[21] The latter exists in two isomeric forms (XXVIII) and (XXIX).[22]

(XXVIII)   (XXIX)

Coronenequinone (XXX) can be obtained from coronene in a mixture of nitrobenzene and acetic acid with sodium dichromate. It can be sublimed and forms dark brown needles which give a red-brown vat with alkaline sodium dithionite solution.

It forms the dark yellow azine (XXXI) with o-phenylenediamine.[23]

Coronenequinone (XXX) gives benzoperylene-dicarboxylic acid (XXXII) when treated with potassium hydroxide in dioxane, with air

(XXX)   (XXXI)

(XXXII)   (XXXIII)   (XXXIV) or hydrogen peroxide, or with a melt of potassium hydroxide and sodium peroxide. Decarboxylation of the dicarboxylic acid (XXXII) leads to 1.12-benzoperylene (XXXIII). A lactonic compound (XXXIV) is obtained from coronenequinone by sublimation with lead dioxide or from the dicarboxylic acid (XXXII) by sublimation.[24]

REFERENCES

1. Clar, E. and Zander, M., J. chem. Soc. 4616 (1957).
2. Scholl, R. and Meyer, K., Ber. dtsch. chem. Ges. 65, 902 (1932).
3. Newman, M. S., J. Amer. chem. Soc. 62, 1683 (1940).
4. Baker, W., McOmie, J. F. W. and Norman, J. M., J. chem. Soc. 1114 (1951).
5. Baker, W., Gockling, F. and McOmie, J. F. W., J. chem. Soc. 1118 (1951).
6. I.G. Farbenindustrie AG, Brit. Patent 470338 (1936); 497089 (1937); French Patent 816162 (1937); Chem. Zbl. 1937 II, 3846; French Patent 49332 (1938); Belg. Patent 427268 (1938); Chem. Zbl. 1939 I, 3832; Brit. Patent 510736 (1938); Orchin, M. and Feldman, J., J. org. Chem. 18, 609 (1953).
7. Boente, L., Brennstoff Chemie 36, 210 (1955).
8. Wieland, H. and Müller, W., Liebigs Ann. 564, 199 (1949).
9. Blumer, M., Geochimica Acta, 26, 228 (1962); Science 134, 3474 (1961).
10. Bowen, E. J. and Brocklehurst, B., J. chem. Soc. 3875 (1954); 4320 (1955).
11. Clar, E. and Zander, M., Chem. Ber. 89, 749 (1956).
12. McClure, D. S., J. chem. Phys. 179, 10 (1944).
13. Zander, M., Naturwissenschaften 47, 443 (1960).
14. Robertson, J. M. and White, J. G., J. chem. Soc. 607 (1945); Ruston, W. R. and Rüdorf, W., Bull. Soc. chim. Belg. 56, 97 (1947).
15. Fromherz, H., Thaler, L. and Wolf, G., Z. Elektrochem. 49, 387 (1943).
16. Zinke, A., Hanus, F. and Ferrari, O., Mh. Chem. 78, 343 (1948).
17. General Anilin & Film Corp., Amer. Patent 2210041 (1939); Chem. Zbl. 1941 I, 1096.
18. Clar, E. and Zander, M., J. chem. Soc. 1577 (1958).
19. Hopff, H. and Schweizer, H. R., Helv. chim. Acta 40, 541 (1957).
20. Zander, M. and Franke, W., Chem. Ber. 91, 2794 (1958).
21. Brown, B. R., Johnson, A. W., Quayle, J. R. and Todd, A. R., J. chem. Soc. 107 (1954).
22. Brown, B. R., Calderbank, A., Johnson, A. W., Joshi, B. S., Quayle, J. R. and Todd, Sir A. R., J. chem. Soc. 959, 114 (1955).
23. Zinke, A., Ott, R., Sobotka, M. and Kretz, R., Mh. Chem. 83, 546 (1952).
24. Zinke, A. and Ott, R., Mh. Chem. 84, 1132.

XXIV. 1.2-BENZOCORONENE

Coronene condenses with succinic anhydride and aluminium chloride in nitrobenzene to form the acid (II). The reduction with hydrazine hydrate and sodium hydroxide in diethylene glycol gives the acid (III) which can be cyclized in a sodium chloride–zinc chloride melt.[1]

(I)   (II)

(III)   (IV)

(V)   (VI)

1.2,4.5-Dibenzopyrene (V) reacts twice with boiling maleic anhydride and chloranil as an oxidizing agent and yields the dianhydride (VI). The decarboxylation is carried out with aqueous potassium hydroxide at 350° under pressure. Sublimation with soda-lime leads to decomposition and the recovery of dibenzopyrene (V).[2]

1.2-Benzocoronene (IV) crystallizes from xylene in pale yellow needles (m.p. 292–294°), which dissolve in hot sulphuric acid with a greenish-yellow colour. The absorption spectrum is given in Fig. 106.

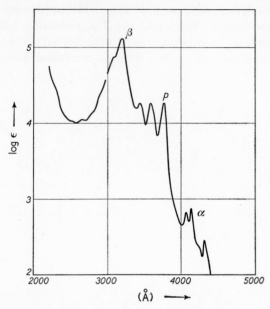

FIG. 106. Absorption spectrum of 1.2-benzocoronene in benzene: α, 4320 (2·50), 4140 (2·91), 4080 (2·85); p, 3760 (4·30), 3580 (4·30), 3430 (4·29); β, 3200 (5·15), 3080 (4·90), from 3000 Å in ethanol.

REFERENCES

1. Clar, E. and Zander, M., *J. chem. Soc.* 1577 (1958).
2. Clar, E., Ironside, C. T. and Zander, M., *Tetrahedron* 6, 358 (1959).

XXV. 1.2,5.6-DIBENZOCORONENE

1.2,4.5,8.9-Tribenzopyrene (I) reacts with maleic anhydride and chloranil as an oxidizing agent to form the dianhydride (II). It appears that two double bonds in tribenzopyrene are fixed as indicated in formula (I) and accessible to a diene synthesis. It is remarkable that no reaction with only one molecule of maleic anhydride can be observed. The obvious reason is that only with two molecules of maleic anhydride can a new aromatic sextet (marked with circles) be formed. The decarboxylation

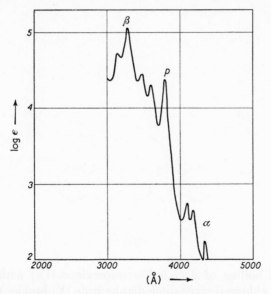

(I)   (II)   (III)

of the dianhydride (II) must be carried out with aqueous potassium hydroxide at 350° under pressure. Sublimation with soda-lime results in almost complete splitting of the compound and the formation of tribenzopyrene.

1.2,5.6-Dibenzocoronene (III) crystallizes from trichlorobenzene in long pale yellow needles (m.p. 327–328°), which do not dissolve in

FIG. 107. Absorption spectrum of 1.2,5.6-dibenzocoronene in 1,2,4-trichlorobenzene: α, 4335 (2·25), 4180 (2·66), 4100 (2·75); p, 3790 (4·38), 3600 (4·31), 3490 (4·45); β, 3280 (5·06), 3140 (4·72).

concentrated sulphuric acid. It can be sublimed *in vacuo*. The absorption spectrum is given in Fig. 107.[1]

REFERENCE

1. Clar, E., Ironside, C. T. and Zander, M., *Tetrahedron* **6**, 358 (1959).

XXVI. 1.2,7.8-DIBENZOCORONENE

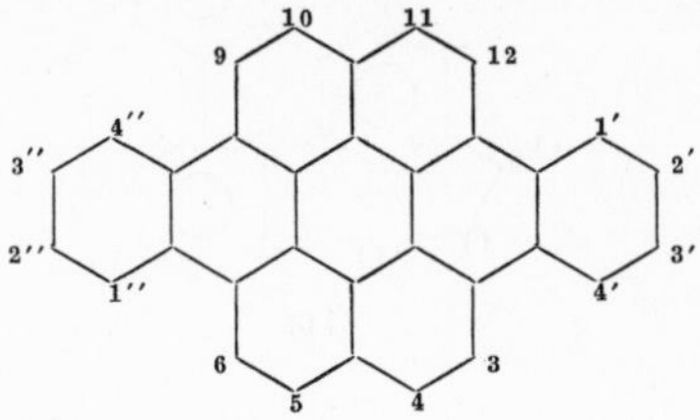

1.12,2.3,8.9-Tribenzoperylene (I) gives dibenzocoronene-dicarboxylic anhydride (II) when heated with maleic anhydride and chloranil. A sublimation *in vacuo* with soda-lime yields 1.2,7.8-dibenzocoronene (III).[1]

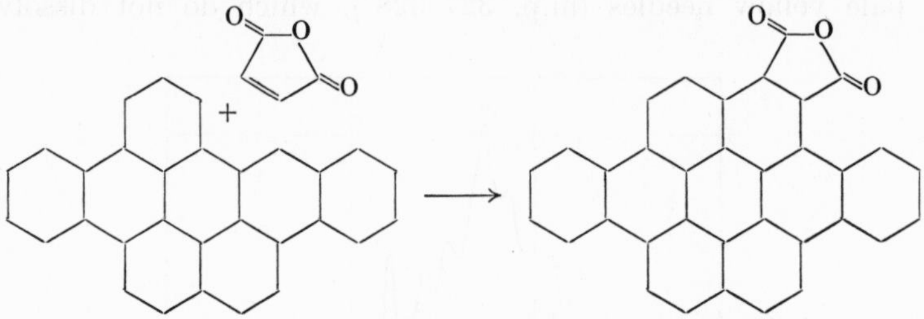

(I)   (II)

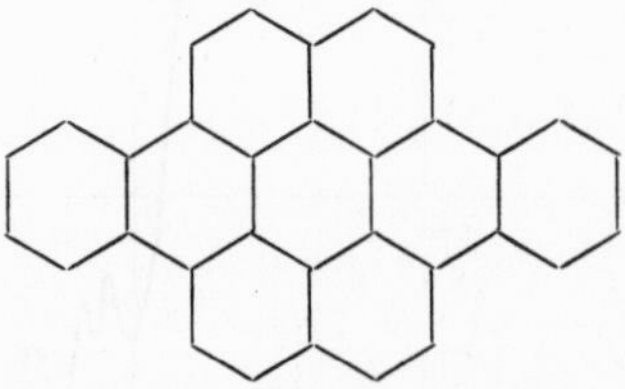

(III)

Prolonged boiling of 2.3,8.9-dibenzoperylene (IV) with maleic anhydride and chloranil gives some dianhydride (V) besides the monoanhydride (see p. 65). The dianhydride (V) also yields dibenzocoronene when sublimed with soda-lime.[2]

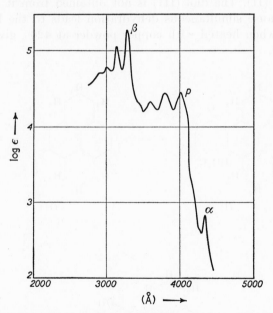

(IV)   (V)

1.2,7.8-Dibenzocoronene (III) crystallizes from 1-methylnaphthalene in yellow needles (m.p. 496–499°), which dissolve in concentrated sulphuric acid to give a blue-violet solution.[1] The crystal structure has been determined and the C—C distances measured.[3] The absorption spectrum is shown in Fig. 108.

FIG. 108. Absorption spectrum of 1.2,7.8-dibenzocoronene in 1,2,4-trichlorobenzene: α, 4350 (2·84); p, 4010 (4·46), 3810 (4·44), 3630 (4·32); β, 3300 (5·29), 3160 (5·07).

REFERENCES

1. Clar, E. and Zander, M., *J. chem. Soc.* 4616 (1957).
2. Lang, K. F., Buffleb, H. and Kalowy, J., *Chem. Ber.* **93**, 303 (1960).
3. Robertson, J. M. and Trotter, J., *J. chem. Soc.* 1115 (1961).

XXVII. 1.2,3.4,5.6-Tribenzocoronene

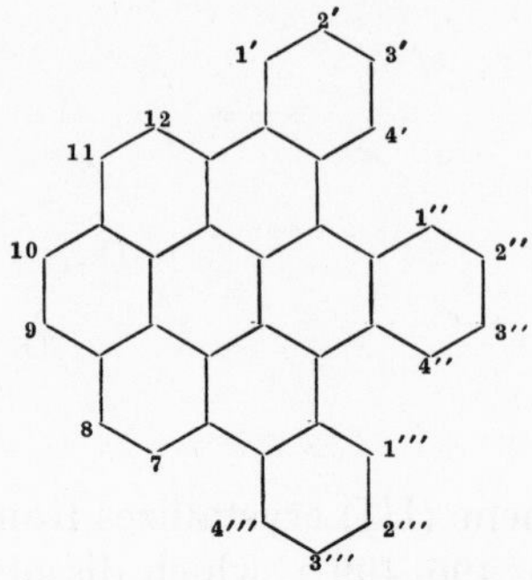

Hexahydropyrene, phthalic anhydride and aluminium chloride give the keto-acid (I). Cyclization with anhydrous hydrogen fluoride yields the quinone (II). The diol (III) is not obtained from it with phenyl lithium, because simultaneous dehydration leads to the hydrocarbon (IV). This, when heated with copper powder at 420°, gives tribenzocoronene (V).

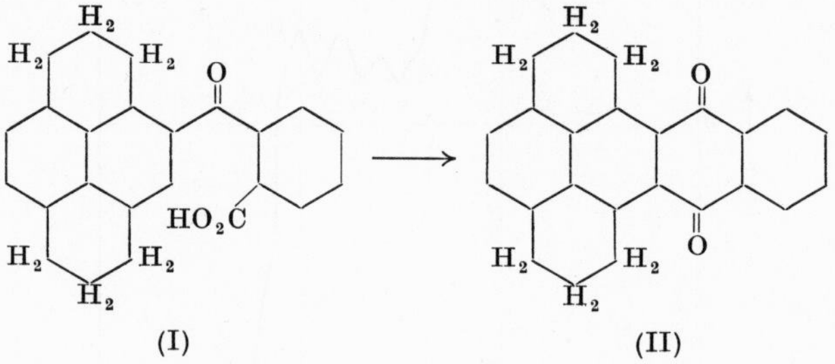

(I)

(II)

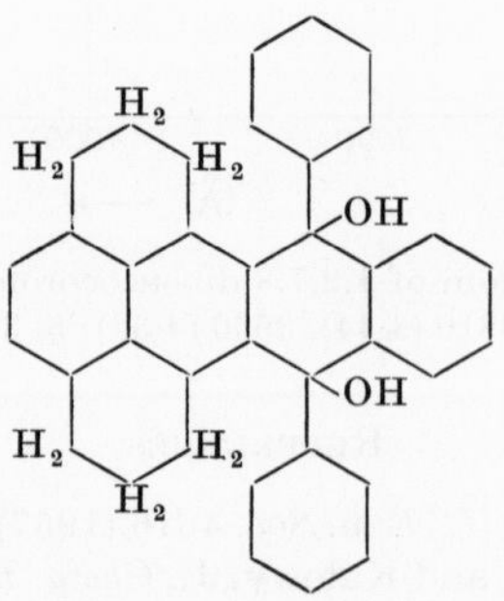

(III)

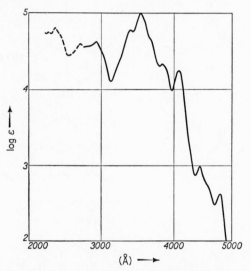

(IV) (V)

1.2,3.4,5.6-Tribenzocoronene crystallizes from benzene in yellow needles (m.p. 350–351°), which do not dissolve in concentrated sulphuric acid. The absorption spectrum is shown in Fig. 109.[1]

FIG. 109. Absorption spectrum of 1.2,3.4,5.6-tribenzocoronene in benzene: α, 4640 (2·62), 4360 (2·98); p, 4070 (4·25), 3840 (4·34); β, 3540 (5·00), 3400 (4·78); β′, 2930 (4·62), in cyclohexane: 2720 (4·60); 2360 (4·81).

REFERENCE

1. Clar, E. and McCallum, A., *Tetrahedron*, in press.

XXVIII. Naphtho-(2'.3':1.2)-coronene

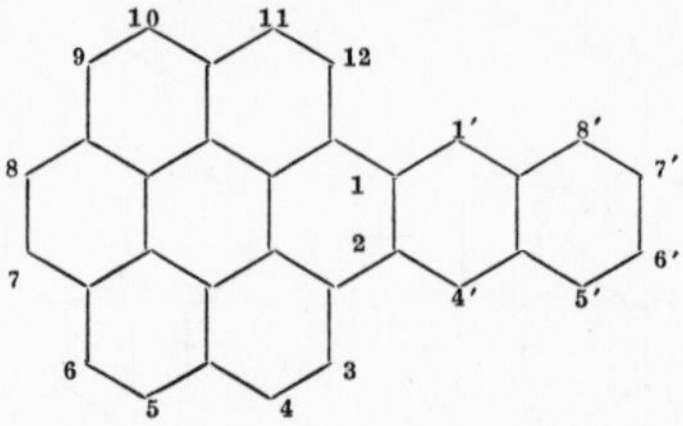

Coronene (I) reacts with phthalic anhydride and aluminium chloride in o-dichlorobenzene solution to form the keto-acid (II). This cyclizes to the quinone (III) when boiled with benzoyl chloride and 1-chloronaphthalene. The quinone (III) can be reduced to the naphthocoronene by the zinc dust, pyridine and acetic acid method.

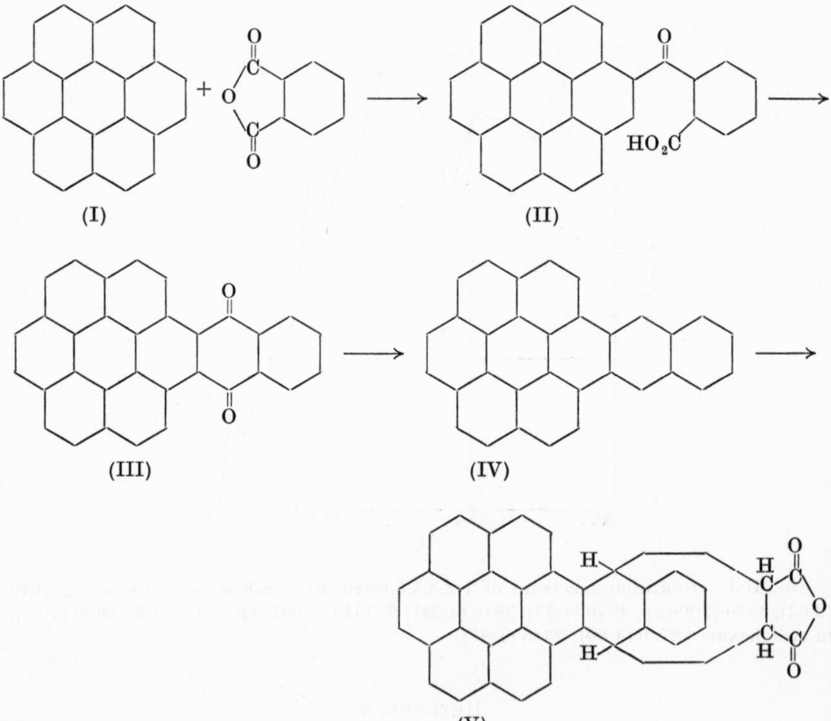

(I) (II)

(III) (IV)

(V)

Naphtho-(2'.3':1.2)-coronene (IV) crystallizes from xylene in yellow needles (m.p. 352–354°), which do not dissolve in cold sulphuric acid but give a yellow solution on warming. The absorption spectrum is given in

Fig. 110. The hydrocarbon adds maleic anhydride to form the adduct (V) whose absorption spectrum shows the coronene complex.[1]

Naphtho-(2'.3':1.2)-coronene-1',4'-quinone (III) forms dark red

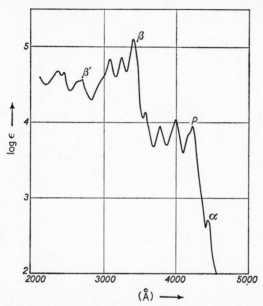

FIG. 110. Absorption spectrum of naphtho-(2'.3':1.2)-coronene in benzene: α, 4440 (2·74); p, 4230 (3·99), 4000 (4·09), 3790 (3·98), 3580 (4·16); β, 3410 (5·12), 3260 (4·88), 3100 (4·86), in ethanol: β', 2720 (4·60), 2480 (4·68), 2390 (4·70).

needles from nitrobenzene (m.p. 347–349°), which dissolve in concentrated sulphuric acid to give a green solution. A violet vat is produced with alkaline sodium dithionite solution.

REFERENCE

1. Clar, E. and Zander, M., J. chem. Soc. 1577 (1958).

XXIX. 1.12,2.3,4.5,6.7,8.9,10.11-HEXABENZOCORONENE

2.3,7.8-Dibenzoperinaphthene (I) in benzene gives a deep brown perbromide with bromine of the composition $C_{21}H_{14}Br_3$. This decomposes on heating or in boiling trichlorobenzene to tetrabenzoperopyrene (II).

(I)   (II)

(III)

Tetrabenzoperopyrene (II) melts at 482° with evolution of hydrogen and resolidifies with the formation of hexahydrocoronene (III), which does not melt below 700°.[1]

(V)   (III)   (IV)

Hexabenzocoronene may be synthesized from hexaphenylbenzene (V) by a sodium chloride–zinc chloride melt. It is also formed together with another hydrocarbon when 2.3,7.8-dibenzoperinaphthone (IV) is submitted to a zinc-dust melt.[2]

Hexabenzocoronene sublimes *in vacuo* as yellow needles or crystallizes from boiling pyrene as long flat pale yellow needles which do not melt

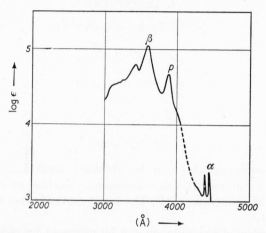

FIG. 111. Absorption spectrum of 1.12,2.3,4.5,6.7,8.9,10.11-hexabenzocoronene in 1,2,4-trichlorobenzene: α, 4440, 4380; p, 3875 (4·68); β, 3600 (5·06), 3425 (4·80). Intensities uncertain.

below 700°. They are insoluble in concentrated sulphuric acid. A weak solution in trichlorobenzene cooled in liquid nitrogen shows a strong orange phosphorescence (band at 5750 Å) of long life after irradiation with a mercury lamp. These properties are typical for aromatic hydrocarbons, which may be considered as condensed polyphenyls as indicated by the aromatic sextets marked with circles in formula (III). The crystal structure and the bond lengths have been determined.[3] The absorption spectrum is shown in Fig. 111.

REFERENCES

1. Clar, E. and Ironside, C. T., *Proc. chem. Soc.* 150 (1958); Clar, E., Ironside, C. T. and Zander, M., *J. chem. Soc.* 142 (1959).
2. Halleux, A., Martin, R. H. and King, G. S. D., *Helv. chim. Acta* **41**, 1177 (1958).
3. Trotter, J. and Robertson, J. M., *J. chem. Soc.* 1280 (1961).

CHAPTER 30

Hydrocarbons derived from Bisanthene

I. BISANTHENE

(meso-*Naphthodianthrene*)

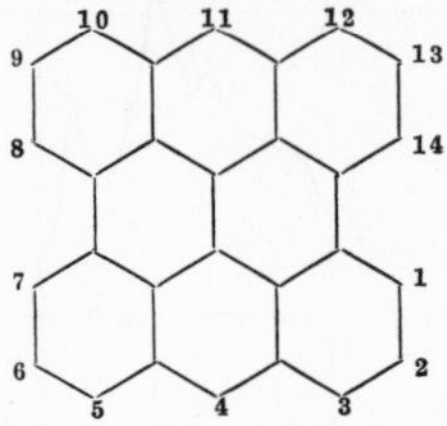

Bisanthenequinone (II) can be obtained from 1.2,11.12-dibenzo-perylene-3,10-quinone (I) with aluminium chloride[1] or by irradiation of solutions of dianthrone (III). The latter method gives a particularly pure product.[2]

The reduction of the quinone can be achieved by reducing it with hydriodic acid and red phosphorus at 200° to a hexahydrobisanthene which is dehydrogenated by a sublimation over copper at 500°.[3] Better results are obtained by a zinc-dust melt or a reduction with zinc dust, pyridine and acetic acid.[4]

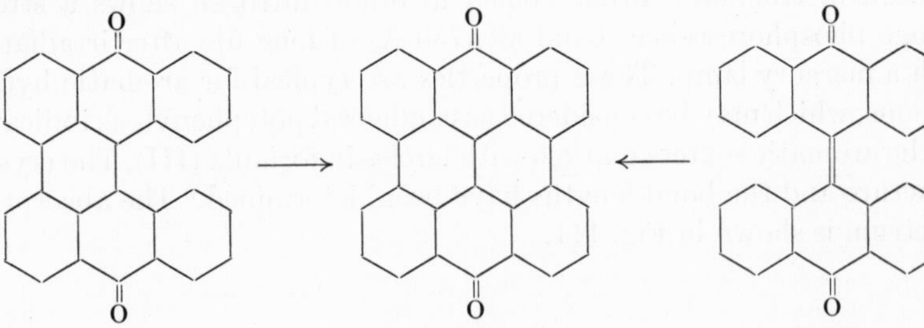

(I)   (II)   (III)

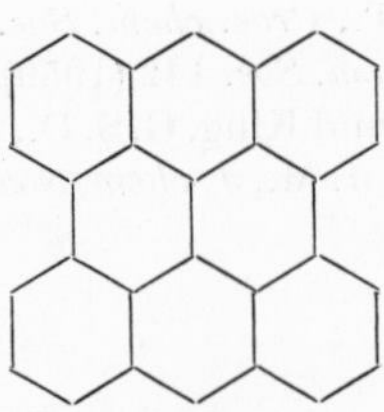

(IV)

Bisanthene (IV, *meso*-naphthodianthrene) sublimes or crystallizes from nitrobenzene as dark blue needles. Its solutions in organic solvents are also blue. Concentrated sulphuric acid gives a green solution which turns to blue-violet on warming. If this solution is poured into water the precipitate gives bisanthenequinone with bichromate. Bisanthene reacts very readily with maleic anhydride in nitrobenzene to give a mono- and a dianhydride (see pp. 101, 103). The absorption spectrum is given in Fig. 112. The spectrum of the photo-oxidized hydrocarbon has also been recorded.[5]

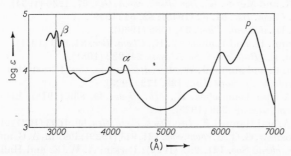

FIG. 112. Absorption spectrum of bisanthene in benzene: p, 6625 (4·70), 6030 (4·32), 5560 (3·67); α, 4240 (4·10), 3990 (4·04); β, 3120 (4·52), 3005 (4·69), 2900 (4·65).

1,14-, 2,13- and 3,12-Dimethylbisanthene can be prepared by reduction of the corresponding quinones. The p-bands of the absorption spectrum of 1,14-dimethylbisanthene (V) show a remarkable shift to the violet in comparison with bisanthene. This unusual shift can be explained by overcrowding of the molecule caused by the methyl groups.[6] Bisanthene and its quinone are semiconductors.[7]

(V)   (VI)

Bisanthene-4,11-quinone (II, *meso*-naphthodianthrone) is a sparingly soluble yellow quinone which dissolves in concentrated sulphuric acid to form a violet-red solution. It forms a vat with alkaline sodium dithionite only by addition of zinc dust.

A number of derivatives of bisanthenequinone have been described, i.e. methyl,[8] chloro,[9] hydroxy derivatives[10] and carboxylic acids.[11] An interesting derivative is hypericin (VI).[12] Bisanthene derivatives occur in fossils, e.g. fringelite.[13]

REFERENCES

1. Scholl, R. and Mansfeld, J., *Ber. dtsch. chem. Ges.* **43**, 1734 (1910).
2. Meyer, H., Bondy and Eckert, *Mh. Chem.* **33**, 1451 (1912); Brockmann, H. and Mühlmann, R., *Chem. Ber.* **82**, 348 (1949).
3. Scholl, R. and Meyer, K., *Ber. dtsch. chem. Ges.* **67**, 1236 (1934).
4. Clar, E., *Chem. Ber.* **81**, 62 (1948); **82**, 54 (1949).
5. Kuroda, H., *J. chem. Phys.* **33**, 1586 (1960).
6. Brockmann, H. and Radebrock, R., *Chem. Ber.* **84**, 533 (1951).
7. Inokuchi, H., *Bull. chem. Soc. Japan* **24**, 222 (1951).
8. Ullmann, F. and Minajew, W., *Ber. dtsch. chem. Ges.* **45**, 689 (1912); Scholl, R. and Tänzer, C., *Liebigs Ann.* **433**, 172 (1923).
9. Eckert A. and Tomaschek, R., *Mh. Chem.* **39**, 839 (1918); Eckert, A., *Ber. dtsch. chem. Ges.* **58**, 322 (1925).
10. Eckert, A. and Hampel, J., *Ber. dtsch. chem. Ges.* **60**, 1693 (1927); Perkin, A. G. and Bradshaw, G. G., *J. chem. Soc.* **121**, 911 (1922); Perkin, A. G. and Whattam, T. W., *J. chem. Soc.* **121**, 297 (1922); Perkin, A. W. E. and Haller, A. G., *J. chem. Soc.* **125**, 231 (1924); Attree, G. F. and Perkin, A. G., *J. chem. Soc.* 144 (1931); Perkin, A. G. and Haddock, N. H., *J. chem. Soc.* 1512 (1933); Brockmann, H., Neef, R. and Mühlmann, E., *Chem. Ber.* **83**, 467 (1950).
11. Scholl, R. and Tänzer, C., *Liebigs Ann.* **433**, 173 (1923).
12. Brockmann, H., Pohl, F., Maier, K. and Haschad, M. N., *Liebigs Ann.* **533**, 11 (1942).
13. Blumer, M., *Geochimica Acta* **26**, 225, 228 (1962).

II. 1.14-BENZOBISANTHENE

(meso-*Anthrodianthrene*)

1.14-Benzobisanthene-4,11-quinone (II, *meso*-anthrodianthrone) is obtained from 1.12,5.6,7.8-tribenzoperylene-4,9-quinone (I) with aluminium chloride. Cyclization can be also effected by irradiation of the quinone (I).[1] It is formed from 2,2'-dimethylbisanthenequinone (III)[2] by heating with alcoholic potassium hydroxide.[3]

The reduction of the quinone (II) to the hydrocarbon (IV) can be achieved by reducing the quinone first to a hexahydrobenzobisanthene which then gives benzobisanthene (IV) by sublimation over copper at 500°.[4] Benzobisanthene can be synthesized from bisanthene (V) with maleic anhydride in nitrobenzene. The reaction proceeds analogously to the one with perylene,[5] and yields the anhydride (VI) quantitatively. Decarboxylation to benzobisanthene (IV) takes place during sublimation with soda-lime. The anhydride (VI) can be oxidized to the quinone-anhydride (VII) with chromic acid.[6]

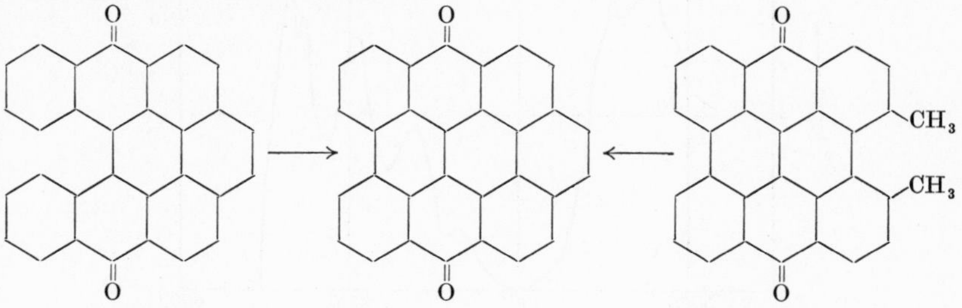

(I)   (II)   (III)

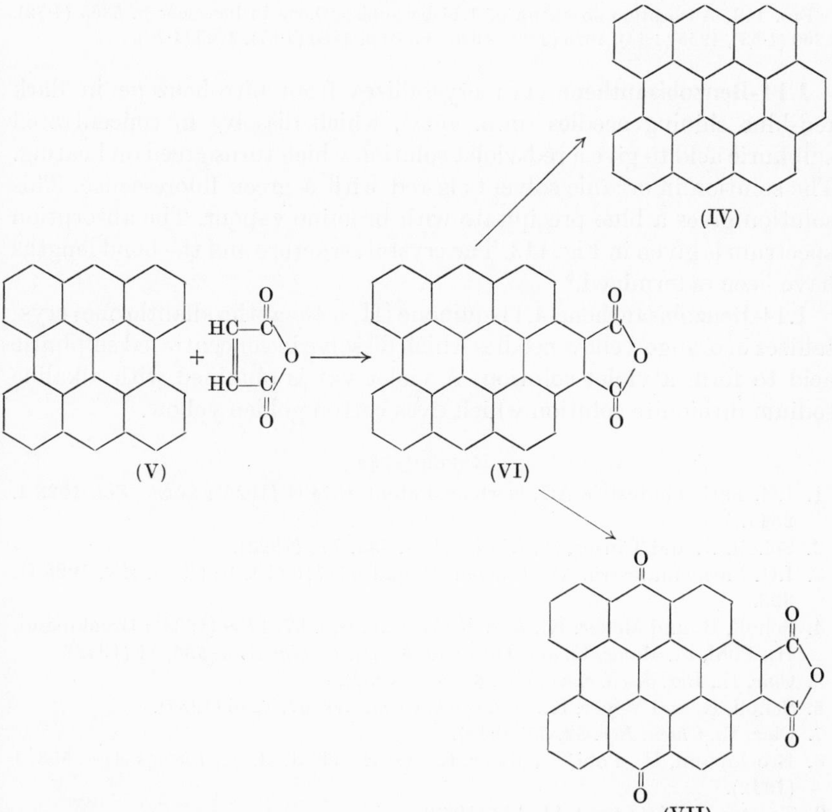

(IV)

(V)   (VI)

(VII)

Benzobisanthene (IV) is most readily obtained from its quinone (II) by a reduction with zinc dust in pyridine and acetic acid. A colourless intermediate product yields benzobisanthene in high yield when re-crystallized in boiling nitrobenzene.[7] It has also been obtained by a zinc-dust melt or a zinc-dust distillation from hypericin[8] (see p. 99).

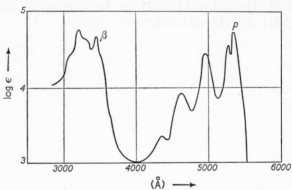

FIG. 113. Absorption spectrum of 1.14-benzobisanthene in benzene: p, 5355 (4·72), 5260 (4·53), 4955 (4·44), 4625 (3·90), 4340 (3·35); β, 3450 (4·67), 3205 (4·75).

1.14-Benzobisanthene (IV) crystallizes from nitrobenzene in dark red-blue shining needles (m.p. 452°), which dissolve in concentrated sulphuric acid to give a red-violet solution which turns green on heating. The solution in organic solvents is red with a green fluorescence. This solution gives a blue precipitate with bromine vapour. The absorption spectrum is given in Fig. 113. The crystal structure and the bond lengths have been determined.[9]

1.14-Benzobisanthene-4,11-quinone (II, *meso*-anthrodianthrone) crystallizes in orange-yellow needles which dissolve in concentrated sulphuric acid to form a violet solution. A violet vat is obtained with alkaline sodium dithionite solution which dyes cotton golden yellow.

REFERENCES

1. I.G. Farbenindustrie AG, German Patent 457494 (1926); *Chem. Zbl.* **1928 I**, 2544.
2. Scholl, R. and Tänzer, C., *Liebigs Ann.* **433**, 172 (1923).
3. I.G. Farbenindustrie AG, German Patent 458710 (1926); *Chem. Zbl.* **1928 II**, 398.
4. Scholl, R. and Meyer, K., *Ber. dtsch. chem. Ges.* **67**, 1229 (1934); Brockmann, H., Pohl, F., Maier, K. and Haschad, M. N., *Liebigs Ann.* **533**, 11 (1942).
5. Clar, E., *Ber. dtsch. chem. Ges.* **65**, 846 (1932).
6. Scholl, R. and Meyer, K., *Ber. dtsch. chem. Ges.* **67**, 1236 (1934).
7. Clar, E., *Chem. Ber.* **82**, 55 (1949).
8. Brockmann, H., Pohl, F., Maier, K. and Haschad, M. N., *Liebigs Ann.* **553**, 1 (1942).
9. Trotter, J., *Acta cryst.* **11**, 423 (1962).

III. OVALENE

1.14-Benzobisanthene (I) condenses with maleic anhydride in boiling nitrobenzene to form the anhydride (II). An analogous reaction takes place with bisanthene (III), which reacts twice with an excess of maleic anhydride and yields the dianhydride (IV). The decarboxylation is carried out by a sublimation with soda-lime *in vacuo*.[1]

Ovalene (V) sublimes or crystallizes from 1-methylnaphthalene in long orange needles (m.p. 473°), which dissolve in concentrated sulphuric acid to give a violet solution which changes to brown. Solutions in organic solvents show an orange fluorescence. Oxidation with selenium dioxide in boiling nitrobenzene gives a quinone which forms a crimson-red

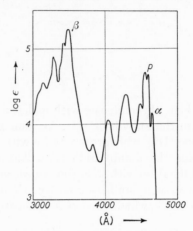

FIG. 114. Absorption spectrum of ovalene in 1-methylnaphthalene: α, 4650 (4·15), 4600 (4·64); p, 4560 (4·68), 4480 (4·25), 4280 (4·39), 4035 (4·05), 3820 (3·72); β, 3490 (5·26), in benzene: 3300 (3·90), 3150 (4·56).

vat and dyes cotton brownish-yellow. The absorption spectrum is given in Fig. 114.

The crystal structure of ovalene has been determined and the C—C distances measured.[2] Ovalene is a semiconductor and shows a high magnetic anisotropy.[3]

REFERENCES

1. Clar, E., *Nature, Lond.* **161**, 238 (1948); *Chem. Ber.* **82**, 55 (1949).
2. Donaldson, D. M. and Robertson, J. M., *Nature, Lond.* **184**, 1002 (1949).
3. Akamatu, H., Inokuchi, H. and Honda, H., *Nature, Lond.* **168**, 520 (1951); Inukuchi, H., *Bull. chem. Soc. Japan* **24**, 222 (1951).

IV. 3.4,10.11-DIBENZOBISANTHENE AND 3.4,11.12-DIBENZOBISANTHENE

8-Chlorobenzanthrone (I) condenses in boiling nitrobenzene with copper powder to 8,8'-dibenzanthronyl (II) which, when submitted to a zinc-dust melt, cyclizes to 3.4,11.12-dibenzobisanthene (III).

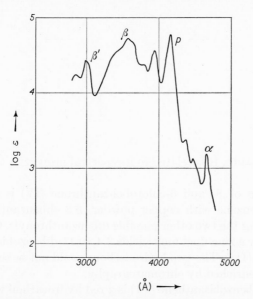

FIG. 115. Absorption spectrum of 3.4,11.12-dibenzobisanthene in benzene: α, 4660 (3·20), 4475 (3·13), 4380 (3·39); p, 4170 (4·80), 3945 (4·58), 3810 (4·40); β, 3580 (4·73); β', 2995 (4·45), 2850 (4·25).

3.4,11.12-Dibenzobisanthene (III) crystallizes from trichlorobenzene in yellow needles (m.p. 432–433°), which dissolve slowly in concentrated sulphuric acid to give a violet colour. The absorption spectrum is given in Fig. 115. It shows a red phosphorescence of long life in solid solution

Cl

O

+

Cl

O

O

O

(I)

(II)

(III)

II—4*

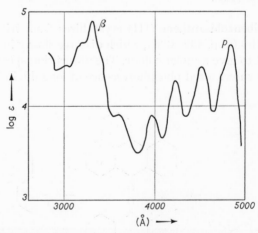

at low temperature. It is related in its spectral properties to hexabenzo-coronene.[1]

If a mixture of 8- and 6-chlorobenzanthrone (IV) is condensed in boiling nitrobenzene with copper powder, 6,8'-dibenzanthronyl (V) is obtained besides the two other possible dibenzanthronyls. Cyclization of this mixture by a zinc-dust melt yields 3.4,10.11-dibenzobisanthene (VI) and its isomer (III). The two hydrocarbons could not be separated, (VI) could only be enriched by chromatography.

3.4,10.11-Dibenzobisanthene (VI) is a red hydrocarbon whose absorption spectrum (Fig. 116) was obtained by the subtraction of (III) from the spectrum of the mixture.

Fig. 116. Absorption spectrum of 3.4,10.11-dibenzobisanthene in benzene: p, 4820 (4·67), 4510 (4·40), 4200 (4·27), 3940 (3·90); 3580 (3·90); β, 3290 (4·90), 3160 (4·68), 3000 (4·42).

REFERENCE

1. Clar, E., Fell, S., Ironside, C. T. and Balsillie, A., *Tetrahedron* **10**, 26 (1960).

V. 1.2,3.4,8.9,10.11-TETRABENZOBISANTHENE

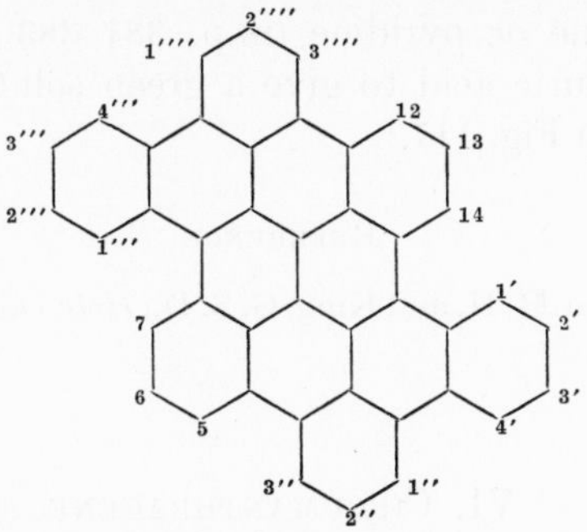

Tetrabenzobisanthene (II) is obtained besides hexabenzocoronene (see p. 96) and tetrabenzoperopyrene (see p. 259) by a zinc-dust melt of 2.3,6.7-dibenzoperinaphthone (I):

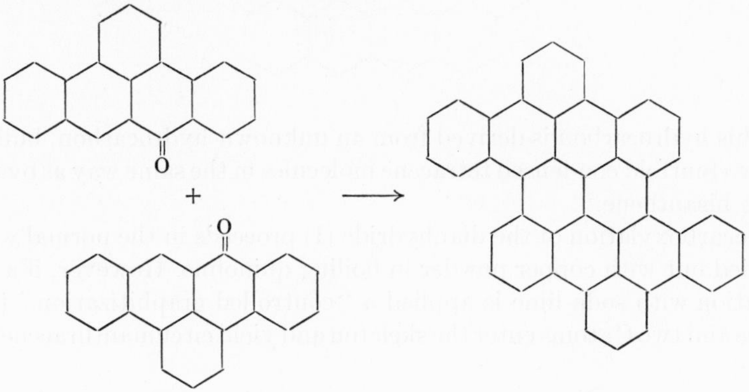

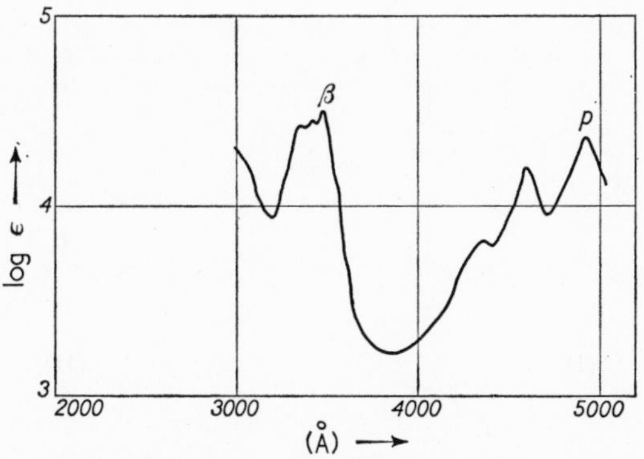

Fig. 117. Absorption spectrum of 1.2,3.4,8.9,10.11-tetrabenzobisanthene in benzene: p, 4930 (4·36), 4600 (4·20), 4370 (3·82); β, 3480 (4·51), 3430 (4·44), 3350 (4·42).

1.2,3.4,8.9,10.11-Tetrabenzobisanthene (II) is the most readily soluble of the three hydrocarbons formed in the above reaction. It forms red crystals from xylene or pyridine (m.p. 381–383°), which dissolve in concentrated sulphuric acid to give a green solution. The absorption spectrum is given in Fig. 117.[1]

REFERENCE

1. Halleux, A., Martin, R. H. and King, G. S. D., *Helv. chim. Acta* **41**, 1177 (1958).

VI. CIRCUMANTHRACENE

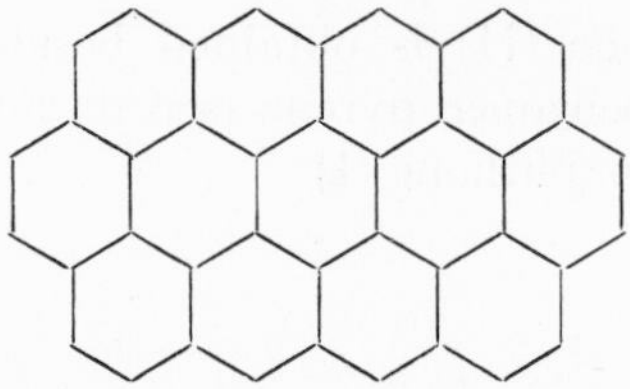

This hydrocarbon is derived from an unknown hydrocarbon, built up of two fourfold condensed tetracene molecules in the same way as ovalene from bisanthene.

Decarboxylation of the dianhydride (I) proceeds in the normal way if carried out with copper powder in boiling quinoline. However, if a sublimation with soda-lime is applied a "controlled graphitization" takes place and two C atoms enter the skeleton and yield circumanthracene (II).

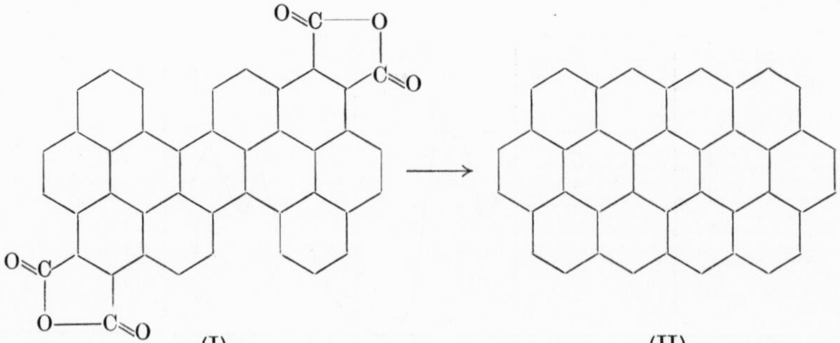

(I)   (II)

Circumanthracene (II) crystallizes from trichlorobenzene in dark red needles, which give an orange solution with concentrated sulphuric acid and begin to decompose at 480°. The crystal structure has been determined and the C—C distances measured. The absorption spectrum is given in Fig. 118.[1]

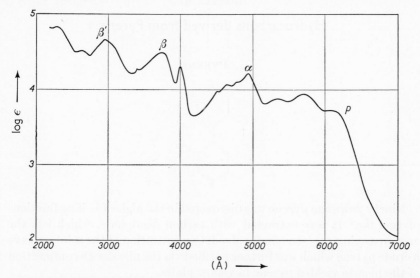

FIG. 118. Absorption spectrum of circumanthracene in 1,2,4-trichlorobenzene: p, 6120 (3·67), 5700 (3·90), 5320 (3·86); α, 4940 (4·20), 4775 (4·06), 4640 (4·08), 4490 (3·95), 4230 (4·71); β, 4000 (4·37), 3420 (4·48); in dioxane: β', 2940 (4·67), 2630 (4·51); 2320 (4·83).

REFERENCE

1. Clar, E., Kelly, W., Robertson, J. M. and Rossmann, M. G., *J. chem. Soc.* 3878 (1956).

CHAPTER 31

Hydrocarbons derived from Pyrene

I. PYRENE

Ninety years ago pyrene was discovered in the highest boiling fractions of coal-tar.[1] It was extracted with carbon disulphide, which left the accompanying chrysene undissolved. Concentration of the solution gave a crude pyrene which was further purified via the picrate. Decomposition of the picrate yielded pyrene in yellow plates.

An improved distillation of coal-tar gave a mixture of fluoranthene and pyrene (b.p. 370–390°), from which the former was removed by treatment with sodium in a mixture of alkylbenzenes (b.p. 160°). Only the fluoranthene formed a sodium compound which could be separated by filtration. The mother liquor was concentrated and the pyrene distilled and recrystallized.[2] Pyrene can be better obtained by a still further improved fractional distillation that separates the fluoranthene from the pyrene. It can now be prepared in large quantities and has found technical application.

Pyrene is formed in many pyrolytic processes, e.g. in the destructive distillation of soft coal-tar,[3] by pyrolysis of acetylene and hydrogen,[4] by the zinc-dust distillation of thebenol and thebenin[5] and from petroleum by the catarol process.[6] An interesting source of pyrene was a special distillation of mercury ore as carried out in Idria. The by-product which was mixed with mercury was called "Stupp" and contained up to 20% pyrene besides other polycyclic hydrocarbons. It was the main starting material for the preparation of pyrene before a modernization of the process prevented its formation in 1882.

The destructive hydrogenation of coal could yield considerable quantities of pyrene besides other polycyclic hydrocarbons.[7] Due to its pyrolytic formation pyrene can be isolated from the polluted air of large cities.[8]

The first synthesis of pyrene started from o,o'-ditolyl. Side chain chlorination gave the dichloro compound which was transformed in the dinitrile and then into the dicarboxylic acid (I). Cyclization afforded 1,6-dihydroxypyrene (II) from which pyrene (III) was obtained by zinc-dust distillation.[9]

(I)   (II)   (III)

In an analogous way the isomeric dicarboxylic acid (IV) gives 1,7-dihydroxypyrene via the dichloride in the presence of aluminium chloride. Zinc-dust distillation of (V) also yields pyrene (III).[10]

(IV)   (V)

Naphthalene tetracarboxylic anhydride (VI) can be condensed with malonic ester to naphthalene-1.8,4.5-di-indandione (VII), the zinc-dust distillation of which yields pyrene (III).[11]

(VI)   (VII)   (III)

peri-Trimethylenenaphthalene (VIII) reacts with malonyl chloride to form the condensation product (IX), which gives pyrene (III) on zinc-dust distillation.[12]

Pyrene can be also synthesized from the ketone (X), which is obtainable from 1-tetralone. The former condenses with bromoacetic ester to (XI).

The isolated double bond is hydrogenated and the $-CH_2CO_2C_2H_5$ group reduced to $-CH_2CH_2OH$. Substitution of the hydroxyl by bromine and reaction with potassium cyanide gives the corresponding nitrile which is

(VIII)   (IX)   (III)

saponified to the acid (XII). Cyclization of the corresponding chloride with aluminium chloride yields keto-decahydropyrene (XIII). Clemmensen reduction of this gives decahydropyrene (XIV) and dehydrogenation with lead dioxide gives pyrene.[13]

(X)   (XI)   (XII)

(XIV)   (XIII)

Starting from naphthalene, pyrene can be obtained by a double chloromethylation leading to (XV). Sodium malonic ester gives (XVI) and saponification and decarboxylation the diacetic acid (XVII). Cyclization with hydrofluoric acid yields the acid (XVIII). Reduction with hydrogen and platinum oxide gives (XIX) and a second cyclization with hydro-fluoric acid the cyclic ketone (XX). Hydrogenation of the latter with platinum oxide in alcohol and sulphuric acid results in the formation of 3,4,5,8,9,10-hexahydropyrene (XXI), and dehydrogenation with palladium–charcoal gives pyrene (III).[14]

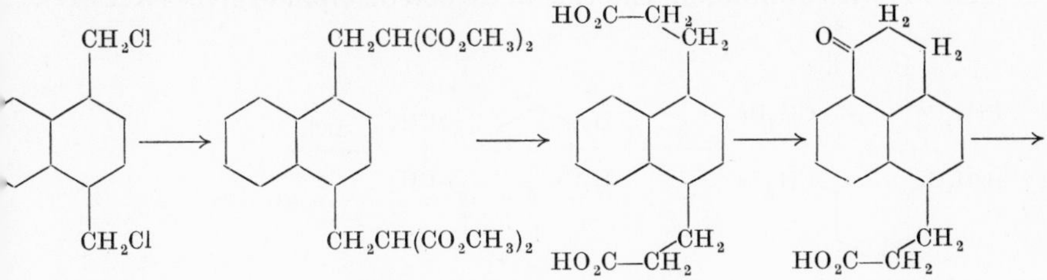

(XV)   (XVI)   (XVII)   (XVIII)

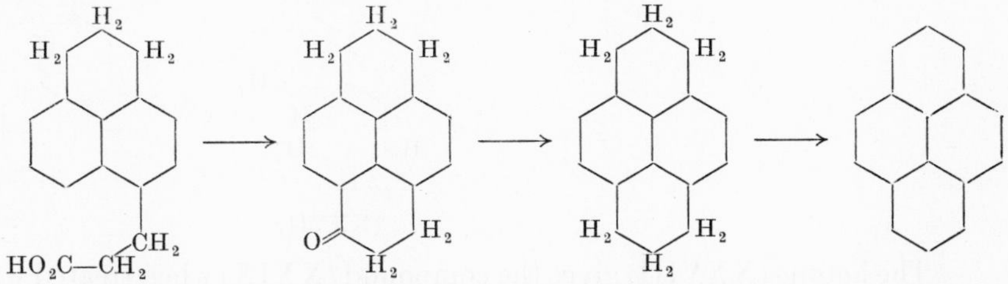

(XIX)   (XX)   (XXI)   (III)

If 4-keto-1,2,3,4-tetrahydrophenanthrene (XXII) is submitted to the Reformatsky reaction with bromoacetic ester and zinc, the ester (XXIII) is obtained. Cyclization with sulphuric acid gives the ketone

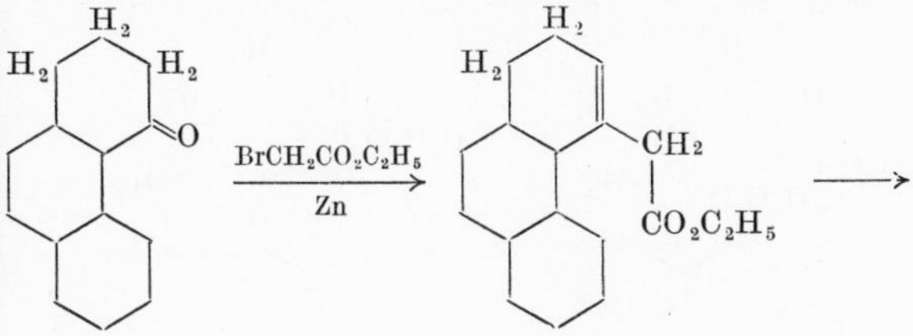

(XXII)   (XXIII)

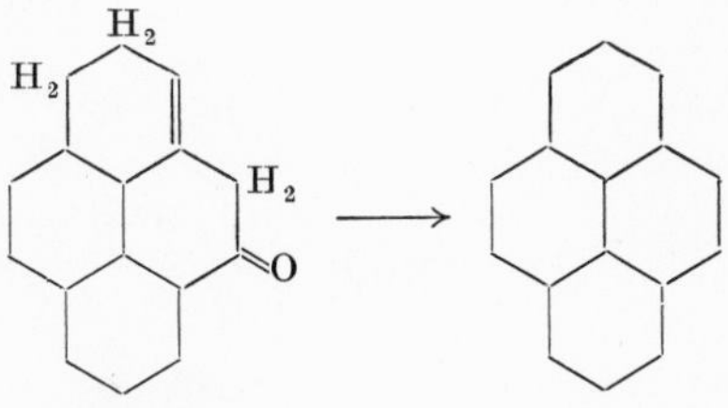

(XXIV)

(XXIV). Reduction followed by dehydrogenation with selenium yields pyrene.[15]

A condensation of *m*-xylylene dibromide (XXV) with sodium leads to the non-planar hydrocarbon (XXVI),[16] which yields pyrene by dehydrogenation with palladium–charcoal at 270–310°.[17] Treatment of (XXVI) with aluminium chloride in carbon disulphide gives (XXVII).[17]

(XXV)   (XXVI)

(XXVII)

The ketone (XXVIII) gives the compound (XXIX) when treated with sodium alcoholate. This can be cyclized with sodium in benzene to the sodium salt of (XXX). Condensation of this with bromoacetic ester yields the acid (XXXI) and cyclization with phosphorus pentoxide in phosphoric acid gives the pyrene derivative (XXXII) from which pyrene is obtained by dehydrogenation with palladium–charcoal.[18]

(XXVIII)   (XXIX)   (XXX)

(XXXI)   (XXXII)

Tetrahydropyrene (XXXIV) which can be easily dehydrogenated to pyrene was obtained from the tetrabromo compound (XXXIII) by treatment with phenyl lithium.[19]

(XXXIII)   (XXXIV)

(XXXV)

A similar cyclization takes place when diphenyltetraldehyde (XXXV) reacts with hydrazine in acetic acid.[20]

The phenanthrene derivative (XXXVI) cyclizes to 1,2-dihydro-pyrene (XXXVII) under the influence of phenyl lithium.[21]

(XXXVI)   (XXXVII)

Pyrene crystallizes in monoclinic prismatic plates (m.p. 156° (corr.)). It boils at 399° at 760 mm. For a long time pyrene was thought to be a yellow hydrocarbon and a quinonoid structure was made responsible for its colour.[22] However, it has been shown that the yellow colour originates from a trace of tetracene which can be removed by treatment with maleic anhydride.[23] Another compound associated with pyrene from coal-tar is brasane.[24]

Pyrene shows a blue fluorescence in solution and forms a dark red picrate (m.p. 222°) with picric acid in alcohol. Tetranitromethane gives a dark violet complex and trinitrobenzene a yellow compound (m.p. 245°).[25] The C—C bond distances in pyrene were determined by X-ray analysis.[26] The absorption spectrum is given in Fig. 119.

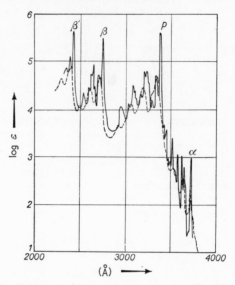

FIG. 119. Absorption spectrum of pyrene in methanol–ethanol (E. Clar, *Spectrochimica Acta* **4**, 118 (1950)).

	At +18° (broken line)	At −170° (full line)		At +18° (broken line)	At −170° (full line)
α-Bands	3715 (2·40)	3712 (3·00)	β-Bands	2720 (4·67)	2741 (5·50)
	3620 (2·60)	3635 (2·80)			2707 (4·72)
		3612 (3·03)			2662 (4·47)
	3560 (2·71)	3565 (3·07)		2615 (4·40)	2638 (4·97)
		3540 (2·68)			2618 (4·74)
	3515 (2·82)	3510 (3·42)			2600 (4·45)
		3490 (2·90)		2510 (4·04)	2532 (4·34)
		3467 (2·96)			
		3440 (3·60)	β′-Bands	2410 (4·90)	2423 (5·60)
		3415 (3·67)			2390 (5·15)
p-Bands	3335 (4·71)	3372 (5·60)		2305 (4·62)	2345 (4·86)
		3328 (4·77)			
		3282 (4·20)			
	3180 (4·47)	3223 (4·79)			
		3202 (4·79)			
		3165 (4·32)			
	3050 (4·06)	3093 (4·40)			
		3070 (4·49)			
		3030 (4·11)			
	2920 (3·62)	2950 (4·06)			

Hydrogenation

Pyrene adds lithium in ethereal solution. The hydrolysis of the metal compound gives an unstable dihydropyrene.[27] Reaction with CO_2 yields a pyrene dicarboxylic acid.[27] Pyrene adds one atom of sodium in solution in ether or liquid ammonia. The hydrolysis gives a monohydro compound of radical character which disproportionates to 1,2-dihydropyrene. Reaction of the monosodium compound with CO_2 yields pyrene-1-carboxylic acid.[28]

Pyrene is reduced to a dihydropyrene with sodium in a solution of ammonia, ether and alcohol. The dihydro compound has the structure (XXXVIII) or (XXXIX), or is a mixture of both. It is a very reactive hydrocarbon. It gives a picrate (m.p. 233° (dec.)), a trinitrobenzene compound (m.p. 213° (dec.)) and reacts with alcoholic potassium hydroxide to form a red solution. Phenyl lithium yields a lithium compound. Triphenylmethyl removes hydrogen with the formation of a green monohydro compound of radical character. A similar blue-green radical is formed under the influence of molecular oxygen. Hydrogenation with hydrogen and nickel affords 3,4,5,8,9,10-hexahydropyrene. Reaction with ethyl nitrite produces a mono- and a dioxime the reduction of which yields the known 3-, 3,8- and 3,10-diaminopyrenes respectively. The absorption spectrum is related to the spectrum of perinaphthene (XL).[29]

(XXXVIII)   (XXXIX)   (XL)

The hydrogenation of pyrene with sodium in amyl alcohol[30] yields two hexahydropyrenes, whose structures, (XLI) and (XLII) respectively, were established by the oxidation of (XLI) to 1,4,5,8-naphthalenetetracarboxylic acid.[31]

The same method yields also 1,2-dihydropyrene (XLV), 1,2,6,7-tetrahydropyrene (XLVI) and the two isomeric decahydropyrenes (XLIII) and (XLIV). The hydrogenation products can be separated by the different stabilities of their picrates. The picrates of (XLI) and (XLVI) are stable in benzene but not in alcohol. Stable picrates are obtained from (XLV) and (XLII) in alcoholic solution. The decahydropyrenes (XLIII) and (XLIV) do not form picrates.[32] Decahydropyrene (XLIII) has also been obtained by synthesis.[33]

The above hydrogenated pyrenes are also formed by catalytic hydrogenation of pyrene with molybdenum sulphide or with nickel.[34] The latter

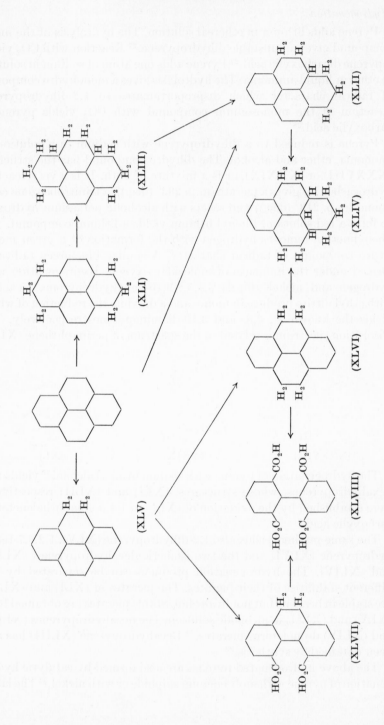

method yields also a perhydropyrene.[35] The constitution of 1,2-dihydro-pyrene (XLV) was established by an oxidation with hydrogen peroxide in acetic acid which yields 9,10-dihydrophenanthrene-4,5-dicarboxylic acid (XLVII). Diphenyltetracarboxylic acid (XLVIII) is formed by oxidation of tetrahydropyrene (XLVI) with potassium permanganate.

Substitutions

Pyrene is a very reactive hydrocarbon and gives readily mono-, di-, tri- and tetra-substitution products in the positions 3-; 3,8-; 3,10-; 3,5,8- and 3,5,8,10-. Chlorination in chloroform solution yields a mixture of 3-chloropyrene (XLIX), 3,8- and 3,10-dichloropyrene (L) and (LI) respectively, trichloropyrene (LII) and tetrachloropyrene (LIII). These

products are rather difficult to separate.[36] 3-Chloropyrene can be more easily obtained with sulphuryl chloride in carbon tetrachloride.[37] Tetra-chloropyrene (LIII) is formed in good yield by chlorination in tetra-chloroethane at 60°. Futher chlorination in trichlorobenzene at 110° leads to the addition of four atoms of chlorine and the formation of the adduct (LIV). Elimination of hydrochloric acid gives the two hexachloropyrenes (LV) and (LVI). Both compounds yield octahydropyrene (LVII) on further chlorination under the catalytic influence of iodine. Pyrene gives decachloropyrene upon chlorination in chlorosulphonic acid and iodine. The adduct eliminates hydrochloric acid on heating and forms decachloropyrene (LVIII).[37] Further chlorination leads to perchloropyrene.[38]

The bromination of pyrene proceeds like the chlorination. Bromine in carbon tetrachloride gives first 3-bromopyrene,[39] then two dibromopyrenes, probably 3,8- and 3,10-dibromopyrene are formed.[40] In benzene solution 3,5,8-tribromopyrene is obtained in addition to the two dibromopyrenes.[40] Bromination in nitrobenzene or in trichlorobenzene at 100–150° gives 3,5,8,10-tetrabromopyrene in quantitative yield.[37] A higher bromination has not been achieved. 3-Iodopyrene is obtained from the lithium compound of pyrene and iodine.[41]

3-Nitropyrene results from the reaction of pyrene with dilute nitric acid[42] or with aqueous potassium nitrite and dilute sulphuric acid[43] or with nitric acid in acetic acid.[37] The same method gives a mixture of dinitropyrenes from which 3,8-dinitropyrene could be obtained in a pure state. Strong nitric acid forms 3,5,8,10-tetranitropyrene.[37, 42]

Pyrene-3-sulphonic acid is prepared from pyrene with sodium bisulphate[44] or in carbon tetrachloride with chlorosulphonic acid at 0–5°.[45] Concentrated sulphuric acid at room temperature yields a mixture of disulphonic acids.[37, 46] More energetic reaction leads to pyrene-3,5,8,10-tetrasulphonic acid.[47]

Pyrene reacts with carbamyl chloride and aluminium chloride to form pyrene-3-carboxylic amide, saponification of which gives pyrene-3-carboxylic acid.[48] Acetyl chloride yields 3-acetylpyrene.[37] Chloroacetyl chloride, pyrene and aluminium chloride yield 3,8- and 3,10-di-(chloroacetyl)-pyrene, which can be oxidized to the corresponding dicarboxylic acids.[37] Propionyl chloride affords 3-propionylpyrene.[37] 3-n-Butyryl- and 3-isovalerylpyrene are obtained from the acid chlorides.[49] Phenylacetyl chloride gives 3-phenylacetylpyrene.[50] Pyrene, phosgene and aluminium chloride form 3,3'-dipyrenyl ketone.[41] 3,8-Di-t-butylpyrene is formed from t-butyl chloride.[51] Succinic anhydride affords 3-pyrenoylpropionic acid.[52]

Benzoyl chloride and aluminium chloride react with pyrene to form 3-benzoylpyrene,[53] a mixture of dibenzoylpyrenes[54] or tetrabenzoylpyrene.[55] Pyranthrone (see p. 208) can be directly obtained from pyrene and benzoyl chloride in a melt of sodium chloride and aluminium chloride.[56] Diketones are also formed with 1- or 2-naphthoyl chloride and thiophene-1-carboxylic chloride.[53] Condensation products are obtained from pyrene or 3-benzoylpyrene and cinnamoyl chloride under the influence of aluminium chloride.[57]

Pyrene, phthalic anhydride and aluminium chloride give 3-pyrenoyl-o-benzoic acid.[58] Excess of phthalic anhydride affords 3,8- and 3,10-(o-carboxybenzoyl)-pyrene[59] and 3,4-phthalylpyrene.[60] A mixture of diphthalylpyrenes can be directly obtained in a sodium chloride–aluminium chloride melt.[37]

Pyrene-3-aldehyde can be synthesized from pyrene, formylmethyl-aniline and phosphorus oxychloride. Pyrenyl-3-acetic acid is obtained from pyrene and monochloroacetic acid in boiling dichlorobenzene.[37] Tetrachloropyrene, benzene and aluminium chloride give 3,5,8,10-tetraphenylpyrene.[37] Benzophenone chloride, pyrene and aluminium chloride yield the naphthanthrene derivative (LIX).[61] 1,8,9-Naphthan-throne (LX) is formed from pyrene, glycerol and sulphuric acid.[37] Diazoacetic ester adds in the 1,2-position of pyrene to form the phenan-threne derivative (LXI). It yields an o-quinone on oxidation.[62] Pyrolysis of pyrene and benzene gives a mixture of phenylpyrenes and 2.3-o-phenylene-pyrene.[63]

(LIX)

(LX)

(LXI)

Alkylpyrenes have been isolated from coal-tar and from soot.[64] Phenylpyrenes and benzylpyrenes are formed by the reaction of phenyl- and benzyl radicals with pyrene.

TABLE XXVI. *Alkyl- and Aryl-pyrenes*

Compound	M.P. (°C)	References
1-Methyl-	149, 146–147	Newmann, M. S., *J. org. Chem.* **16**, 860 (1951); Chatterjee, D. N., *J. Amer. chem. Soc.* **77**, 5131 (1955).
3-Methyl-	72, 74–75	Vollmann, Becker, Corell and Streeck, *Liebigs Ann.* **531**, 36 (1937).
4-Methyl-	142·5–143·5	Vollmann, Becker, Corell and Streeck, *Liebigs Ann.* **531**, 36 (1937).
1-Ethyl-	74–75	Chatterjee, D. N., *J. Amer. chem. Soc.* **77**, 5131 (1955).
3-Ethyl-	94–95	Vollmann, Becker, Corell and Streeck, *Liebigs Ann.* **531**, 36 (1937).
1,2-Dimethyl-	211	Newmann, M. S., *J. org. Chem.* **16**, 860 (1951); Dannenberg, H. and Brachert, H., *Ber. dtsch. chem. Ges.* **84**, 504 (1951).
3,4-Dimethyl-	103–104	Martin and Senders, *Bull. Soc. chim. Belg.* **64**, 221 (1955); Clemo, G. R. and Ghatge, N. D., *J. chem. Soc.* 1069 (1956).
3,5-Dimethyl-	98–99	de Clercq, M. and Martin, R. H., *Bull. Soc. chim. Belg.* **64**, 367 (1955).
3,8-Dimethyl-	165–166	de Clercq, M. and Martin, R. H., *Bull. Soc. chim. Belg.* **64**, 367 (1955).
3,10-Dimethyl-	129–130	de Clercq, M. and Martin, R. H., *Bull. Soc. chim. Belg.* **64**, 367 (1955).
4,8-Dimethyl-	62	de Clercq, M. and Martin, R. H., *Bull. Soc. chim. Belg.* **64**, 367 (1955).
4,9-Dimethyl-	238	Orchin, Reggel and Friedel, *J. Amer. chem. Soc.* **74**, 332 (1952); Runge and Meckelburg, *Ber. dtsch. chem. Ges.* **86**, 373 (1953).
3,4-Diethyl-	84	Clemo, G. R. and Ghatge, N. D., *J. chem. Soc.* 1069 (1956).
3,5,8-Trimethyl-	178–179	
3,5,8,10-Tetramethyl	269–270	de Clercq, M. and Martin, R. H., *Bull. Soc. chim. Belg.* **64**, 367 (1955).
1-Benzyl-	89	Norman, R. O. C., Thompson, G. A. and Waters, W. A., *J. chem. Soc.* 175 (1958).
2-Benzyl-	170	Norman, R. O. C., Thompson, G. A. and Waters, W. A., *J. chem. Soc.* 175 (1958).
1,2-Dibenzyl-	158	Norman, R. O. C., Thompson, G. A. and Waters, W. A., *J. chem. Soc.* 175 (1958).
1-Phenyl-	170–171	Vollmann, Becker, Corell and Streeck, *Liebigs Ann.* **531**, 112 (1937).
3-Phenyl-	84	Norman, R. O. C., Thompson, G. A. and Waters, W. A., *J. chem. Soc.* 175 (1958).
3,5,8,10-Tetraphenyl-		Vollmann, Becker, Corell and Streeck, *Liebigs Ann.* **531**, 112 (1937).

Oxidation products

Oxidation of pyrene with chromic acid gives pyrenequinone.[65] Further oxidation yields 1,8-perinaphthone-4,5-dicarboxylic acid (LXIV), from which perinaphthone (LXV) can be obtained by decarboxylation, and naphthalene-1,4,5,8-tetracarboxylic acid (LXVI).[66] These results show that the carbonyls must be in the two rings with the positions 3,4,5,8,9,10. Later it was demonstrated that pyrenequinone is a mixture of two quinones which could be separated by means of the diacetates of the corresponding dihydroxypyrenes. One of the quinones, the 3,8-quinone (LXII), could be obtained by oxidation of 3,8-diaminopyrene, whose constitution is established. The other quinone is thus obviously the 3,10-quinone (LXIII).[67]

Pyrene-3,8-quinone (LXII) crystallizes from nitrobenzene in long, golden-yellow needles (m.p. 309°), which dissolve in concentrated sulphuric acid to form a yellow-orange solution. Alkaline sodium dithionite solution forms a light yellow blue-fluorescing vat.

(LXII)   (LXIII)

(LXIV)   (LXV)   (LXVI)

Pyrene-3,10-quinone (LXIII), which is the main constituent of the quinone mixture, forms long brownish-red needles (m.p. 270°). It dissolves in concentrated sulphuric acid to give an olive-green colour. Alkaline sodium dithionite gives a light yellow vat with an intense bluish-green fluorescence.[66, 67]

(LXVII)   (LXVIII)   (LXIX)   (LXX)

Halogenated pyrenequinones are readily accessible from halogenated pyrenes. 3,5,8,10-Tetrachloropyrene (LXVII) and 20% oleum at 85° yield a mixture of the two dichloropyrenequinones (LXVIII) and (LXIX). Both compounds give 3,5,8,10-tetraoxo-3,4,5,8,9,10-hexahydropyrene (LXX).[67]

Ozonolysis of pyrene in acetic acid gives first phenanthrene-4-alde-hyde-5-carboxylic acid (LXXI) from which phenanthrenequinone-4,5-dicarboxylic acid (LXXII) is obtained on further oxidation with chromic acid in acetic acid. The oxidation proceeds to diphenyl-o,o,o',o'-tetra-carboxylic acid (LXXIII) on application of alkaline potassium perman-ganate. Phenanthrene-4-aldehyde-5-carboxylic acid (LXXI) yields pyrene-1,2-quinone (LXXIV) under the influence of alcoholic potassium hydroxide or potassium cyanide. Further oxidation with chromic acid in acetic acid leads to pyrene-1.2,6.7-diquinone (LXXV).[67] The two aldehydes (LXXVI) and (LXXVII) can be obtained from the mono- and diozonides of pyrene.[68]

(LXXI)   (LXXII)   (LXXIII)

(LXXIV)   (LXXV)   (LXXVI)   (LXXVII)

Pyrene-1,2-quinone can be obtained also by oxidation of 1-hydroxy-2-aminopyrene. It crystallizes from chlorobenzene in long orange needles (m.p. 310°), which dissolve in concentrated sulphuric acid to give a greenish-blue solution. Alkaline sodium dithionite produces a yellow vat. As an o-quinone it condenses readily with o-phenylenediamine to form a phenazine derivative.[67]

Pyrene-1.2,6.7-diquinone (LXXV) crystallizes in yellow needles (m.p. 365° (dec.)), which give a yellow solution with concentrated sulphuric acid and a yellow vat with alkaline sodium dithionite solution. It condenses twice with o-phenylenediamine.[67]

Pyrene shows no carcinogenic activity and no growth inhibiting action.[69]

REFERENCES

1. Graebe, C., *Liebigs Ann.* **158**, 285 (1871).
2. Kruber, O., *Ber. dtsch. chem. Ges.* **64**, 84 (1931).
3. Schultz, G. and Würth, K., *Chem. Zbl.* **1905 I**, 1444.
4. Meyer, R., *Ber. dtsch. chem. Ges.* **45**, 1632 (1912); Meyer, R. and Taeger, K., *Ber. dtsch. chem. Ges.* **53**, 1263 (1920).
5. Freund, M. and Michaelis, H., *Ber. dtsch. chem. Ges.* **30**, 1357, 1383 (1897); Vongerichten, E., *Ber. dtsch. chem. Ges.* **34**, 768 (1901).
6. Steiner, H., *J. Inst. Petroleum* **33**, 410 (1947); *Chem. & Ind.* (*Rev.*) 457 (1949).
7. I.G. Farbenindustrie AG, French Patent 781543; Brit. Patent 435254; German Patents 639240, 640580, 654201; Brit. Patents 493447, 49508, 497089; French Patents 816162, 834062, 49332; Belg. Patent 427268; *Chem. Zbl.* **1937 II**, 3846; **1939 I**, 3296, 3832.
8. Cooper, R. L. and Lindsay, A. J., *Chem. & Ind.* (*Rev.*) 957 (1953).
9. Weitzenböck, R., *Mh. Chem.* **34**, 193 (1913).
10. Chatterjee, N. N., Bose, A. and Roy, H. B., *J. Ind. chem. Soc.* **24**, 169 (1947); *Amer. Abstr.* 2613 (1949).
11. Freund, M. and Fleischer, K., *Liebigs Ann.* **402**, 77 (1914).
12. Fleischer, K. and Retze, E., *Ber. dtsch. chem. Ges.* **55**, 3280 (1923).
13. von Braun, J. and Rath, E., *Ber. dtsch. chem. Ges.* **61**, 956 (1928).
14. Lock, J. and Walter, E., *Ber. dtsch. chem. Ges.* **72**, 286 (1944); Lock, J., *Ber. dtsch. chem. Ges.* **75**, 1158 (1942).
15. Cook, J. W., *J. chem. Soc.* 366 (1934).
16. Pellegrin, M., *Rec. trav. chim.* **18**, 458 (1899); Baker, W., McOmie, J. F. W. and Norman, J. M., *Chem. & Ind.* (*Rev.*) **77** (1950); *J. chem. Soc.* 1114 (1951).
17. Baker, W., McOmie, J. F. W. and Norman, J. M., *Chem. & Ind.* (*Rev.*) **77** (1950); *J. chem. Soc.* 1114 (1951).
18. Baker, W., McOmie, J. F. W. and Warburton, W. K., *J. chem. Soc.* 2991 (1952); Saha, N. N. and Bagchi, P., *J. org. Chem.* **20**, 1392 (1955).
19. Pelchowicz, Z. and Bergmann, E. D., *Bull. Res. Council Israel* **3**, 91 (1953).
20. Bacon, R. G. R. and Lindsay, W. S., *J. chem. Soc.* 1375 (1958).
21. Marvel, C. S. and Wilson, B. D., *J. org. Chem.* **23**, 1483 (1958).
22. Goldschmiedt, G., *Liebigs Ann.* **351**, 218 (1907).
23. Clar, E., *Ber. dtsch. chem. Ges.* **65**, 1427 (1932).
24. Winstein, W., Schön, K. and Vetter, H., *Hoppe-Seyl. Z.* **230**, 162 (1934).
25. Hertel, E., *Liebigs Ann.* **451**, 179 (1926).
26. Robertson, J. M. and White, J. G., *J. chem. Soc.* 358 (1947).
27. Bergmann, E. D. and Bograchov, E., *J. Amer. chem. Soc.* **62**, 3016 (1940).
28. Neunhoeffer, O. and Woggon, H., *Liebigs Ann.* **600**, 34 (1956).
29. Neunhoeffer, O., Woggon, H. and Dähne, S., *Liebigs Ann.* **612**, 98 (1958).
30. Graebe, C., *Liebigs Ann.* **158**, 297 (1871); Goldschmiedt, G., *Liebigs Ann.* **351**, 226 (1907).
31. Cook, J. W. and Hewett, C. L., *J. chem. Soc.* 401 (1933).
32. Coulson, E. A., *J. chem. Soc.* 1298 (1937); Fieser, L. F. and Novello, F. C., *J. Amer. chem. Soc.* **62**, 1855 (1940).
33. von Braun, J. and Rath, E., *Ber. dtsch. chem. Ges.* **61**, 956 (1928).
34. Kagehira, I., *Bull. chem. Soc. Japan* **6**, 241 (1931).
35. Treibs, W. and Mann, G., *Ber. dtsch. chem. Ges.* **91**, 1910 (1958).
36. Goldschmiedt, G. and Wegscheider, R., *Mh. Chem.* **4**, 238 (1883).
37. Vollmann, H., Becker, H., Corell, M. and Streeck, H., *Liebigs Ann.* **531**, 1 (1937).

38. Farbwerke Höchst, German Patent 863794 (1953).
39. Lock, G., *Ber. dtsch. chem. Ges.* **70**, 926 (1937); I.G. Farbenindustrie AG, French Patent 803820; *Chem. Zbl.* **1937** I, 1550.
40. Graebe, C., *Liebigs Ann.* **158**, 294 (1871); Clar, E., *Ber. dtsch. chem. Ges.* **69**, 1685 (1936).
41. Berg, A., *Acta chem. scand.* **3**, 665 (1949).
42. Graebe, C., *Liebigs Ann.* **158**, 292 (1871).
43. Goldschmiedt, G., *Monatsh. Chem.* **2**, 580 (1881).
44. Abe, Y. and Nagai, Y., *Koggo Kagaku Zasshi* **62**, 1025 (1959).
45. Gesellschaft für Chemische Industrie in Basel, Swiss Patent 172726 (1933); *Chem. Zbl.* **1935** II, 923.
46. Goldschmiedt, G., *Mh. Chem.* **4**, 681 (1883).
47. Tietze, E. and Bayer, O., *Liebigs Ann.* **540**, 189 (1939).
48. Gesellschaft für Chemische Industrie in Basel, Swiss Patent 190716 (1936); *Chem. Zbl.* **1937** II, 4107; Imp. Chem. Ind. Brit. Patent 486668 (1936); *Chem. Zbl.* **1938** II, 3317.
49. Bachmann, W. E. and Carmack, M., *J. Amer. chem. Soc.* **63**, 2494 (1941).
50. Buu-Hoï, N. P. and Royer, R., *Bull. Soc. chim. Fr.* 659 (1946).
51. Buu-Hoï, N. P. and Cagniant, P., *Ber. dtsch. chem. Ges.* **77**, 121 (1944).
52. Cook, J. W. and Hewett, C. L., *J. chem. Soc.* 398 (1933); Fieser, L. F., Hershberg, E. B., Long, L., Jr. and Newmann, M. S., *J. Amer. chem. Soc.* **59**, 475 (1937).
53. Scholl, R. and Seer, C., *Liebigs Ann.* **394**, 162 (1912); Scholl, R., Meyer, K. and Donat, J., *Ber. dtsch. chem. Ges.* **70**, 2180 (1937).
54. Vollmann, H., Becker, H., Corell, M. and Streeck, H., *Liebigs Ann.* **531**, 38 (1937).
55. Vollmann, H., Becker, H., Corell, M. and Streeck, H., *Liebigs Ann.* **531**, 46 (1937).
56. I.G. Farbenindustrie AG, Brit. Patent 382877 (1932); *Chem. Zbl.* **1933** I, 1525.
57. Scholl, R. and Meyer, K., Swiss Patent 176919 (1934); *Chem. Zbl.* **1936** I, 2637.
58. I.G. Farbenindustrie AG, German Patent 589145; *Chem. Zbl.* **1934** I, 771; Cook, J. W. and Hewett, C. L., *J. chem. Soc.* 403 (1933); Clar, E., *Ber. dtsch. chem. Ges.* **69**, 1684 (1936).
59. Clar, E., *J. chem. Soc.* 2013 (1949).
60. Verein für Chemische und Metallurgische Produktion, Aussig, German Patent 574189; *Chem. Zbl.* **1932** II, 447.
61. Clar, E., *Ber. dtsch. chem. Ges.* **69**, 1685 (1936); *Chem. Ber.* **81**, 524 (1948).
62. Badger, G. M., Cook, J. W. and Gibb, A. R. M., *J. chem. Soc.* 3456 (1951).
63. Lang, K. F. and Buffleb, H., *Chem. Ber.* **90**, 2894.
64. Clemo, G. R. and Miller, E. W., *Chem. & Ind. (Rev.)* 38 (1955).
65. Graebe, C., *Ber. dtsch. chem. Ges.* **3**, 742 (1870); *Liebigs Ann.* **158**, 285 (1871).
66. Bamberger, E. and Philip, M., *Ber. dtsch. chem. Ges.* **19**, 1427 (1886); **20**, 365 (1887); *Liebigs Ann.* **240**, 147 (1887).
67. Vollmann, H., Becker, H., Corell, M. and Streeck, H., *Liebigs Ann.* **531**, 5 (1937).
68. Fieser, L. F. and Novello, F. C., *J. Amer. chem. Soc.* **62**, 1885 (1940).
69. Haddow, A., Scott, C. M. and Scott, J. D., *Proc. roy. Soc.* **B122**, 477 (1937); Haddow, A., *J. path. Bact.* **47**, 567 (1938).

II. 1.2-BENZOPYRENE

3,4,5,8,9,10-Hexahydropyrene (I) condenses with succinic anhydride and aluminium chloride in nitrobenzene to form the acid (II). Wolff-Kishner reduction yields the reduced acid (III). Cyclization to (IV) is carried out with 80% sulphuric acid. Reduction with sodium and alcohol gives a hydrocarbon and dehydrogenation yields 1.2-benzopyrene (V).[1]

Reaction of propylmagnesium iodide with benzanthrone (VI) gives a dihydropropylbenzanthrone which is readily oxidized to 4-propyl-benzanthrone (VII). Cyclization and dehydrogenation to 1.2-benzo-pyrene (V) can be effected by a zinc-dust distillation.[2]

Dihydroanthracene (VIII) undergoes a two-fold condensation with acrolein and anhydrous hydrofluoric acid. The resulting hydrogenated benzopyrene is dehydrogenated by distillation with mercury.[3]

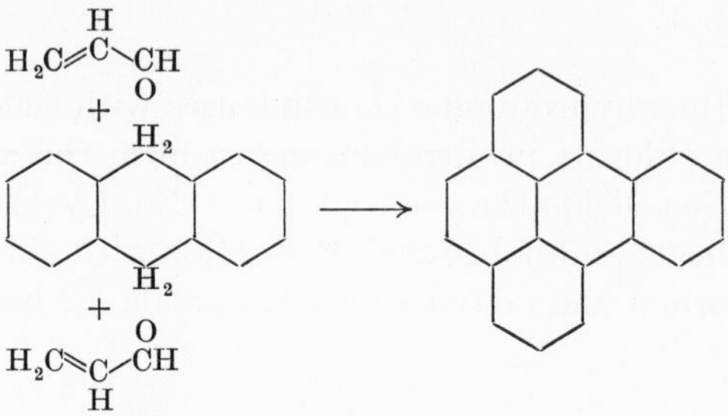

(VIII)   (V)

Benzanthrene (IX) condenses with maleic anhydride to form the substituted succinic acid (X). The cyclization via (XI) to benzopyrene (V) is carried out in a sodium chloride–aluminium chloride melt. About 0·4% perylene (XII) is obtained as a by-product. It can be separated from benzopyrene by chromatography.[4]

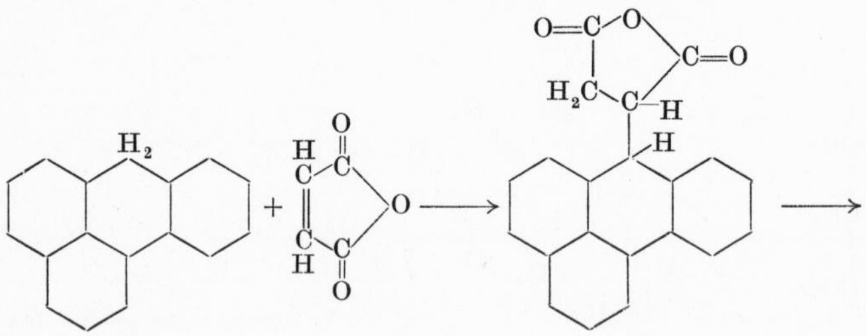

(IX)   (X)

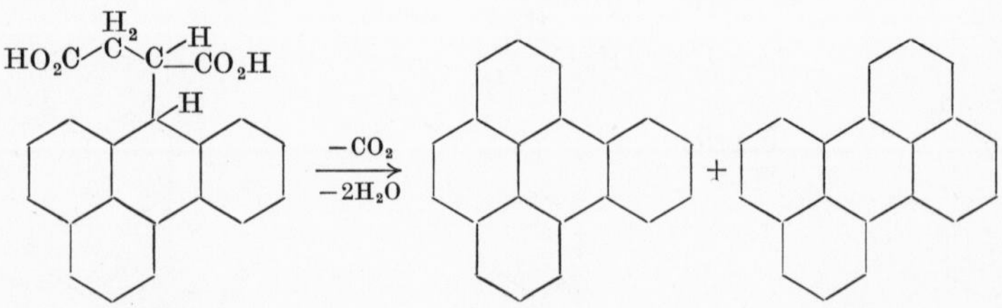

(XI)   (V)   (XII)

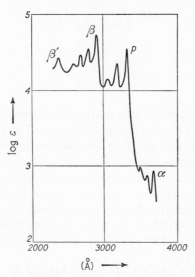

(XIII)   (XIV)

(XV)   (V)

2-Naphthyl-propiolic acid (XIII) and phenylpropiolic acid condense to the anhydride (XIV) when boiled with acetic anhydride. Sublimation with soda-lime and copper powder yields 4-phenylphenanthrene (XV) and 1.2-benzopyrene (V).[5]

1.2-Benzopyrene is a constituent of the high-boiling coal-tar. It can be isolated from the isomeric 3.4-benzopyrene by its more stable and less

Fig. 120. Absorption spectrum of 1.2-benzopyrene in ethanol: α, 3660 (2·80), 3570 (2·75), 3480 (2·90); p, 3315 (4·52), 3165 (4·34), 3040 (4·12); β, 2890 (4·72), 2780 (4·54), 2670 (4·46), 2570 (4·34); β' 2370 (4·42).

soluble picrate.[6] Pyrolysis of acetylene also yields 1.2-benzopyrene.[7] It has been isolated from soil.[8]

1.2-Benzopyrene crystallizes in large colourless prisms or plates (m.p. 178–179°). It forms a red picrate which crystallizes in needles (m.p. 229–230°). It has no carcinogenic properties.[7] The absorption spectrum is given in Fig. 120.

REFERENCES

1. Cook, J. W. and Hewett, C. L., *J. chem. Soc.* 401 (1933).
2. Charier, G. and Ghigi, E., *Ber. dtsch. chem. Ges.* **69**, 2220 (1936); Ghigi, *Atti X. Congr. Intern. Chimica, Roma* **3**, 178 (1938).
3. Weinmayr, V. (E. I. du Pont de Nemours & Co.), Amer. Patent 2145905 (1939); *Chem. Zbl.* **1939 II**, 230.
4. Clar, E., *Ber. dtsch. chem. Ges.* **76**, 609 (1943).
5. Campbell, A. D., *J. chem. Soc.* 3659 (1954).
6. Cook, J. W., Hewett, C. L. and Hieger, I., *J. chem. Soc.* 396 (1933).
7. Meyer, R. and Taeger, K., *Ber. dtsch. chem. Soc.* **53**, 1261 (1920).
8. Blumer, M., *Science* **134**, 474 (1961).

III. 3.4-BENZOPYRENE

This hydrocarbon, which was and still is of very great importance for cancer research, has been synthesized in several ways.

Condensation of pyrene with succinic anhydride and aluminium chloride in nitrobenzene solution gives the propionic acid (I). The reduction can be carried out with zinc dust and ammonia, zinc dust and sodium hydroxide under pressure or by the Wolff–Kishner method. Cyclization of the resulting butyric acid (II) can be effected with stannic chloride or via the acid chloride with aluminium chloride. Direct dehydrogenation of the ketone (III) or following reduction of the carbonyl yields 3.4-benzopyrene (IV).[1]

It can also be synthesized from perinaphthone (V). This is first reduced to *peri*-trimethylenenaphthalene (VI). Reaction with benzoyl chloride and aluminium chloride gives the ketone (VII). Cyclization to (VIII) takes place in a sodium chloride–aluminium chloride melt. Zinc-dust distillation of the benzanthrone derivative (VIII) yields 3.4-benzo-pyrene.[2]

Perinaphthanone (IX) reacts with the Grignard compound of o-chlorobromobenzene to form the compound (X). Dehydration followed by hydrogenation gives the compound (XI). The chlorine atom can be replaced by the CN-group whose hydrolysis yields the acid. Cyclization with hydrofluoric acid leads to trimethylenebenzanthrone (VIII) and dehydrogenation to 3.4-benzopyrene.[3]

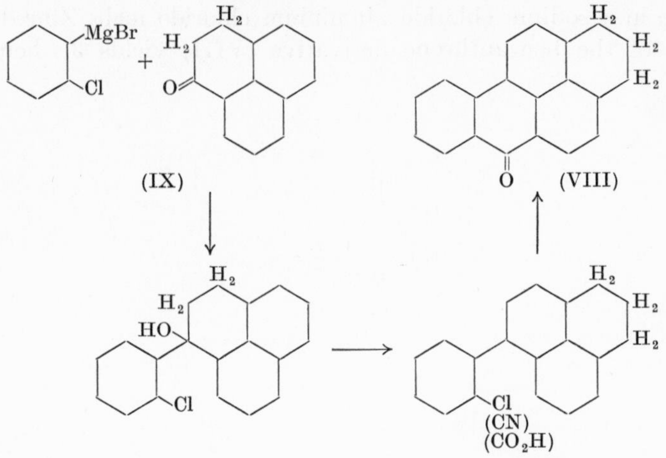

(IX)

(VIII)

(X)

(XI)

Another starting material for the synthesis of 3.4-benzopyrene is the ketone (XII). Condensation with bromoacetic ester and zinc gives the compound (XIII). Dehydration followed by dehydrogenation yields the propionic acid (XIV), and cyclization with hydrofluoric acid gives 2-hydroxy-3.4-benzopyrene (XV) from which 3.4-benzopyrene can be obtained by zinc-dust distillation.[4]

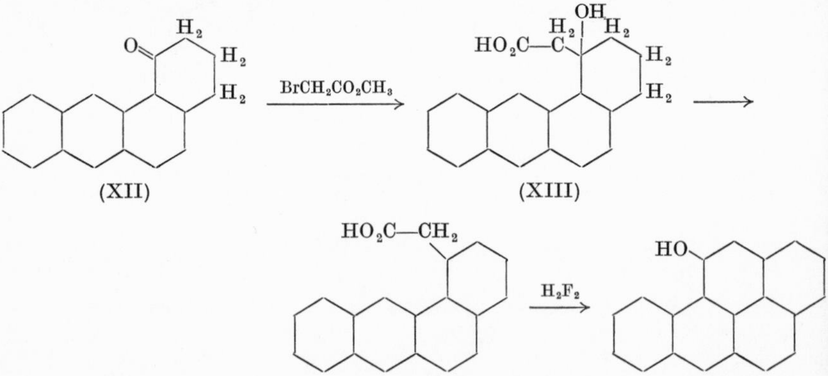

(XII)

(XIII)

(XIV)

(XV)

Anthracene can also be used as a starting material for the synthesis of 3.4-benzopyrene. It is converted into the 9-aldehyde from which the anthracenyl-acrylic acid (XVI) is obtained by a condensation with malonic ester. Hydrogenation with sodium and amyl alcohol gives (XVII) and cyclization with hydrofluoric acid gives the compound (XVIII). The latter condenses with ethyl succinate and potassium t-butoxide to the ester (XIX) from which the benzanthrene-propionic acid (XX) and the acid (XXI) are obtained with hydrobromic acid in acetic acid. The compound (XXI) exists in two stereomeric forms which both are formed by hydrogenation of (XX). Both forms of (XXI) cyclize to the ketone (XXII) by a treatment with hydrofluoric acid. Dehydrogenation of (XXII) with palladium in boiling 1-methylnaphthalene leads to 8-hydroxy-3.4-benzopyrene (XXIII). This is one of the biological degradation products of 3.4-benzopyrene and can be oxidized to benzopyrene-3,10-quinone (XXIV) or reduced to 3.4-benzopyrene.[5]

The reaction of perinaphthone (XXV) with o-tolylmagnesium bromide gives o-tolyl-perinaphthone (XXVI) from which 3.4-benzopyrene is obtained by cyclization.[6]

The chrysene derivative (XXVII) reacts with bromoacetic ester to form the acid (XXVIII). Reduction gives (XXIX) and cylization (XXX). Reduction of the carbonyl in (XXX) yields the hydrogenated 3.4-benzopyrene (XXXI) and dehydrogenation 3.4-benzopyrene.[7]

3.4-Benzopyrene can be isolated from coal-tar if the mother liquor from the crystallization of the picrate of 1.2-benzopyrene (p. 129) is freed from the picric acid, distilled and the distillate repeatedly recrystallized,[8] 3.4-Benzopyrene is a by-product of crude picene from coal-tar.[9]

(XXV)

(XXVI)

(XXVII)

(XXXI)

(XXVIII)

(XXIX)

(XXX)

3.4-Benzopyrene is one of the pyrolytic products from styrene, tetralin, acetylene and phenylbutylnaphthalene.[10] It is also found in the tar from tobacco smoke (see below) and polluted air (smog).[11] It has been isolated from soil.[12]

3.4-Benzopyrene crystallizes from a mixture of benzene and methylalcohol in long, pale-yellow needles (m.p. 176·5–177·5°). It dissolves in concentrated sulphuric acid to form an orange-red solution with a green fluorescence. It can be recovered unchanged from this solution on dilution with water. 3.4-Benzopyrene forms a picrate, dark red needles (m.p. 197–198°). The absorption spectrum is given in Fig. 121. It has a phosphorescence spectrum with bands at 6815, 6975, 7135, 7455, 7640, 7835, 8420, 8650 Å.[13]

The hydrogenation of 3.4-benzopyrene with platinum oxide gives 5,6-dihydro-3.4-benzopyrene (**XXXII**) and tetrahydro-3.4-benzopyrene (**XXXIII**) and, finally, perhydro-3.4-benzopyrene. Compound (**XXXII**) has the absorption spectrum of a chrysene and (**XXXIII**) the spectrum of a pyrene derivative.[14]

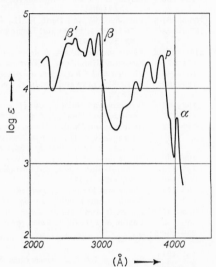

FIG. 121. Absorption spectrum of 3.4-benzopyrene in ethanol: α, 4030 (3·60); p, 3845 (4·44), 3635 (4·36), 3470 (4·10), 3300 (3·76); β, 2965 (4·76), 2843 (4·66), 2740 (4·50); β′, 2655 (4·66), 2540 (4·60); β″, 2250 (4·44).

3.4-Benzopyrene with bromine in carbon disulphide gives tribromo-3.4-benzopyrene.[15] It reacts with nitric acid in acetic acid to form 5-nitro-3.4-benzopyrene and a dinitro derivative.[15-17] Isomeric mono-nitro derivatives are also formed.[18] Sulphuric acid in acetic acid yields a monosulphonic acid.[15] Rhodanation gives the 5-rhodano-3.4-benzo-

(XXXII)   (XXXIII)

pyrene.[19] Acetic anhydride and aluminium chloride yield 10-acetyl-3.4-benzopyrene from which 3.4-benzopyrene-10-carboxylic acid is obtained by oxidation with sodium hypochlorite solution. A diacetyl-3.4-benzopyrene was prepared in an analogous way.[15, 20] 3.4-Benzopyrene-5-aldehyde is formed by the reaction with methylformanilide in o-dichlorobenzene.[21]

TABLE XXVII. *Alkyl-3.4-benzopyrenes*

Alkyl group	M.P.(°C)	References
1-Methyl-	155–156·5	Doyle, W. C. and Daub, G. H., *J. Amer. chem. Soc.* **80**, 5252 (1958).
2-Methyl-	166·5–167·5 167·4–168·4	Patton, J. W. and Daub, G. H., *J. Amer. chem. Soc.* **79**, 709 (1957); Fieser and Heymann, *J. Amer. chem. Soc.* **63**, 2333 (1941).
5-Methyl-	215·7–216·2	Fieser and Hershberg, *J. Amer. chem. Soc.* **60**, 2542 (1938).
6-Methyl-	171–171·5	Fieser and Hershberg, *J. Amer. chem. Soc.* **60**, 1658 (1938).
7-Methyl-	187–188 188–189	Phillips and Chatterjee, *J. Amer. chem. Soc.* **80**, 4360 (1958); Comp and Daub, *J. Amer. chem. Soc.* **80**, 6049 (1958).
8-Methyl-	192–193	Windaus and Raichle, *Liebigs Ann.* **537**, 157 (1939).
9-Methyl-	176–177	Adelfang and Daub, *J. Amer. chem. Soc.* **79**, 1751 (1956).
10-Methyl-	177–178	Adelfang and Daub *J. Amer. chem. Soc.* **77**, 3297 (1955); Campbell, A. D., *J. chem. Soc.* 1938 (1956); Comp and Daub, *J. Amer. chem. Soc.* **80**, 6049 (1958).
1'-Methyl-	190–190·8 ⎱	Fieser and Hersberg, *J. Amer. chem. Soc.* **60**, 1658 (1938); Bachmann and Carmack, *J. Amer. chem. Soc.* **63**, 2494 (1941).
2'-Methyl-	139–140 ⎰	
3'-Methyl-	147·5–148	
4'-Methyl-	217·5–218	Fieser and Fieser, *J. Amer. chem. Soc.* **57**, 782 (1935).
10-Ethyl-	112	Windaus and Raichle, *Liebigs Ann.* **537**, 157 (1939).
1,8-Dimethyl-	136·5–137	Doyle, Jr. and Daub, *J. Amer. chem. Soc.* **80**, 5252 (1958).
2,8-Dimethyl-	140–142	Patton and Daub, *J. Amer. chem. Soc.* **79**, 709 (1957).
5,8-Dimethyl-	239–239·5 ⎱	Adelfang and Daub, *J. Amer. chem. Soc.* **80**, 1405 (1958).
5,10-Dimethyl-	227·5–230 ⎰	
6,7-Dimethyl-	181–184 ⎱	Comp and Daub, *J. Amer. chem. Soc.* **80**, 6049 (1958).
7,10-Dimethyl-	222–223 ⎰	
8,9-Dimethyl-	214·5–217	Adelfang and Daub, *J. Amer. chem. Soc.* **79**, 1751 (1956).
8,10-Dimethyl-	235–238	Adelfang and Daub, *J. Amer. chem. Soc.* **77**, 3297 (1955).
9,10-Dimethyl-	174–175·5	Adelfang and Daub, *J. org. Chem.* **23**, 749 (1958).
3',4'-Dimethyl-	215–216	Bachmann and Carmack, *J. Amer. chem. Soc.* **63**, 2494 (1941).
5,8,10-Trimethyl-	290–292	Adelfang and Daub, *J. Amer. chem. Soc.* **80**, 1405 (1958).

Sulphuryl chloride in carbon tetrachloride gives 5-chloro-3.4-benzo-pyrene from which 3.4-benzopyrene-5-nitrile can be prepared with copper cyanide.[20] Lead tetra-acetate in acetic acid yields 5-acetoxy-3.4-benzopyrene.[17, 21] 3.4-Benzopyrene-5-acetic acid can be obtained from

(XXXIV)   (XXXV)

the hydrocarbon and thioglycocol under the influence of radiation.[22] A 3.4-benzopyrene with ^{14}C in the position 5 has been synthesized.[23]

The two fluorene derivatives (XXXIV) and (XXXV) of 3.4-benzo-pyrene have also been synthesized.[24]

3.4-Benzopyrenequinones

Like pyrene, 3.4-benzopyrene yields two isomeric quinones on oxidation with chromic acid. They can be separated by reduction to the corresponding hydroquinols and fractional crystallization of their diacetates. Hydrolysis and mild oxidation give the pure quinones (XXXVI) and (XXXVII).[25]

(XXXVI)   (XXXVII)   (XXXVIII)

(XXXIX)   (XL)

3.4-Benzopyrene-5,8-quinone (XXXVII) may also be prepared by oxidation of 3.4-benzopyrene-10-carboxylic acid (XXXIX) to (XL) followed by decarboxylation.[26] Both quinones give benzanthrone-dicarboxylic anhydride (XXXVIII) on further oxidation.[25] The latter has also been synthesized in a different way.[27]

II—5*

3.4-Benzopyrene-5,10-quinone (XXXVI) crystallizes in orange needles (m.p. 295°), which dissolve in concentrated sulphuric acid to form a red solution. Alkaline sodium dithionite gives an orange-yellow vat.

3.4-Benzopyrene-5,8-quinone (XXXVII) forms orange-red needles (m.p. 245°) from acetic acid. It gives an olive-brown solution with concentrated sulphuric acid and a reddish-yellow vat with alkaline sodium dithionite. The two quinones (XXXVI) and (XXXVII) can also be obtained by ozonolysis of benzopyrene which further leads to the anhydride (XXXVIII).[28]

3.4-Benzopyrene-1,5-quinone (XLII) can be prepared by a condensation of phthalidene acetic acid (XLI) with naphthalene and aluminium chloride. It forms yellow crystals (m.p. 327°) from o-dichlorobenzene.[29]

(XLI)   (XLII)

(XLIII)   (XLIV)

Methyl derivatives and benzologues of the quinone (XLII) can be prepared by the same method. In a similar synthesis naphthoylbenzoic ester (XLIII) is submitted to a modified Stobbe reaction. The resulting ester (XLIV) is hydrolysed and cyclized via the dichloride with aluminium chloride.[30]

Carcinogenic Properties of 3.4-Benzopyrene

3.4-Benzopyrene is one of the most powerful cancer-producing agents. When applied in benzene solution to the skin of mice, tumours appear within 90–100 days. Injection causes the fast development of sarcomas. These properties which were discovered by Cook, Hewett and Hieger[31] were soon studied extensively in other laboratories.[32]

Biological degradation of 3.4-benzopyrene in rabbits yields 8-hydroxy- and 10-hydroxy-3.4-benzopyrene, 3.4-benzopyrene-5,8-quinone and 3.4-benzopyrene-5,10-quinone.[33]

The carcinogenic activity disappears in the following substitution products: tribromo, mononitro, dinitro, monoamino and sulphonic acid.[34] 4'-Methoxy-3.4-benzopyrene is weakly active, while 4'-hydroxy-3.4-benzopyrene is inactive.[35] 3.4-Benzopyrene shows a distinct oestrogenic activity.[36] 3.4-Benzopyrene is a constituent of the tar condensed from cigarette smoke.[37] $2 \cdot 2$ γ could be isolated from 100 cigarettes.[38] 3.4-Benzopyrene besides other carcinogenic hydrocarbons, has also been obtained from the soot filtered from the polluted air in large cities.[39]

REFERENCES

1. Cook, J. W., Hewett, C. L. and Hieger, I., *J. chem. Soc.* 398 (1933); Maisin, J. and Liégeois, P., *C. R. Soc. Biol., Paris* 115, 733 (1934); Winterstein, W., Vetter, H. and Schön, K., *Ber. dtsch. chem. Ges.* 68, 1082 (1935); *Hoppe-Seyl. Z.* 230, 173 (1934); Fieser, L. F. and Fieser, M., *J. Amer. chem. Soc.* 57, 782 (1935); Rondoni, P. and Corbellini, A., *Atti R. Accad. naz. Lincei, Rend.* 21, 128 (1935); Windaus, A. and Rennhak, S., *Hoppe-Seyl. Z.* 249, 256 (1937); Vollmann, H., Becker, H., Corell, M. and Streeck, H., *Liebigs Ann.* 531, 48 (1937); Fieser, L. F. and Novello, F. C., *J. Amer. chem. Soc.* 62, 1855 (1940).
2. Fieser, L. F. and Hershberg, E. B., *J. Amer. chem. Soc.* 60, 1658 (1938).
3. Fieser, L. F. and Gates, M. D., Jr., *J. Amer. chem. Soc.* 62, 2335 (1940).
4. Fieser, L. F. and Heymann, H., *J. Amer. chem. Soc.* 63, 2333 (1941).
5. Cook, J. W., Ludwiczak, R. S. and Schoental, R., *J. chem. Soc.* 1112 (1950).
6. Arbuzov, B. A. and Grechkin, N. P., *Zh. obshch. Khim.* 22, 1692 (1952); *Amer. Abstr.* 9953 (1953).
7. Phillips, D. D. and Chatterjee, D. N., *J. Amer. chem. Soc.* 80, 4360 (1958).
8. Cook, J. W., Hewett, C. L. and Hieger, I., *J. chem. Soc.* 396 (1933).
9. Winterstein, W., Schön, K. and Vetter, H., *Hoppe-Seyl. Z.* 230, 163 (1934); *Naturwissenschaften* 22, 237 (1934).
10. Badger, G. M. and Kimber, R. W. L., *J. chem. Soc.* 2453, 2455 (1958).
11. Cooper, R. L. and Lindsey, A. J., *Chem. & Ind. (Rev.)* 1205 (1953); Badger, G. M. and Buttery, R. G., *J. chem. Soc.* 2458 (1958).
12. Blumer, M., *Science* 134, 447 (1961).
13. Muel, B. and Hubert-Habart, M., *J. chem. Phys.* 55, 377 (1958).
14. Jacobs, T. L. and Scott, W. R., Jr., *J. Amer. chem. Soc.* 75, 5497; Lijinski, W. and Zechmeister, *J. Amer. chem. Soc.* 75, 5495 (1953).
15. Windaus, A. and Rennhak, S., *Hoppe-Seyl. Z.* 249, 256 (1937).
16. Cook, J. W. and Hewett, C. L., *J. chem. Soc.* 403 (1933).
17. Fieser, L. F. and Hershberg, E. B., *J. Amer. chem. Soc.* 61, 1565 (1939).
18. Dewar, M. J. S., Mole, T., Urch, D. S. and Warford, E. W. T., *J. chem. Soc.* 3572 (1956).
19. Wood, J. L. and Fieser, L. F., *J. Amer. chem. Soc.* 63, 2323 (1941).
20. Windaus, A. and Raichle, K., *Liebigs Ann.* 537, 157 (1939).
21. Fieser, L. F. and Hershberg, E. B., *J. Amer. chem. Soc.* 60, 2542 (1938).
22. Conway, W. and Tarbell, D. S., *J. Amer. chem. Soc.* 78, 2228 (1956).
23. Heidelberger, C. and Rieke, H. S., *Cancer Res.* 11, 640 (1951).

24. Saint-Ruf, G., Buu-Hoï, N. P. and Jacquinon, P., *J. chem. Soc.* 48 (1958).
25. Vollmann, H., Becker, H., Corell, M. and Streeck, H., *Liebigs Ann.* 531, 51 (1937).
26. Windaus, A. and Raichle, K., *Liebigs Ann.* 537, 157 (1939).
27. I.G. Farbenindustrie AG, German Patent 494111 (1927); *Chem. Zbl.* 1930 II, 820.
28. Moriconi, E. J., Rakoczy, B. and O'Connor, W. F., *J. Amer. chem. Soc.* 83, 4618 (1961).
29. E. I. du Pont de Nemours & Co. (H. E. Schroeder) Amer. Patent 2653, 953 (1953); *Amer. Abstr.* 11494 (1954); Schroeder, H. E., Stilmar, F. B. and Palmer, F. S., *J. Amer. chem. Soc.* 78, 446 (1956); Dakunikhin, N. S. and Moiseeva, Z. Z., *Zh. Vseroguzo Khim. Obshch. Mendeleeva* 6, 235 (1961).
30. Norman, R. O. C. and Waters, W. A., *J. chem. Soc.* 2379 (1956).
31. Cook, J. W., Hewett, C. L. and Hieger, I., *J. chem. Soc.* 395 (1933).
32. Barry, G., Cook, J. W., Haslewood, G. A. D., Hewett, C. L., Hieger, I. and Kennaway, E. L., *Proc. roy. Soc.* B117, 318 (1935); Maisin, J. and Coolen, M. L., *C. R. Soc. Biol., Paris* 117, 109 (1934); Maisin, J. and Liégeois, P., *C. R. Soc. Biol., Paris* 115, 733 (1934); Oberling, C., Sannie, C. and Guérin, M. and P., *Bull. Assoc. Franç. Etude Cancer* 25, 156 (1936); Rondoni, P. and Corbellini, A., *Atti. R. Accad. naz. Lincei Rend.* 21, VI, 128 (1936); Schürch, O. and Winterstein, A., *Hoppe-Seyl. Z.* 236, 79 (1935); Shear, M., *Amer. J. Cancer* 1936, 322; Fieser, L. F., *Nucleus* 15, 107 (1938); *Amer. J. Cancer* 34, 37 (1938); Bachmann, W. E., Cook, J. W., Dansi, A., de Worms, C. G. M., Haslewood, G. A. D., Hewett, C. L. and Robinson, A. M., *Proc. roy. Soc.* B123, 343 (1937); Cook, J. W., Haslewood, G. A. D., Hewett, C. L., Hieger, I., Kennaway, E. L. and Mayneord, W. V., *Amer. J. Cancer* 29, 119 (1937); Cook, J. W. and Kennaway, E. L., *Amer. J. Cancer* 33, 50 (1938).
33. Berenblum, I. and Schoental, R., *Cancer Res.* 3, 145 (1943); Berenblum, I., Crowfoot, D., Holiday, E. R. and Schoental, R., *Cancer Res.* 3, 151 (1943); Berenblum, I., Schoental, R., Holiday, E. R. and Jope, E. M., *Cancer Res.* 6, 699 (1946); Cook, J. W., Ludwiczak, R. S. and Schoental, R., *J. chem. Soc.* 1112 (1950).
34. Windaus, A. and Rennhak, S., *Hoppe-Seyl. Z.* 249, 256 (1937).
35. Fieser, L. F., Hershberg, E. B., Long, L., Jr. and Newman, M. S., *J. Amer. chem. Soc.* 59, 475 (1937); Cook, J. W., Haslewood, G. A. D., Hewett, C. L., Hieger, I., Kennaway, E. L. and Mayneord, W. V., *Amer. J. Cancer* 29, 220 (1937).
36. Cook, J. W., Dodds, E. C., Hewett, C. L. and Lawson, W., *Proc. roy. Soc.* B114, 272 (1934).
37. Roffo, A. H., *Bol. Inst. med. exp. Cancer* 15, 349 (1938); Commins, B. T., Cooper, R. L. and Lindsey, A. J., *Brit. J. Cancer* 8, 296 (1954); Cooper, R. L., Lindsay, A. J. and Waller, R. E., *Chem. & Ind. (Rev.)* 1418 (1954); Wright, G. and Wynder, E., *Cancer Res.* 2, 55 (1955); Lettré, H. and Jahn, A., *Naturwissenschaften* 42, 210 (1955); Kuratsune, M., *J. nat. Cancer Res.* 16, 1485 (1956).
38. Bonnet, J., Neukomm, S., *Helv. chim. Acta* 39, 1724 (1956).
39. Clemo, G. R., *Chem. & Ind. (Rev.)* 957 (1953).

IV. 1.2,3.4-DIBENZOPYRENE

The synthesis of 1.2,3.4-dibenzopyrene starts from 1-naphthoyl-*o*-benzoic acid the chloride of which reacts in the presence of aluminium chloride with benzene in the pseudo form (I) to give the phthalide (II). This re-arranges to the acid (III) when heated in boiling benzene with aluminium chloride. Zinc-dust distillation of (III) causes cyclization and reduction to 1.2,3.4-dibenzopyrene (IV). The latter can be also obtained directly from the phthalide (II) in a melt with aluminium chloride.[1]

However, this synthesis is not unambiguous and could have resulted in the formation of isomeric hydrocarbons. The following synthesis confirms the adopted constitution (IV).[2] 1-Benzoyl-2-methylnaphthalene (V) is oxidized with aqueous selenium dioxide under pressure at

220° to the acid (VI). The corresponding chloride of this acid reacts with benzene and aluminium chloride in the pseudo form to yield the phthalide (VII). Reduction with zinc dust in alcoholic potassium hydroxide solution gives the acid (VIII) and cyclization with sulphuric acid the anthrone–anthranol derivative (IX, IXa). A direct condensation of (IX) in a sodium chloride–aluminium chloride melt or after reduction to 12-phenyltetraphene (X) gives 1.2,3.4-dibenzopyrene (IV). A hydrogenated dibenzopyrene and the red 2.3,6.7-dibenzofluoranthene (p. 306) are formed as by-products and can be removed by chromatography.

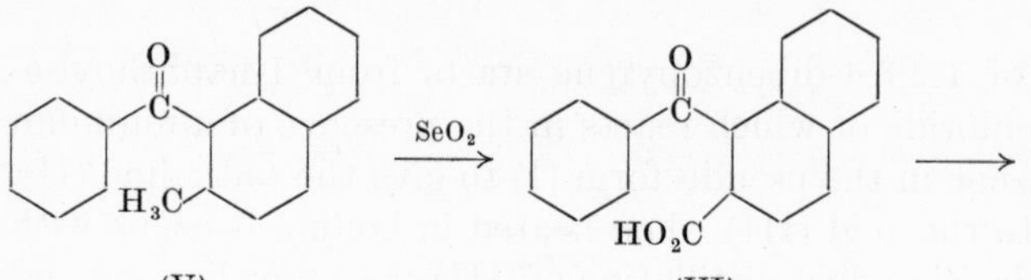

(V) $\xrightarrow{\text{SeO}_2}$ (VI)

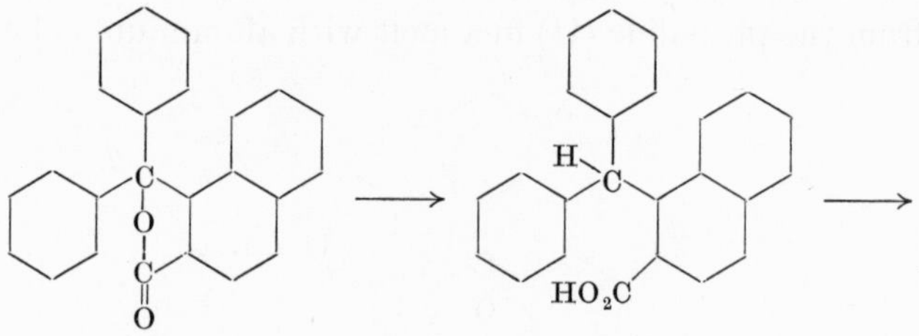

(VII)

(VIII)

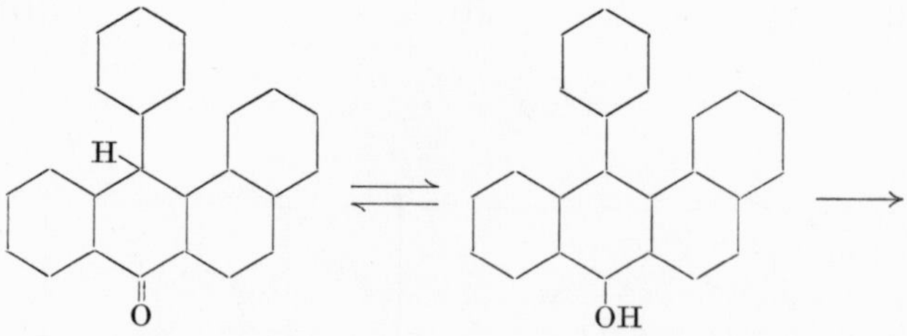

(IX) $\rightleftharpoons$ (IXa)

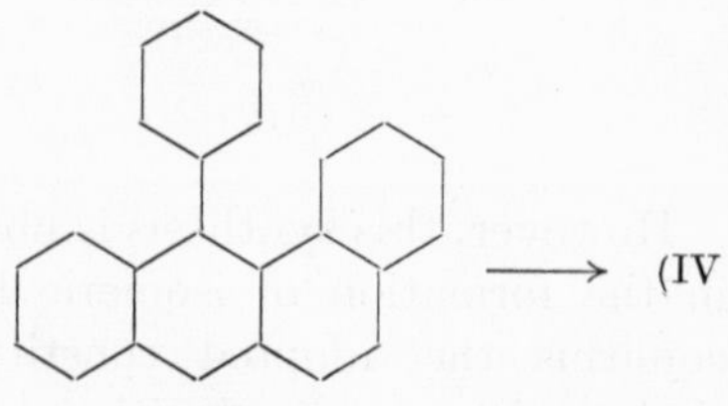

(X) $\longrightarrow$ (IV

The reaction of tetraphene (XI) with boiling benzene, stannic chloride and aluminium chloride also gives 1.2,3.4-dibenzopyrene (IV).[3]

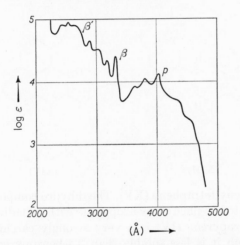

(XI)   (IV)

1.2,3.4-Dibenzopyrene crystallizes from benzene in long yellow needles (m.p. 224–226°), which dissolve in concentrated sulphuric acid to form a bordeaux-red solution which soon changes to olive-green. Solutions in organic solvents show a green fluorescence. Dibenzopyrene forms a picrate which crystallizes in dark red needles (m.p. 231°). The absorption spectrum is given in Fig. 122.

Fig. 122. Absorption spectrum of 1.2,3.4-dibenzopyrene in ethanol: α, 4540 (3·56), 4330 (3·76), 4120 (3·88); p, 4010 (4·08), 3790 (4·02), 3590 (3·90); β, 3305 (4·38), 3150 (4·36), 3010 (4·58), 2890 (4·68), 2710 (4·80), 2610 (4·85), 2530 (4·83), 2400 (4·78).

The synthesis of a number of methyldibenzopyrenes has been reported: 2′-methyl- (m.p. 210–211°), 3′-methyl (m.p. 213–214°), 4′-methyl- (m.p. 206–207°), 5-methyl-(m.p. 221–222°),[4] 1′,4′-dimethyl- (m.p. 207–209°), 1′,3′-dimethyl- (m.p. 215–216:), 2′,4′-dimethyl- (m.p. 198–199°), 3′,4′-dimethyl- (m.p. 201–202°).[5]

5-Phenyl-1.2,3.4-dibenzopyrene (XIV) can be synthesized from tetraphene-7,12-quinone, which reacts with phenylmagnesium bromide to form the diol (XII). Treatment with boiling benzene and aluminium chloride splits out two molecules of water and gives phenyl-1.2,3.4-dibenzopyrene and its dihydro compound (XIII) as a by-product. The dehydro compound is the sole condensation product if the diol is first

(XII)   (XV)

(XIII)   (XIV)

reduced to diphenyltetraphene (XV). The dihydro compound can easily be dehydrogenated to phenyldibenzopyrene with palladium–charcoal.[1]

1.2,3.4-Dibenzopyrene (IV) is a very strongly carcinogenic hydrocarbon. Although it is less soluble than 3.4-benzopyrene it produces tumours in a very short time.[6]

REFERENCES

1. Clar, E., *Ber. dtsch. chem. Ges.* **63**, 112 (1930).
2. Clar, E. and Stewart, D., *J. chem. Soc.* 687 (1951).
3. Zander, M., *Chem. Ber.* **92**, 2749 (1959).
4. Buu-Hoï, N. P. and Lavit-Lamy, D., *C.R. Acad. Sci., Paris* **225**, 2614 (1962).
5. Vingiello, F. A. and Zajac, W. W., *J. org. Chem.* **26**, 2228 (1961).
6. Bachmann, W. E., Cook, J. W., Dansi, A., de Worms, C. G. M., Hewett, C. L. and Robinson, A. M., *Proc. roy. Soc.* **B123**, 350 (1937); Cook, J. W. and Kennaway, E. L., *Amer. J. Cancer* **33**, 53 (1938).

V. 1.2,4.5-DIBENZOPYRENE

4.5,7.8-Dibenzoperinaphthene (I) can be condensed with maleic anhydride to form the succinic anhydride (II). The acid (III) derived from it cyclizes in a sodium chloride–aluminium chloride melt to 1.2,4.5-dibenzopyrene (IV).[1]

Condensation of chrysene (V) with aluminium chloride in boiling benzene gives a hydrocarbon which was believed to be a dinaphthoperylene.[2] However, it is identical with 1.2,4.5-dibenzopyrene (IV).[3]

Benzanthrone (VI) reacts with o-tolyl magnesium bromide to form a dihydrobenzanthrone derivative which after mild oxidation gives o-tolylbenzanthrone (VII). The latter can be cyclized to 1.2,4.5-dibenzopyrene (IV).[4]

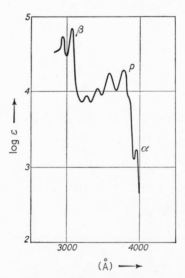

$$\text{(VI)} \longrightarrow \qquad \text{(VII)} \longrightarrow \text{(IV)}$$

1.2,4.5-Dibenzopyrene forms pale yellow needles from xylene (m.p. 233–234°), which dissolve in concentrated sulphuric acid to give a red solution which turns brown. Solutions in organic solvents show a blue fluorescence. The absorption spectrum is given in Fig. 123.

The oxidation[3] of 1.2,4.5-dibenzopyrene yields first the quinone (VIII) and then the acid (IX). This acid gives two different esters one

Fig. 123. Absorption spectrum of 1.2,4.5-dibenzopyrene in benzene: α, 3960 (3·20); p, 3780 (4·30), 3600 (4·25), 3430 (4·05), 3275 (3·90); β, 3065 (4·83), 2945 (4·72).

of them derived from the lactone form of the acid (IX). Zinc-dust distillation leads to the fluorene derivative (X) and a melt with potassium hydroxide to a mixture of phenanthrene-monocarboxylic and dicarboxylic acids (XI) and (XII) respectively. Both give phenanthrene on decarboxylation. Decarboxylation of the acid (IX) yields 1.2,3.4-dibenzanthraquinone (XIII).

(VIII)   (IX)   (X)

(XI)   (XII)   (XIII)

2'-Methyl-1.2,4.5-dibenzopyrene (m.p. 224–225°) has been prepared from chrysene, toluene and aluminium chloride.[5] 2''-Methyl-1.2,4.5-dibenzopyrene (m.p. 172–174°), 2'',4''-dimethyl-1.2,4.5-dibenzopyrene (m.p. 166–167·5°), 3''-isopropyl-1.2,4.5-dibenzopyrene (m.p. 124·5–126·5°) and the compound (IX) (m.p. 241–242·5°) are synthesized from benzanthrone and Grignard compounds. The tetralylbenzanthrone (X) was obtained in the same way. A melt with sulphur gives the compound

(IX)   (X)   (XI)

(XI) (m.p. 206–207°), which, however, cannot be considered a benzologue of pyrene but rather a benzanthrene derivative.[6]

1.2,4.5-Dibenzopyrene is a very strong carcinogenic hydrocarbon.[6] The compound (IX) produces leukaemia.[6]

REFERENCES

1. Clar, E., *Chem. Ber.* **76**, 609 (1943).
2. I.G. Farbenindustrie AG, French Patent 795447 (1935); *Chem. Zbl.* **1936 II**, 4051.
3. Zinke, A., Zimmer, W., *Monatsh. Chem.* **81**, 783; **82**, 348 (1951); Zinke, A. and Ott, R., *Mh. Chem.* **82**, 946 (1951).
4. Ghigi, E., *Atti. X Congr. Intern. Chimica, Roma* **3**, 178 (1938); *Chem. Zbl.* **1939 II**, 3984; Arbuzov, B. A. and Grechkin, N. P., *Zh. obshch. khim.* **22**, 1692 (1952); *Amer. Abstr.* 9953 (1953).
5. Zinke, A., Ott, R. and Pack, L., *Mh. Chem.* **82**, 359 (1951); Buu-Hoï, N. P. and Lavit-Lamy, D., *Bull. Soc. chim. Fr.* 341 (1963).
6. Arbuzov, B. A. and Grechkin, N. P., *Zh. Obshch. khim.* **22**, 1692 (1953); *Amer. Abstr.* 9953 (1953).

VI. 1.2,6.7-DIBENZOPYRENE

Dinitrodiphenylbiphenyl (I) can be prepared by an Ullmann synthesis. Reduction of the nitro groups to amino groups gives the compound (II). Tetrazotization and decomposition yield 1.2,6.7-dibenzopyrene (III).[1]

(I)

(II)

(III)

2.3,7.8-Dibenzoperinaphthene (IV) adds maleic anhydride to form the substituted succinic anhydride (V). Hydrolysis to (VI) followed by a melt with sodium chloride and zinc chloride gives 1.2,6.7-dibenzopyrene (III). This is accompanied by its 3-hydroxy compound (VII), which has very weak phenolic character and dissolves only in alcoholic potassium hydroxide. Its formation can be avoided if zinc dust is added to the melt.[2] Dibenzopyrene is formed by cyclodehydrogenation of o-quaterphenyl (IX).[3] This may also be achieved with lithium in ether.[4]

1.2,6.7-Dibenzopyrene is also obtained from the reaction of diphenyl-ether with sodium and potassium. It was assumed that the intermediate stage is the o-phenylene radical.[5]

This view was later supported by the synthesis of dibenzopyrene from 2,2'-dilithiumdiphenyl and titanium tetrachloride. Diphenyl and o-quaterphenyl are obtained as by-products. In this reaction as in many other ones the formation of benzyne (VIII) was assumed as an intermediate product.[6]

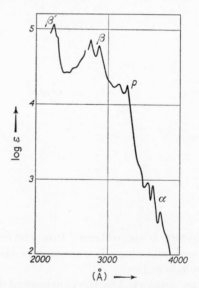

1.2,6.7-Dibenzopyrene crystallizes or sublimes in very pale yellow plates or prisms (m.p. 340–342°), which do not dissolve in concentrated sulphuric acid. Solutions in organic solvents show a blue fluorescence. The absorption spectrum is given in Fig. 124. Dibenzopyrene in solid

Fig. 124. Absorption spectrum of 1.2,6.7-dibenzopyrene in benzene: α, 3720 (2·56), 3620 (2·90), 3550 (2·96); p, 3280 (4·24), 3150 (4·26); β, 2880 (4·78), 2780 (4·86), in heptane: β', 2250 (5·04).

alcoholic solution at $-190°$ shows a strong phosphorescence of long life with bands at 4900, 4980, 5050, 5240, 5350, 5440, 5560, 5650, 5730 and 5820 Å.

REFERENCES

1. Sako, S., *Bull. chem. Soc. Japan* **9**, 55 (1934).
2. Clar, E., *Ber. dtsch. chem. Ges.* **76**, 609 (1943).
3. Copeland, P. G., Dean, R. E. and McNeil, D., *J. chem. Soc.* 4522 (1960).
4. Wittig, G., Hahn, E. and Tachtermann, W., *Chem. Ber.* **95**, 439 (1962).
5. Lüttringhaus, A. and Schubert, K., *Naturwissenschaften* **42**, 17 (1955).
6. Wittig, G. and Lehmann, G., *Ber. dtsch. chem. Ges.* **90**, 875 (1957).

VII. 3.4,8.9-DIBENZOPYRENE

3.4,8.9-Dibenzopyrene-5,10-quinone (I) is a technically important dyestuff which can be obtained from benzanthrone and benzoyl chloride in a sodium chloride–aluminium chloride melt with simultaneous

(I)   (II)

introduction of molecular oxygen. It can be prepared from 1,5-dibenzoyl-naphthalene (II) in the same way.[1]

The reduction to 3.4,8.9-dibenzopyrene (III) is carried out in a zinc-dust melt.[2] A lower yield is obtained by a zinc-dust distillation.[3]

Reduction with hydriodic acid and phosphorus followed by dehydrogenation has also been used.[4] A reduction of the quinone with zinc dust and cyclohexyl-p-toluenesulphonate in trichlorobenzene is reported.[5]

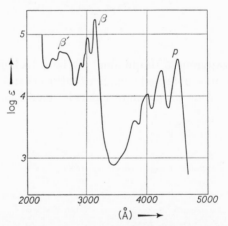

(III)

3.4,8.9-Dibenzopyrene crystallizes from xylene in golden yellow plates (m.p. 308°), which dissolve in concentrated sulphuric acid to form a red solution which changes to violet and then to blue. The absorption spectrum is given in Fig. 125.

Fig. 125. Absorption spectrum of 3.4,8.9-dibenzopyrene in benzene: p, 4510 (4·59), 4240 (4·40), 4010 (4·03), 3790 (3·60); β, 3135 (5·23), 3010 (4·94), 2900 (4·54); in ethanol: β', 2640 (4·70), 2560 (4·73), 2420 (4·60).

Chlorination of dibenzopyrene in o-dichlorobenzene solution gives the 5,10-dichloro derivative.[6] Nitration with nitric acid in nitrobenzene yields the 5-nitro- and 5,10-dinitro compounds.[7] The 5-aldehyde can be prepared with formyl-methylanilide. Reduction gives 5-methyl-3.4,8.9-dibenzopyrene (m.p. 329°). Repetition of these two reactions with the latter yields 5,10-dimethyl-3.4,8.9-dibenzopyrene (m.p. 373°).[6] Carbazole derivatives of dibenzopyrene have been synthesized.[8]

3.4,8.9-Dibenzopyrene is very carcinogenic.[9] Injection as a solution in olive oil produced tumours in all cases.[10] From the smoke of 100 cigarettes, 1 γ dibenzopyrene has been isolated.[11]

3.4,8.9-Dibenzopyrene-5,10-quinone (I) forms yellow crystals (m.p. 391–392°) from nitrobenzene. It gives a violet solution with sulphuric acid. Alkaline sodium dithionite produces a red vat.

REFERENCES

1. Höchster Farbwerke, German Patents 412053 (1922); 423720 (1924); 420412 (1923); 423283 (1923); I.G. Farbenindustrie AG, German Patents 430558 (1924); 440890 (1924); 426711 (1924); 483229 (1927); 518316; 555180; *Chem. Zbl.* **1932 II**, 3627.
2. Clar, E., Amer. Patent 2172020 (1936); *Ber. dtsch. chem. Ges.* **72**, 1645 (1939).
3. Vollmann, H., Becker, H., Corell, M. and Streeck, H., *Liebigs Ann.* **531**, 129 (1937).
4. Silbermann, G. B., *J. gen. Chem. U.S.S.R.* **7**, 234 (1937); *Chem. Zbl.* **1937 I**, 4787.
5. Kelly, W. and Shannon, J. S., *Aust. J. Chem.* **13**, 103 (1960).
6. Buu-Hoï, Ng. Ph. and Lavit, D., *Rec. trav. chim.* **76**, 321 (1957).
7. Ioffe, I. S. and Efros, L. S., *J. gen. Chem. U.S.S.R.* **16**, 111 (1946); *Amer. Abstr.* 116 (1947).
8. I.G. Farbenindustrie AG, German Patent 728333 (1937); *Chem. Zbl.* **1943 I**, 2144.
9. Bachmann, W. E., Cook, J. W., Dansi, A., de Worms, C. G. M., Haslewood, G. A. D., Hewett, C. L. and Robinson, A. M., *Proc. roy. Soc.* **B123**, 350 (1937); Cook, J. W. and Kennaway, E. L., *Amer. J. Cancer* **33**, 53 (1938).
10. Kleinenberg, G. E., *Arch. d. Sci. biol.* **51**, 127 (1938); **56**, 39, 48 (1939); *Chem. Zbl.* **1940 II**, 1031.
11. Bonnet, J. and Neukomm, S., *Helv. chim. Acta* **39**, 1724 (1956).

VIII. 3.4,9.10-DIBENZOPYRENE

A twofold reaction of naphthalene-1,4-dicarboxylic dichloride with benzene and aluminium chloride gives 1,4-dibenzoylnaphthalene (I).

This can be cyclized to the quinone (II) when heated with aluminium chloride.[1] The cyclization gives better results in a sodium chloride–aluminium chloride melt into which oxygen is introduced by vigorous stirring. The same method yields good results in the cyclization of benzoylbenzanthrone (III) which can be prepared from benzanthrone carboxylic chloride, benzene and aluminium chloride.[2]

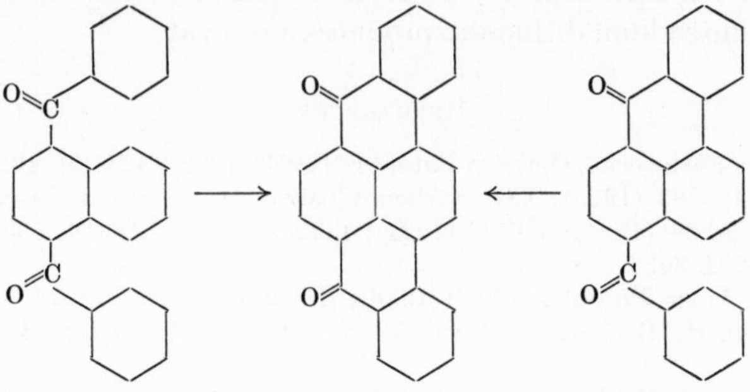

(I)   (II)   (III)

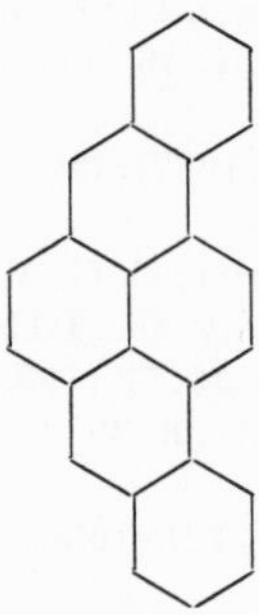

(IV) 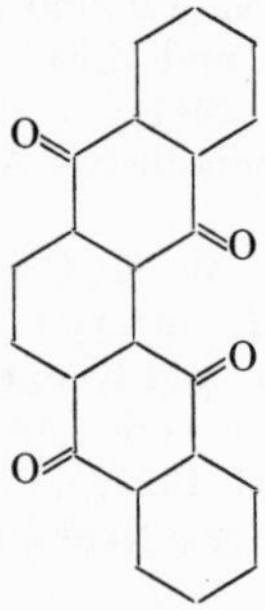   (V)

The reduction of the quinone (II) to 3.4,9.10-dibenzopyrene (IV) can be achieved by a zinc-dust melt[3] or a zinc-dust distillation.[1] Reduction with aluminium in cyclohexanol also gives a good yield.[4]

3.4,9.10-Dibenzopyrene was isolated from the coal-tar fraction following 3.4-benzopyrene by fractional crystallization of the picrates

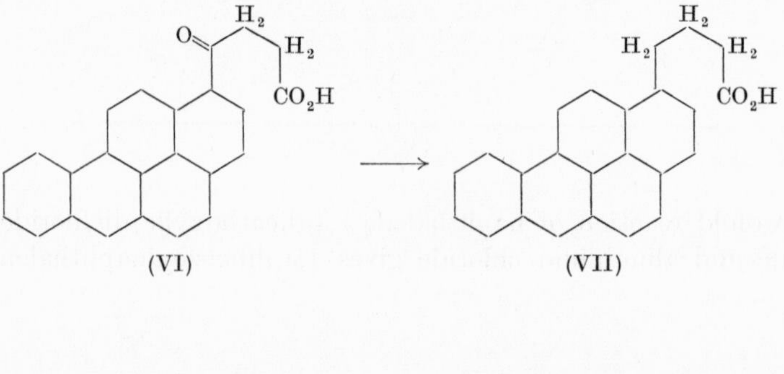

(VI)   (VII)

obtained from this fraction. The chromatographic decomposition of the picrate gave dibenzopyrene (IV).[5]

3.4,9.10-Dibenzopyrene can be synthesized from 3.4-benzopyrene. This gives the acid (VI) on condensation with succinic anhydride and aluminium chloride. Reduction with hydrazine and potassium hydroxide yields the butyric acid (VII) and cyclization with stannic chloride the ketone (VIII). Reduction to the tetrahydro compound followed by dehydrogenation with chloranil in xylene gives dibenzopyrene (IV).[6]

Another synthesis starts from the ketone (IX) which reacts with o-tolyl magnesium bromide to give the hydrocarbon (X). Dehydrogenation with palladium–charcoal yields dibenzopyrene.[7]

3.4,9.10-Dibenzopyrene crystallizes from xylene in greenish-yellow needles (m.p. 280°), which dissolve in concentrated sulphuric acid to form a blue solution with a red fluorescence. It shows a blue fluorescence in organic solvents. The absorption spectrum is given in Fig. 126.

The reduction of dibenzopyrene with sodium in amyl alcohol gives the tetrahydro derivative (XI). Hydrogenation with platinum oxide and hydrogen yields the dihydro derivative (XII) and then the octahydro derivative (XIII). (XI) has the spectrum of a 2,2′-dinaphthyl, (XII) of a picene and (XIII) of a pyrene derivative.[8]

Dibenzopyrene has a very high activity in producing cancer.[9] It is extremely effective in producing sarcomata in the very short time of about 78 days.[9] Dibenzopyrene is also a constituent of tobacco smoke.[10]

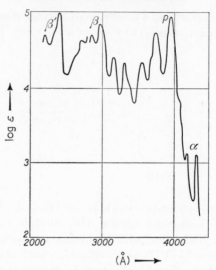

FIG. 126. Absorption spectrum of 3.4,9.10-dibenzopyrene in benzene: α, 4330 (3·10),
4190 (3·10); p, 3970 (4·94), 3750 (4·74), 3565 (4·34), 3320 (4·32), 3170 (4·40); β, 2970 (4·84),
2850 (4·70); in ethanol: 2720 (4·63); β', 2420 (5·00), 2220 (4·70).

3.4,9.10-Dibenzopyrene reacts with formylmethylanilide in boiling
dichlorobenzene to form the 5-aldehyde. Reduction of this yields
5-methyl-3.4,9.10-dibenzopyrene. A repetition of these two reactions
gives 5,8-dimethyl-3.4,9.10-dibenzopyrene.

Dibenzopyrene forms 5,8-dinitro-3.4,9.10-dibenzopyrene when submitted to nitration with nitric acid in nitrobenzene. Sulphuryl chloride gives the 5,8-dichloro compound.[11]

The oxidation of dibenzopyrene with chromic acid yields first the quinone (II). This forms red needles from nitrobenzene (m.p. 365°), which dissolve in concentrated sulphuric acid with an olive-green colour. Alkaline sodium dithionite solution produces a yellow-red vat. Further oxidation of the quinone leads to pentaphene-diquinone(V).[12] The quinone may also be obtained with selenium dioxide in nitrobenzene; oxidation with lead tetra-acetate gives the diacetate (XIV).

REFERENCES

1. Scholl, R. and Neumann, H., *Ber. dtsch. chem. Ges.* **55**, 118 (1922).
2. I.G. Farbenindustrie, AG, German Patents 518316 (1927); 555180 (1929); Brit. Patent 287050; *Chem. Zbl.* **1932 II**, 3627; **1928 I**, 3000.
3. Clar, E., *Ber. dtsch. chem. Ges.* **72**, 1645 (1939).
4. Tilak, B. D., Unni, M. K. and Venkataraman, K., *Tetrahedron* **3**, 62 (1958).
5. Schoental, R., *Nature, Lond.* **180**, 606 (1957).
6. Buu-Hoï, N. and Lavit, D., *Tetrahedron* **8**, 1 (1960).
7. Daub, G. H. and Smith, M. A., *J. org. Chem.* **25**, 2043 (1960).
8. Unseren, E. and Fieser, L. F., *J. org. Chem.* **27**, 1386 (1962).
9. Lacassagne, A., Zajdela, F., Buu-Hoï, N. P. and Chalvet, *C. R. Acad. Sci., Paris* **244**, 273 (1957); Lacassagne, A., Buu-Hoï, N. P. and Zajdela, F., *C. R. Acad. Sci., Paris* **246**, 95 (1958); Schoental, R., *Acta Union Internationale contre le Cancer* **15**, 216 (1959).
10. Bonnet, J. and Neukomm, S., *Helv. chim. Acta* **31**, 1724 (1956).
11. Buu-Hoï, N. P. and Lavit, D., *Rec. trav. chim.* **75**, 1194 (1956).
12. Scholl, R. and Neumann, H., *Ber. dtsch. chem. Ges.* **55**, 118 (1922).

IX. 1.2,4.5,8.9-TRIBENZOPYRENE

Octahydroanthracene reacts two-fold with benzyl chloride and aluminium chloride to form the dibenzoyloctahydroanthracene (I). Dehydrogenation with copper powder at 400–420° is accompanied by

cyclization and the formation of tribenzopyrene in small yield. 2.3,8.9-
Dibenzoperylene (III) is obtained as a by-product and can be separated
by chromatography.[1]

(I)   (II)   (III)

Tribenzopyrene can be more easily prepared by a condensation of
picene (IV) with benzene and aluminium chloride.[2] The yield is considerably improved if stannic chloride is used as a dehydrogenating
agent.[3] Tribenzopyrene can also be prepared from 1.2,5.6-dibenzanthra-
cene (V), benzene, aluminium chloride and stannic chloride. This reaction
involves a remarkably smooth re-arrangement of the dibenzanthracene
in one of the intermediate reaction stages.[3] 2'-Methyltribenzopyrene has
been prepared in an analogous way.

(IV)   (V)

1.2,4.5,8.9-Tribenzopyrene crystallizes from xylene in pale yellow
needles (m.p. 320–321°), which dissolve in concentrated sulphuric acid
to form a green solution which changes to red on heating. The absorption
spectrum is given in Fig. 127.

The oxidation of tribenzopyrene with sodium bichromate in acetic
acid gives the red-violet 3,10-quinone (VI). Further oxidation leads to
6,7-benzopentaphene-5.14,8.13-diquinone (VII) (m.p. 287°) which has
also been prepared by another method (see Vol. 1, p. 365). It forms a red
azine (VIII) with hydrazine in pyridine.[4]

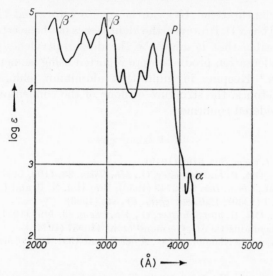

FIG. 127. Absorption spectrum of 1.2,4.5,8.9-tribenzopyrene in cyclohexane: α, 4180 (2·86); p, 3850 (4·76), 3640 (4·60), 3465 (4·24), 3230 (4·26), 3070 (4·70); β, 2965 (4·94), 2850 (4·70); 2680 (4·73); β′, 2260 (4·92).

(VI)   (VII)   (VIII)

(IX)   (X)

Dibenzoylanthracene (IX) can be cyclized to a red-violet quinone which could be (VI). However, the identity has not been established. It is equally possible that it might be the dibenzoperylene-quinone (X).[5] Similar condensation products were reported using isomeric dibenzoyl-anthracenes.[6] Keeping in mind that aluminium chloride tends to isomerize ketones, the structure of none of the condensation products can be considered confirmed.

REFERENCES

1. Clar, E., *J. chem. Soc.* 2168 (1949).
2. Zinke, A., Ott, R. and Schuster, O., *Mh. Chem.* **83**, 1100, 1497 (1952).
3. Zander, M., *Chem. Ber.* **92**, 2749 (1959); Buu-Hoï, N. P. and Lavit, D., *Tetrahedron* **8**, 1 (1960); *Bull. Soc. chim. Fr.* 341 (1963).
4. Zinke, A., Ott, R. and Schuster, O., *Mh. Chem.* **83**, 1497 (1951).
5. I.G. Farbenindustrie AG, German Patent 430557 (1924).
6. E. I. du Pont de Nemours & Co., Amer Patent 1991, 1687; *Chem. Zbl.* **1935 II**, 2454.

X. 1.2,3.4,9.10-TRIBENZOPYRENE

1,4-Dimethylanthraquinone (I) reacts with phenyl lithium to form the diol (II). This exists in two stereoisomeric forms. Both give tribenzo-pyrene (III) with copper powder at 400°.

1.2,3.4,9.10-Tribenzopyrene crystallizes from benzene in orange-yellow leaflets (m.p. 238°), which dissolve in concentrated sulphuric acid to give a green solution which changes to brown on standing. Solutions

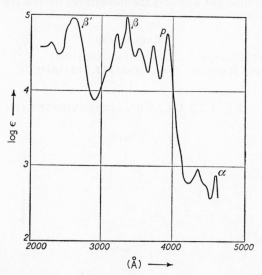

FIG. 128. Absorption spectrum of 1.2,3.4,9.10-tribenzopyrene in ethanol: α, 4610 (2·88), 4340 (2·98); p, 3930 (4·78), 3730 (4·58), 3540 (4·56); β, 3375 (5·00), 3220 (4·76); β', 2600 (4·96), 2290 (4·62).

in organic solvents show a green fluorescence. The absorption spectrum is given in Fig. 128.

Tribenzopyrene gives a blue quinone when oxidized in nitrobenzene with selenium dioxide. This gives a red solution in sulphuric acid and an orange-red vat with alkaline sodium dithionite solution.[1]

II—6

A dimethyl derivative of the 5,8-quinone can be prepared from the lactone (IV). Reduction yields the anthracene derivative (V) and cyclization with sulphuric acid the quinone (VI). The dimethyl derivative ($R = CH_3$) is a blue vat dye and the dimethoxy derivative ($R = OCH_3$) a green vat dye.[2]

REFERENCES

1. Clar, E. and Holker, J. R., *J. chem. Soc.* 3259 (1951).
2. Scholl, R. and Meyer, K., *Liebigs Ann.* **512**, 112 (1934).

XI. 1.2,3.4,6.7,8.9-TETRABENZOPYRENE

1.2,3.4,6.7,8.9-Tetrabenzopyrene-5,10-quinone (II) can be prepared by cyclization of the ester (I) with concentrated sulphuric acid. This quinone, which has been called Ixene-quinone, crystallizes in greenish-black cubes (m.p. 393–394°). Its solution shows absorption bands at 6960, 6350, 3070 and 2700 Å. An orange-red vat is formed with alkaline sodium dithionite. This dyes cotton green.[1]

(I)   (II)

REFERENCE

1. Dufraisse, Ch. and Loury, M., *C. R. Acad. Sci., Paris* **213**, 689 (1941); Loury, *Ann. chim. Fr.* **10**, 807 (1955).

XII. Naphtho-(2'.3':1.2)-pyrene

Decahydropyrene (I) can be condensed with phthalic anhydride and aluminium chloride to form the acid (II). Cyclization in a sodium chloride–aluminium chloride melt gives a hydrogenated derivative of (III) which is dehydrogenated with copper powder at 400–410°.[1]

2-Naphthylpropiolic acid (V) condenses to the anhydride (VI) when boiled with acetic anhydride. Decarboxylation with soda-lime and copper powder gives the two fluorenone derivatives (VII) and (VIII). When these are submitted to a melt with potassium hydroxide they yield the potassium salts of two different acids which both give naphthopyrene (III) on sublimation with copper powder.

Decarboxylation with copper powder in boiling quinoline, however, yields naphthylphenanthrene (IX). This can be cyclized to naphthopyrene in a sodium chloride–aluminium chloride melt.

A similar condensation of the tetralyl-propiolic acid (X) yields the anhydride (XI). This can be dehydrogenated to (VI) with palladium–charcoal. The sodium salt of (XI) can be dehydrogenated and decarboxylated to naphthopyrene (III) with palladium–charcoal or copper powder.[2]

Naphtho-(2′.3′:1.2)-pyrene crystallizes from xylene in long, pale-yellow needles (m.p. 259–260°), which dissolve in concentrated sulphuric acid to give a reddish-brown solution. The solution in xylene shows a blue

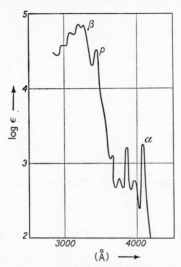

FIG. 129. Absorption spectrum of naphtho-(2′.3′: 1.2)-pyrene in benzene: α, 4075 (3.26), 3960 (2·74), 3860 (3.20), 3750 (2·80), 3670 (3·08); p, 3450 (4·52), 3280 (4·80); β, 3210 (4·85), 3090 (4·74), 2970 (4·53); in cyclohexane: β′, 2730 (4·44); β″, 2470 (5·06), 2300 (4·80).

fluorescence. The absorption spectrum is given in Fig. 129. It forms a picrate (m.p. 212–213°) and gives the adduct (IV) in boiling xylene with maleic anhydride.[1]

REFERENCES

1. Clar, E., *J. chem. Soc.* 2168 (1949).
2. Campbell, A. D., *J. chem. Soc.* 3659 (1954).

XIII. NAPHTHO-(1′.2′:3.4)-PYRENE

Perinaphthone (I) reacts with the Grignard compound of 1-bromo-2-methylnaphthalene with 1,4-addition. The resulting dihydro compound is readily oxidizable to (II). Cyclization gives naphtho-(1′.2′:3.4)-pyrene (III) which melts at 216–218°.[1]

(I)   (II)   (III)

REFERENCE

1. Arbuzov, B. A. and Grechkin, N. P., *Zh. Obshch. khim.* **22**, 1692 (1952); *Amer. Abstr.* 9953 (1953).

XIV. NAPHTHO-(2′.3′:3.4)-PYRENE

The reaction of phthalic anhydride and aluminium chloride with pyrene gives the 3-pyrenoyl-*o*-benzoic acid (I). This can by cyclized in the same reaction[1] or after reduction of the acid (I) with sodium hydroxide solution and zinc dust to the acid (III). Cyclization is effected by a zinc-chloride melt and gives the anthrone derivative (IV). This can be reduced to naphthopyrene (V) with sodium hydroxide solution and zinc dust.[2] Naphthopyrene (V) can be also obtained by a pyrolysis of the ketone (VI). This can be prepared from *o*-toluyl chloride, pyrene and aluminium chloride.[2,3]

Naphtho-(2′.3′:3.4)-pyrene (V) crystallizes from xylene in orange-red leaflets (m.p. 273°), which dissolve in concentrated sulphuric acid first violet gradually changing to brown and finally to green. The solution in xylene shows a strong green fluorescence. The absorption spectrum is at ca. 0.1% (Fig. 27.3). The solid in benzene gives a pleasant odor. 205°. When an ice-cold chloroform solution is treated with sodium sulfoxide to yield the aldehyde (VII) in ... being too ... to ... too readily troublesome.

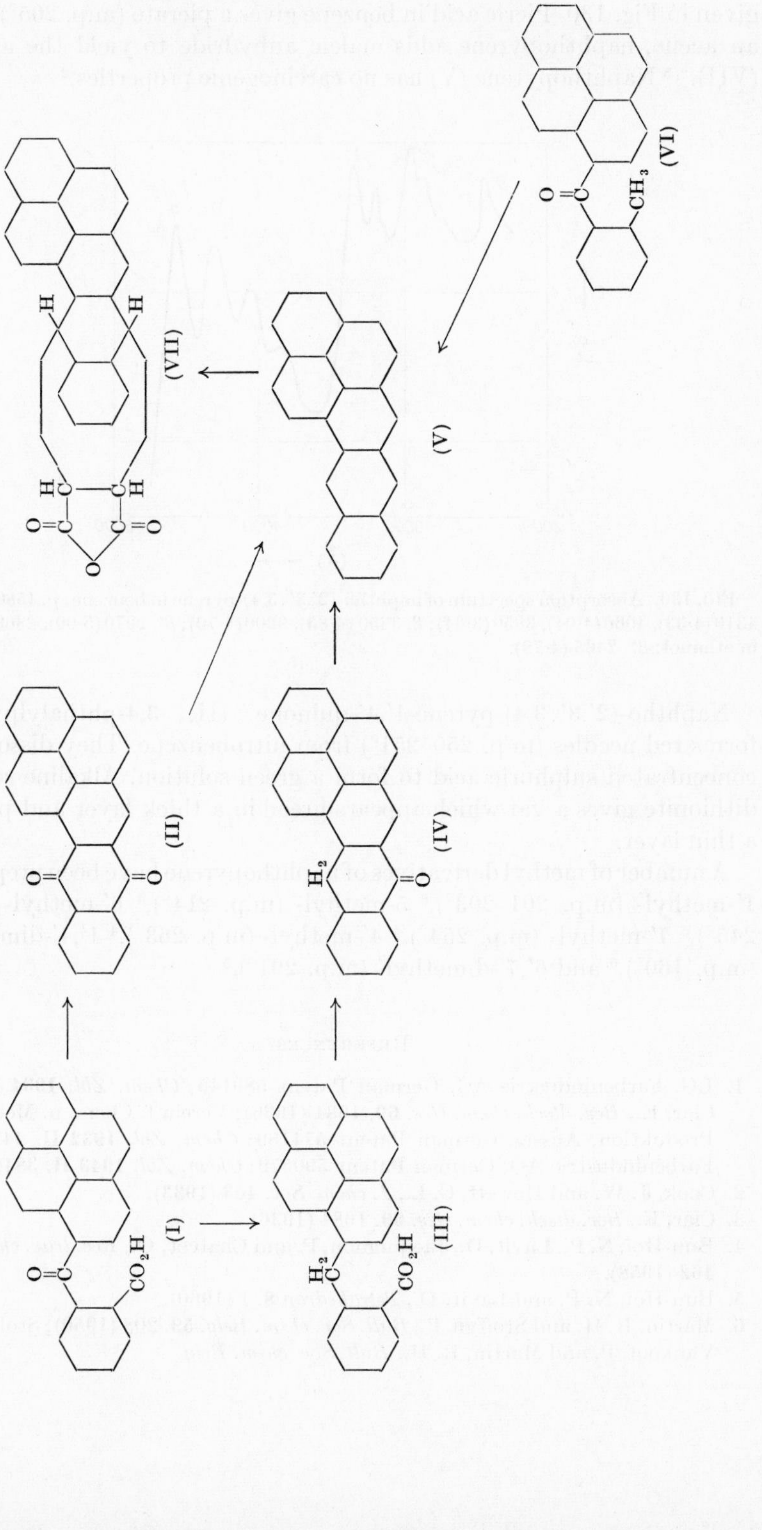

(VI)

(V)

(VII)

(II)

(IV)

(I)

(III)

CH₃

H

H

O

CO₂H

CO₂H

H₂

H₂

given in Fig. 130. Picric acid in benzene gives a picrate (m.p. 205°). Like an acene, naphthopyrene adds maleic anhydride to yield the adduct (VII).[2, 3] Naphthopyrene (V) has no carcinogenic properties.[2]

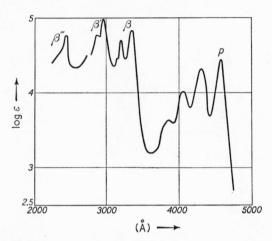

FIG. 130. Absorption spectrum of naphtho-(2′.3′ : 3.4)-pyrene in benzene: p, 4580 (4·43), 4310 (4·33), 4060 (4·04), 3850 (3·64); β, 3350 (4·85), 3200 (4·70); β', 2970 (5·00), 2860 (4·77), in ethanol: β'', 2465 (4·78).

Naphtho-(2′.3′ : 3.4)-pyrene-1′,4′-quinone (II, 3,4-phthalylpyrene) forms red needles (m.p. 250–251°) from nitrobenzene. They dissolve in concentrated sulphuric acid to form a green solution. Alkaline sodium dithionite gives a vat which appears green in a thick layer and pink in a thin layer.

A number of methyl derivatives of naphthopyrene have been prepared: 1′-methyl- (m.p. 201–203°),[6] 5-methyl- (m.p. 214°),[4] 6′-methyl- (m.p. 245°),[5] 7′-methyl- (m.p. 254°),[4] 4′-methyl- (m.p. 263°),[4] 1′,4′-dimethyl- (m.p. 160°),[6] and 6′,7′-dimethyl- (m.p. 291°).[5]

REFERENCES

1. I.G. Farbenindustrie AG, German Patent 589145; *Chem. Zbl.* **1934 I**, 771; Clar, E., *Ber. dtsch. chem. Ges.* **69**, 1684 (1936); Verein f. Chem. u. Metallurg. Produktion, Aussig, German Patent 574189; *Chem. Zbl.* **1932 II**, 447; I.G. Farbenindustrie AG, German Patent 590579; *Chem. Zbl.* **1943 II**, 3846.
2. Cook, J. W. and Hewett, C. L., *J. chem. Soc.* 403 (1933).
3. Clar, E., *Ber. dtsch. chem. Ges.* **69**, 1684 (1936).
4. Buu-Hoï, N. P., Lavit, D., Jacquignon, P. and Chalvet, O., *Rec. trav. chim.* **77**, 462 (1958).
5. Buu-Hoï, N. P. and Lavit, D., *Tetrahedron* **8**, 1 (1960).
6. Martin, R. H. and Stoffyn, P., *Bull. Soc. chim. Belg.* **59**, 208 (1950); Stoffyn, P. Vankoof, P. and Martin, R. H., *Bull. Soc. chim. Belg.*

XV. 1.2-BENZONAPHTHO-(2″.3″:4.5)-PYRENE

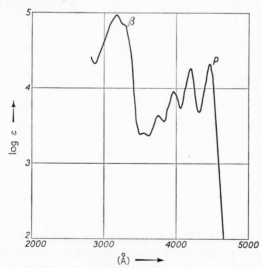

Benzanthrone reacts with methyl magnesium iodide to give a hydrocarbon which was thought to have formula (I).[1] This contains the complex of the very unstable 2,3-dihydronaphthalene and is therefore better formulated with the diene structure (II). In accordance with this it reacts readily with 1,4-naphthoquinone to yield the quinone (III). Reduction with pyridine, zinc dust and acetic acid leads to the hydrocarbon (IV).[2]

1.2-Benzopyrene, phthalic anhydride and aluminium chloride give the keto-acid (V). Cyclization with benzoyl chloride and a little sulphuric acid yields the quinone (III). The hydrocarbon (IV) is also obtained from the pyrolysis of the ketone (VI) which, however, gives also an isomeric hydrocarbon (see below).[3]

FIG. 131. Absorption spectrum of 1.2-benzonaphtho-(2″.3″:4.5)-pyrene in benzene: p, 4460 (4·34), 4200 (4·26), 3965 (3·96), 3750 (3·64); β, 3270 (4·85), 3170 (4·98).

II—6*

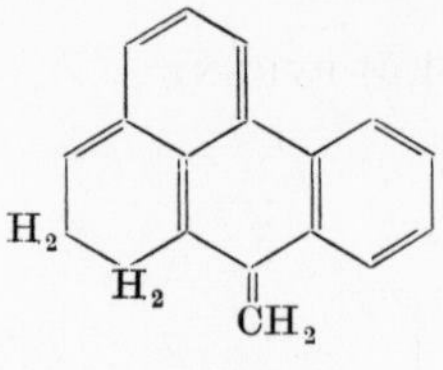

(I)

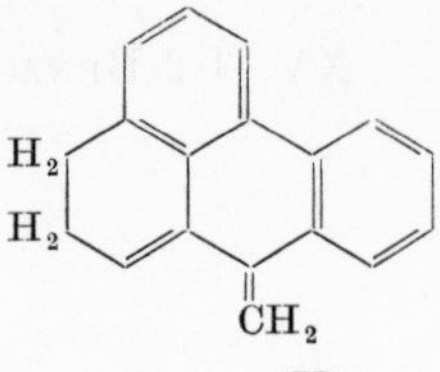

(II)

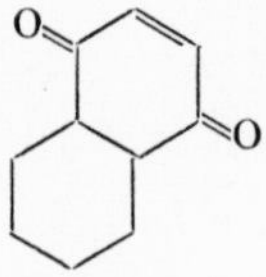

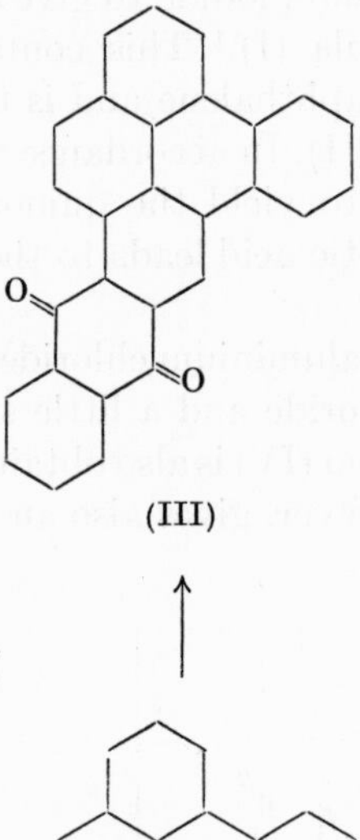

+

(III)

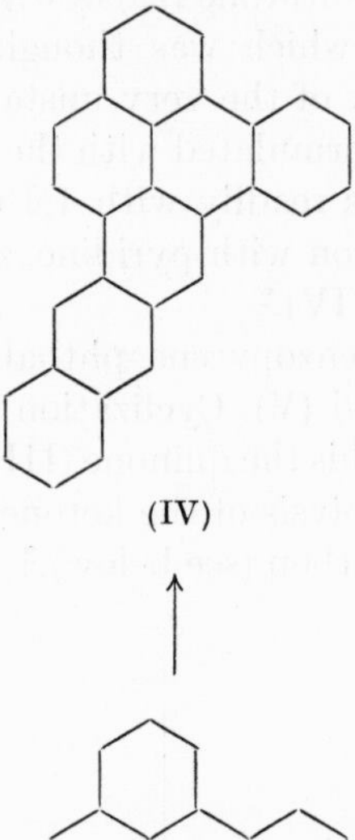

(IV)

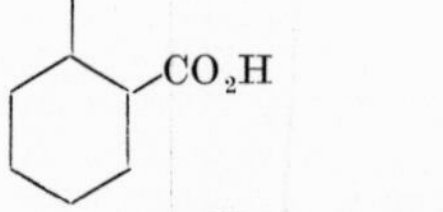

↑

↑

(V)

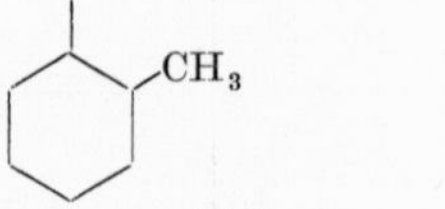

(VI)

1.2-Benzonaphtho-(2″.3″:4.5)-pyrene crystallizes from xylene in yellow needles (m.p. 262–263°), which dissolve in concentrated sulphuric acid to give a violet solution. The absorption spectrum is given in Fig. 131.

The quinone (III) forms orange-red needles (m.p. 298–299°), which dissolve in concentrated sulphuric acid with a blue-green colour.

(VII)   (VIII)

The reaction of the compound (II) with benzoquinone yields a quinone which has the structure (VII) or a corresponding plane symmetric structure (VIII) or is a mixture of both.[2]

REFERENCES

1. Charrier, O. and Ghigi, F., *Gazz. chim. ital.* **62**, 928 (1932); *Ber. dtsch. chem. Ges.* **69**, 2211 (1936).
2. Zander, M., *Chem. Ber.* **94**, 2894 (1961).
3. Clar, E. and Zander, M., *Tetrahedron* **19**, 521 (1963).

XVI. 1.2-BENZONAPHTHO-(2″.3″:6.7)-PYRENE

(5.6,13.14-*Dibenzopentacene*)

1.2-Benzopyrene reacts with o-toluyl chloride and aluminium chloride to form the ketone (I). Its pyrolysis gives mainly 1.2-benzo-naphtho-(2″.3″:4.5)-pyrene (II) but also small quantities of 1.2-benzo-naphtho-(2″.3″:6.7)-pyrene (III).[1] It can also be obtained from decahydro-1.2-benzopyrene (IV), which condenses with phthalic anhydride and aluminium chloride to yield the keto-acid (V). A melt with sodium chloride and zinc chloride, followed by dehydrogenation with copper powder gives benzonaphthopyrene (III).[2]

1.2-Benzo-naphtho-(2″.3″:6.7)-pyrene (III) crystallizes from xylene in colourless needles (m.p. 314°) which do not dissolve in concentrated sulphuric acid. The absorption spectrum is given in Fig. 132.

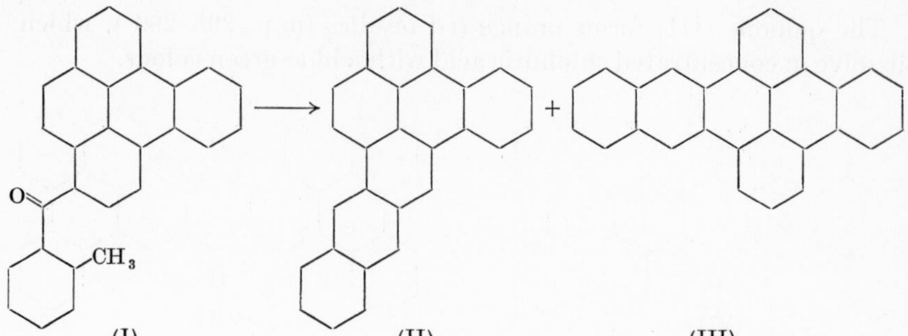

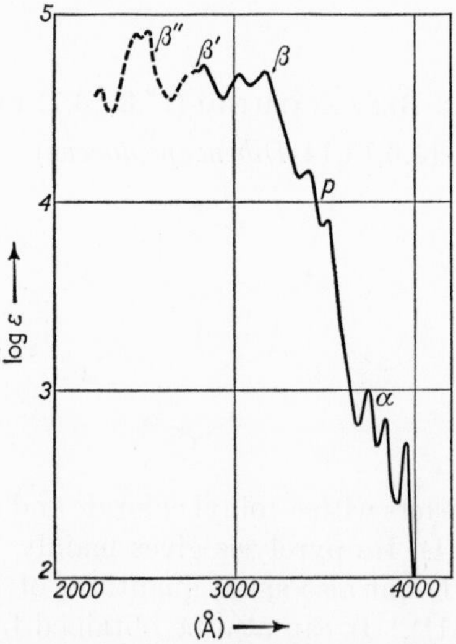

FIG. 132. Absorption spectrum of 1.2-benzonaphtho-(2'.3':6.7)-pyrene in dioxane: α, 3960 (2·70), 3845 (2·74), 3750 (2·92); p, 3500 (3·81), 3400 (4·14); β, 3160 (4·71), 3020 (4·72); β', 2820 (4·77), 2740 (4·72): β", 2520 (4·96), 2460 (4·93).

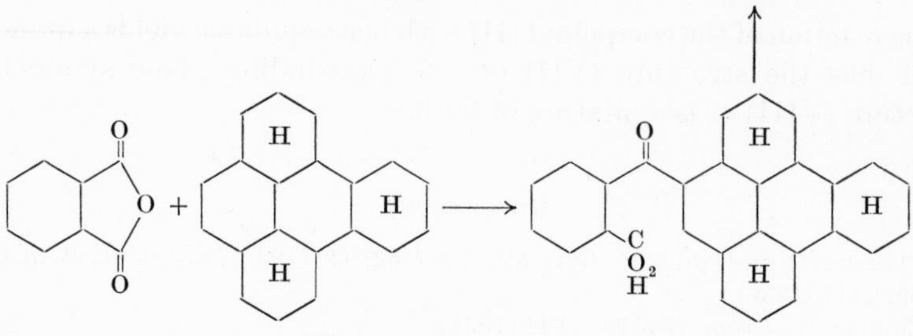

REFERENCES

1. Clar, E. and Zander, M., *Tetrahedron* **19**, 521 (1963).
2. Clar, E., Guye-Vuillème, J. F., Macpherson, I. A. and McCallum, A., *Tetrahedron* **19**, 2185 (1963).

XVII. 8.9-BENZONAPHTHO-(2″.1″:3.4)-PYRENE AND 3.4-BENZANTHRACENO-(2″.1″:8.9)-PYRENE

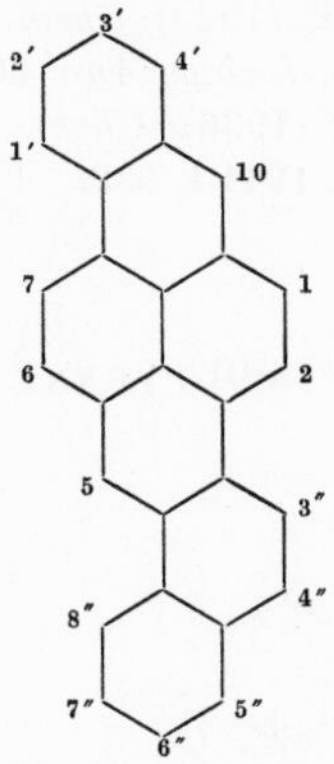

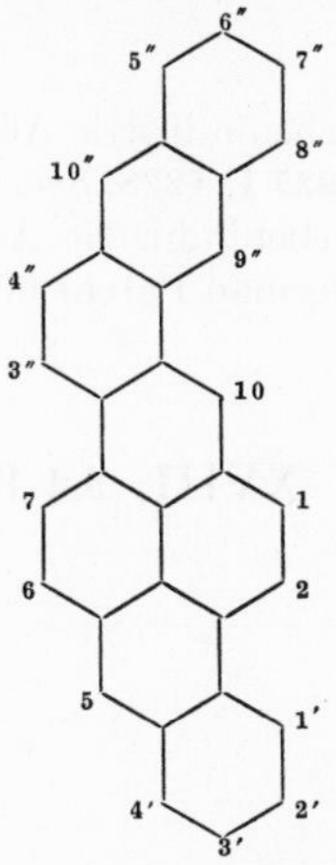

Only quinones have been prepared from these hydrocarbons. If naphthoyl-benzanthrone (I) is submitted to an aluminium chloride–sodium chloride melt into which oxygen is stirred, 8.9-benzonaphtho-(2″.1″,3.4)-pyrene-5,10-quinone (II) is obtained. It is a brown-orange vat dye.[1] A similar vat dye was prepared when the naphthoyl group in (I) was replaced by an α-acenaphthoyl group.[1]

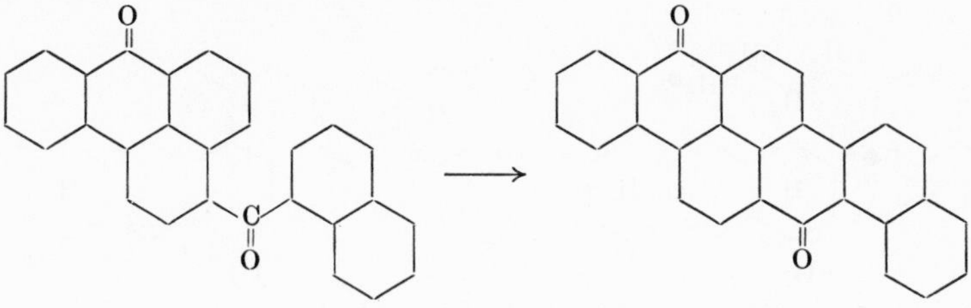

(I)   (II)

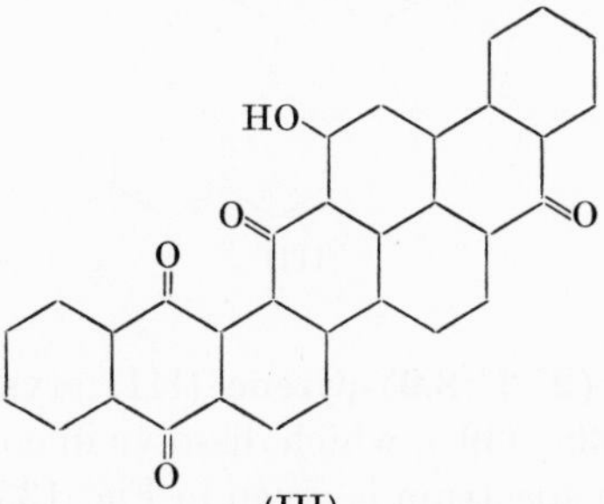

(III)

The benzanthracenopyrene derivative (III) can be prepared by oxidation of violanthronequinone (see p. 253).[2]

REFERENCES

1. I.G. Farbenindustrie AG, German Patent 446187 (1925); *Chem. Zbl.* **1927 II,** 1096; **1927 I,** 1228. See, however, Vollmann, H., *Liebigs Ann.* **669,** 22 (1963).
2. I.G. Farbenindustrie AG, Brit. Patent 480882 (1936); *Chem. Zbl.* **1938 II,** 1134; German Patent 695031 (1936); *Chem. Zbl.* **1941 I,** 582.

XVIII. 3.4-BENZONAPHTHO-(2″.3″:8.9)-PYRENE

The treatment of octahydroanthracene (I) with aluminium chloride gives a yellow high molecular hydrocarbon of the assumed constitution (II). This structure was confirmed by dehydrogenation, which yielded a red hydrocarbon (III) whose absorption spectrum is completely in accordance with the predictions of the annellation principle. The reaction is analogous to the formation of 3.4-benzopyrene from tetralin.

3.4-Benzonaphtho-(2″.3″:8.9)-pyrene (III) crystallizes from xylene in red leaflets (m.p. 338–339°), which dissolve in concentrated sulphuric acid.[1] The absorption spectrum is given in Fig. 133.

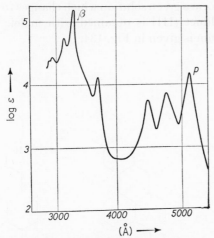

Fig. 133. Absorption spectrum of 3.4-benzonaphtho-(2″.3″:8.9)-pyrene in benzene:
p, 5160 (4·15), 4800 (3·87), 4500 (3·75); β, 3660 (4·10); β, 3250 (5·17), 3110 (4·74), 2900 (4·43),
2840 (4·34) (Grove, J. F., J. chem. Soc. 483 (1953)).

REFERENCE

1. Grove, J. F., J. chem. Soc. 453 (1953). See also Vollmann, H., Liebigs Ann. **669**,
22 (1963).

XIX. 3.4-BENZONAPHTHO-(2″.3″:9.10)-PYRENE

3.4-Benzopyrene condenses with o-toluyl chloride and aluminium
chloride to form the ketone (I) which, on pyrolysis, cyclizes to benzonaphthopyrene (II).

3.4-Benzonaphtho-(2″.3″:9.10)-pyrene (II) crystallizes from xylene
in yellow leaflets (m.p. 292–292·5°) which dissolve in concentrated

sulphuric acid to form a green solution which changes to blue on standing. The colourless adduct (III) is obtained with maleic anhydride.[1] The absorption spectrum is given in Fig. 134.

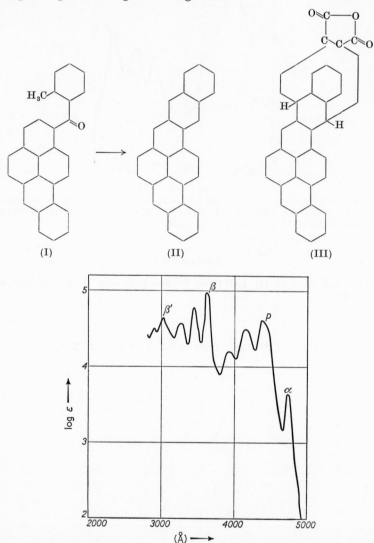

(I)   (II)   (III)

Fig. 134. Absorption spectrum of 3.4-benzonaphtho-(2″.3″:9.10)-pyrene in benzene: α, 4720 (3·66); p, 4380 (4·62), 4150 (4·50), 3930 (4·20); β, 3620 (5·00), 3450 (4·78), 3280 (4·57): β′, 3030 (4·64), 2900 (4·50).

REFERENCE

1. Clar, E. and Zander, M., *Tetrahedron* **19**, 521 (1963).

XX. DINAPHTHO-(2'.3' : 1.2); (2".3" : 4.5)-PYRENE

Under certain conditions 1-vinylnaphthalene (I) condenses twice with naphthoquinone in boiling nitrobenzene to give the diquinone (II). Reduction to dinaphthopyrene (III) can be carried out in pyridine, zinc dust and acetic acid or in a zinc-dust melt.

(III)

Dinaphtho-(2'.3':1.2); (2".3":4.5)-pyrene crystallizes from xylene in yellow needles (m.p. 300–301°), which dissolve in concentrated sulphuric acid to form a blue solution which changes to green. The absorption spectrum is given in Fig. 135.

Dinaphtho-(2′.3′ : 1.2); (2″.3″ : 4.5)-pyrene-1′.4′,1″.4″-diquinone   gives
wine-red needles (m.p. 344·5–345·5°) on sublimation or on crystallization

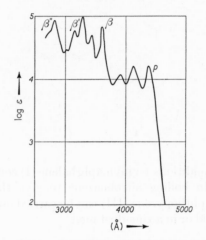

FIG. 135. Absorption spectrum of dinaphtho-(2′.3′ : 1.2); (2″.3″ : 4.5)-pyrene in benzene :
p, 4380 (4·19), 4130 (4·20), 3930 (4·06); β, 3610 (4·83), 3440 (4·68); β', 3290 (4·98), 3160
(4·76); β'', 2840 (4·92).

from trichlorobenzene. It dissolves in concentrated sulphuric acid with
a green colour. A brown vat is formed with alkaline sodium dithionite.[1]
Dinaphthopyrene yields the adduct (IV) with maleic anhydride.

(IV)

REFERENCE

1. Zander, M. and Franke, W., *Ber. dtsch. chem. Ges.* **94**, 446 (1961).

XXI. DINAPHTHO-$(2'.3':1.2)$; $(2''.3'':6.7)$-PYRENE

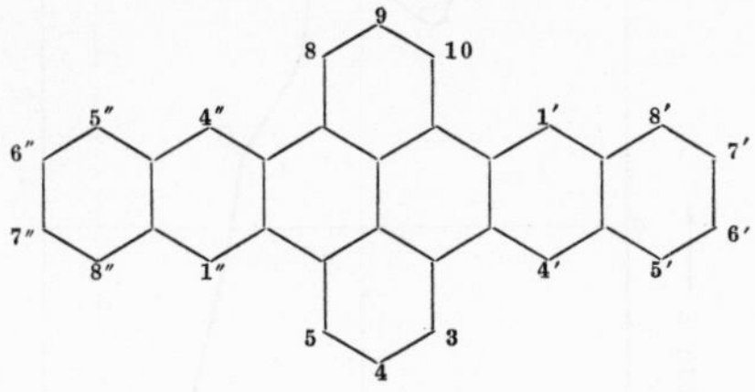

Phthalic anhydride can be twice condensed with hexahydropyrene and aluminium chloride in tetrachloroethane. The diketo-acid (I) is reduced to the acid (II) with sodium hydroxide and zinc dust. A melt with sodium chloride and zinc chloride gives dinaphthopyrene (III).

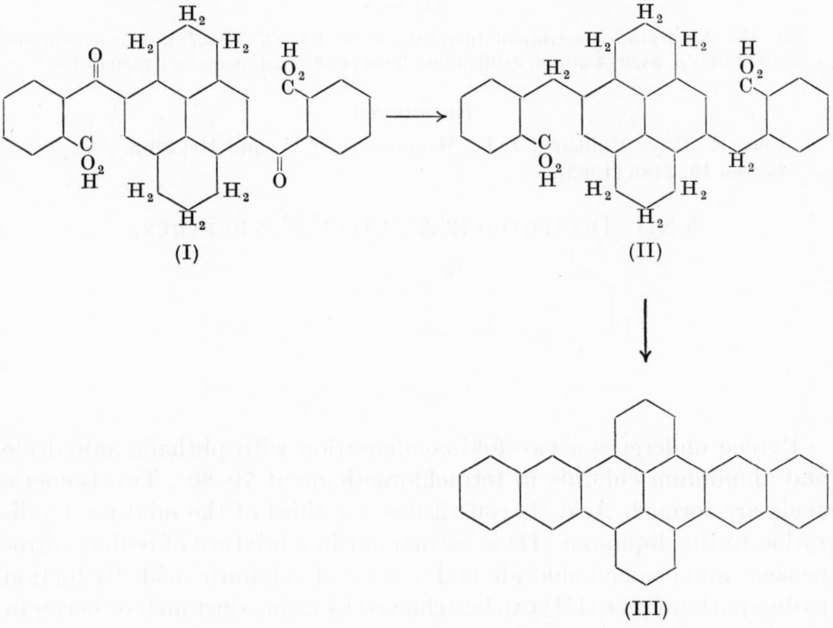

(I)   (II)

(III)

Dinaphtho-$(2'.3':1.2)$; $(2''.3'':6.7)$-pyrene (III) crystallizes from 1-methylnaphthalene or 1,2,4-trichlorobenzene or sublimes in colourless needles (m.p. 405°), which do not dissolve in concentrated sulphuric acid. The absorption spectrum is given in Fig. 136.[1]

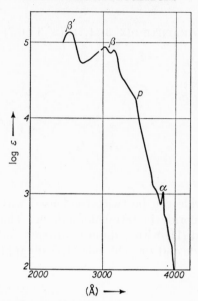

FIG. 136. Absorption spectrum of dinaphtho-(2′.3′:1.2); (2″.3″:6.7)-pyrene in benzene: α, 3840 (3·04); p, 3420 (4·30); β, 3160 (4·90), 3030 (4·96), in dioxane: β′, 2530 (5·14).

REFERENCE

1. Clar, E., Guye-Vuillème, J. F., Macpherson, I. A. and McCallum, A., *Tetrahedron* **19**, 2185 (1963).

XXII. DINAPHTHO-(2′.3′:3.4),(2″.3″:8.9)-PYRENE

Pyrene undergoes a two-fold condensation with phthalic anhydride and aluminium chloride in tetrachloroethane at 70–80°. Two isomeric acids are formed. Acid (I) constitutes one-third of the mixture. Cyclization to the diquinone (II) is carried out in a mixture of boiling nitrobenzene and benzoyl chloride and a trace of sulphuric acid. Reduction to dinaphthopyrene (III) can be achieved by a zinc-dust melt or better in pyridine with zinc dust and acetic acid.

Naphtho-(2′.3′:3.4); (2″.3″:8.9)pyrene (III) crystallizes from 1-methylnaphthalene or sublimes *in vacuo* in blue leaflets (m.p. 460°), which dissolve in concentrated sulphuric acid to give a brownish-yellow solution. The hydrocarbon reacts readily with maleic anhydride with decolorization. The absorption spectrum is given in Fig. 137.

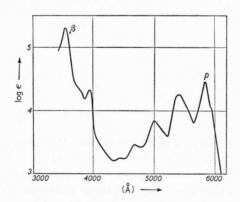

Naphtho-$(2'.3':3.4)$; $(2''.3'':8.9)$-pyrene-5,10-quinone (IV) can be obtained from the hydrocarbon in boiling nitrobenzene and selenium dioxide. It sublimes *in vacuo* in red-brown, silky needles (m.p. 479°), which dissolve in concentrated sulphuric acid with a green colour. Alkaline sodium dithionite gives a brownish olive-red vat, from which cotton is dyed in deep red shades.

Naphtho-$(2'.3':3.4)$; $(2''.3'':8.9)$-pyrene-1'.4',1'',4''-diquinone (II) crystallizes from nitrobenzene in orange needles (m.p. 450° dec.). Alkaline sodium dithionite solution produces a brownish-red vat.[1]

FIG. 137. Absorption spectrum of dinaphtho-$(2'.3':3.4)$; $(2''.3'':8.9)$-pyrene in 1-methyl naphthalene: p, 5820 (4·44), 5390 (4·26), 4990 (3·84), 4660 (3·46), 4400 (3·25); 3930 (4·32); β, 3530 (5·30).

REFERENCE

1. Clar, E., *J. chem. Soc.* 2013 (1949).

XXIII. Dinaphtho-(2'.3' : 3.4); (2".3" : 9.10)-pyrene

The mixture of acids that is obtained from pyrene, excess phthalic anhydride and aluminium chloride in tetrachloroethane contains as the main constituent the acid (I). Cyclization with benzoyl chloride in boiling nitrobenzene and a trace of sulphuric acid yields the diquinone (II). The reduction can be carried out by the zinc-dust melt or in pyridine with zinc dust and acetic acid.

(I)   (II)   (III)   (IV)

Dinaphtho-(2'.3' : 3.4); (2".3" : 9.10)-pyrene (III) crystallizes from 1-methylnaphthalene in yellow leaflets (m.p. 420°), which dissolve in concentrated sulphuric acid to give a brown solution which afterwards turns to green and then blue. The solution in xylene shows a strong green fluorescence. The hydrocarbon reacts readily with maleic anhydride; however, markedly more slowly than its isomer (p. 180). The absorption spectrum is given in Fig. 138.

Dinaphtho-(2'.3' : 3.4); (2".3" : 9.10)-pyrene-5,8-quinone (IV) is prepared from the hydrocarbon with selenium dioxide in boiling nitrobenzene. It sublimes in dark violet needles (m.p. 460° dec.), which dissolve in concentrated sulphuric acid with a brown colour. A violet vat is formed with alkaline sodium dithionite solution from which cotton is dyed violet.

Dinaphtho - (2'.3' : 3.4); (2".3" : 9.10) - pyrene - 1'.4',1".4" - diquinone (II)

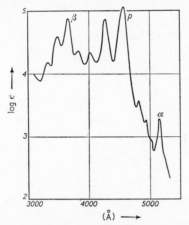

FIG. 138. Absorption spectrum of dinaphtho-(2'.3' : 3.4); (2".3" : 9.10)-pyrene in 1,2,4-trichlorobenzene: α, 5150 (3·30), 4940 (3·25), 4820 (3·55); p, 4560 (5·10), 4270 (4·85), 4030 (4·34), 3820 (4·35); β, 3655 (4·86), 3490 (4·60), 3310 (4·18).

forms orange needles (m.p. 450–455°), which dissolve in concentrated sulphuric acid with a green colour. A brownish-red vat is formed with alkaline sodium dithionite solution.[1]

REFERENCE

1. Clar, E., J. chem. Soc. 2013 (1949).

XXIV. 1.2-BENZODINAPHTHO-(2".3" : 4.5); (2'''.3''' : 8.9)-PYRENE

The ketone (I) is obtained from 1.2-benzopyrene with o-tolyl chloride and aluminium chloride. Pyrolysis gives the hydrocarbons (II), (III) and (IV).

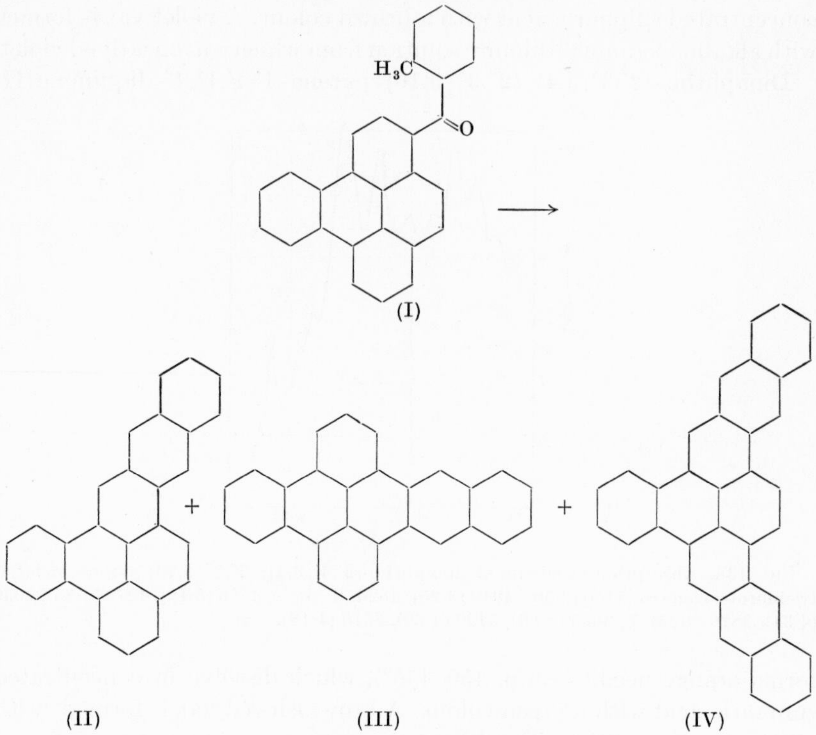

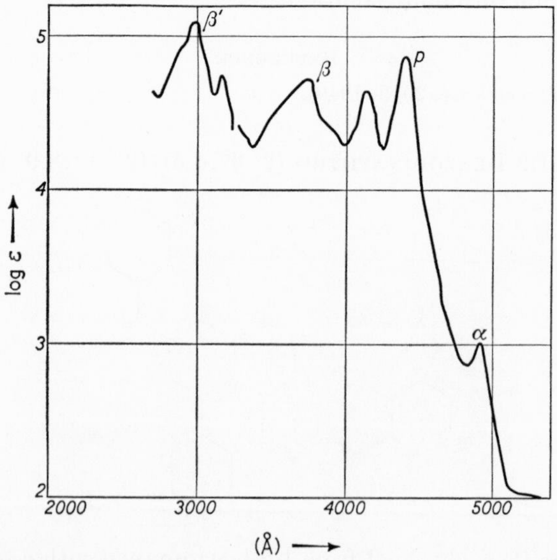

FIG. 139. Absorption spectrum of 1.2-benzonaphtho-(2″.3″:4.5); (2‴.3‴:8.9)-pyrene in 1,2,4-trichlorobenzene: α, 4930 (3·01); p, 4430 (4·87), 4150 (4·65), 3900 (4·40); β, 3760 (4·71); in benzene: β′, 3180 (4·74), 3010 (5·10).

1.2-Benzodinaphtho-(2″.3″:4.5); (2‴.3‴:8.9)-pyrene (IV) crystallizes from 1-methylnaphthalene in brownish yellow needles (m.p. 393–394°) which dissolve in concentrated sulphuric acid with a blue colour. The absorption spectrum is given in Fig. 139.[1]

REFERENCE

1. Clar, E. and Zander, M., *Tetrahedron* **19**, 521 (1963).

XXV. 1.14,4.5-DIBENZOPENTACENE

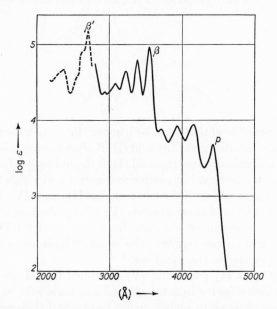

A condensation of 2,3-naphthalene-dicarboxylic anhydride and aluminium chloride with hexahydropyrene yields the keto-acid (I). This can be cyclized in a sodium chloride–zinc chloride melt to dibenzopentacene (II).

FIG. 140. Absorption spectrum of 1.14,4.5-dibenzopentacene in benzene: p, 4420 (3·68), 4150 (3·94), 3930 (3·92), 3720 (3·83); β, 3555 (4·96), 3390 (4·80), 3225 (4·65), 3080 (4·48), 2950 (4·38); in cyclohexane (broken line): β', 2715 (5·19); 2380 (4·68).

(I)   (II)

1.14,4.5-Dibenzopentacene (II) crystallizes from xylene or sublimes in golden yellow plates (m.p. 285°) which dissolve in concentrated sulphuric acid to give a violet solution which changes through red to olive-green. The absorption spectrum is given in Fig. 140.[1]

REFERENCE

1. Clar, E., Guye-Vuillème, J. F., Macpherson, I. A. and McCallum, A., *Tetrahedron* **19**, 2185 (1963).

XXVI. NAPHTHO-(1′.7′:2.14-)-PENTACENE

Condensation of naphthalene-2,3-dicarboxylic anhydride with pyrene and aluminium chloride gives the acid (I). Boiling benzoyl chloride and a trace of zinc chloride cyclizes the acid (I) to the quinone (II). The reduction of this with zinc dust in pyridine and acetic acid yields the dihydro compound, which consists of the two isomers (III) and (IV). Both can be dehydrogenated to naphthopentacene (V) with palladium–charcoal.

Napthopentacene can be obtained by pyrolysis of the ketone (VII) in the presence of copper powder. The isomeric hydrocarbon (VIII, see p. 188) is also formed in the pyrolysis. [1]

Naphtho-(1′.7′:2.14)-pentacene (V) sublimes in red crystals (m.p. 348–350°), which dissolve in concentrated sulphuric acid to give a blue solution which changes to violet, green, brown and then red-brown on standing. It is a hydrocarbon of considerable reactivity which, however, does not approach that of pentacene. The red solutions are photo-oxidizable and react readily with maleic anhydride to form the adduct (VI). The absorption spectrum is given in Fig. 141.[1]

Naphtho-(1′.7′:2.14)-pentacene-6,13-quinone (II) crystallizes from

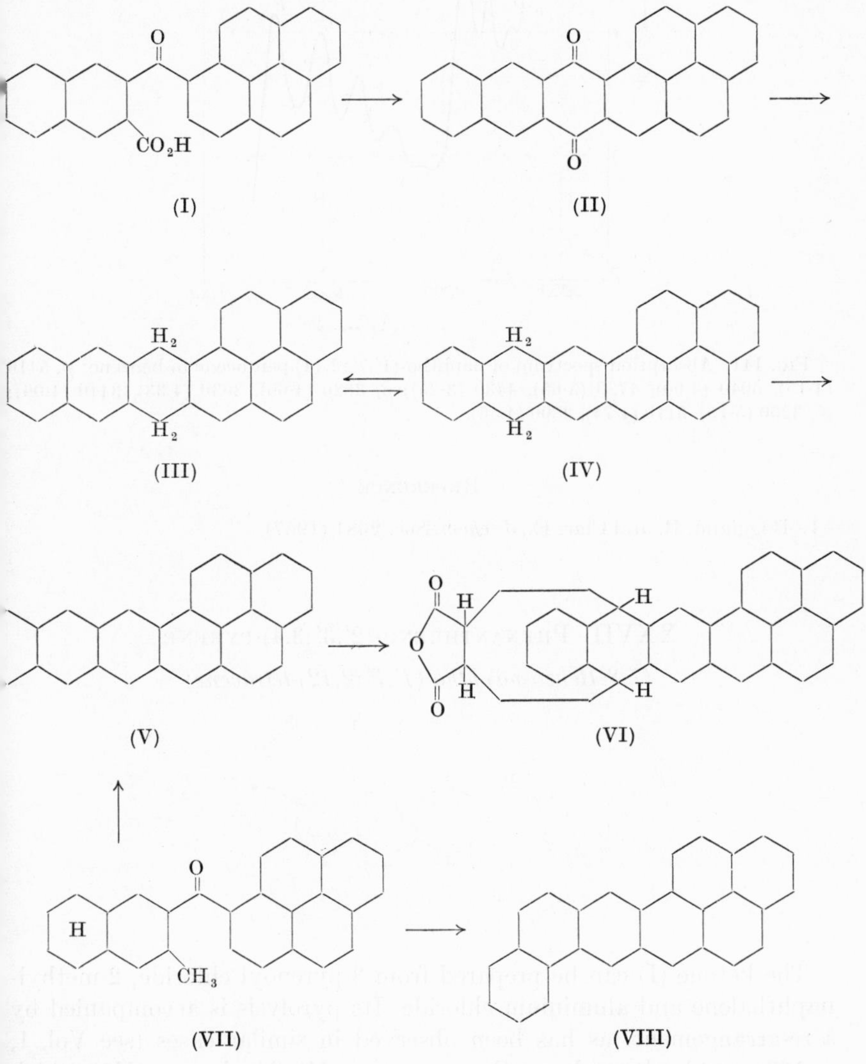

(I)   (II)

(III)   (IV)

(V)   (VI)

(VII)   (VIII)

nitrobenzene in orange plates (m.p. 340–341°), which dissolve in concentrated sulphuric acid to give a leaf-green solution. No vat is obtained with sodium dithionite solution.

188   POLYCYCLIC HYDROCARBONS

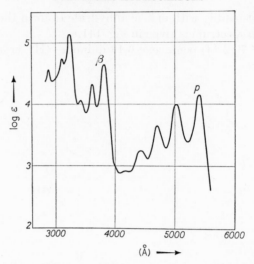

FIG. 141. Absorption spectrum of naphtho-(1'.7':2.14)-pentacene in benzene: *p*, 5410
(4·15), 5040 (4·00), 4720 (3·65), 4430 (3·25); *β*, 3820 (4·65), 3630 (4·33), 3440 (4·06);
β', 3250 (5·15), 3110 (4·74), 2890 (4·56).

REFERENCE

1. Boggiano, B. and Clar, E., *J. chem. Soc.* 2681 (1957).

XXVII. Phenanthreno-(2'.3':3.4)-pyrene

(7.8-Benzo-naphtho-(1'.7':2.12)-tetracene)

The ketone (I) can be prepared from 3-pyrenoyl chloride, 2-methyl-
naphthalene and aluminium chloride. Its pyrolysis is accompanied by
a re-arrangement, as has been observed in similar cases (see Vol. 1,
p. 177), and leads to phenanthreno-pyrene (II). The ketone (III), which
is obtained from pyrenoyl chloride, tetralin and aluminium chloride, is
dehydrogenated and partly re-arranged when pyrolysed in the presence
of copper powder and yields phenanthrenopyrene besides naphtho-
(1'.7':2.14)-pentacene (see p. 186).[1]

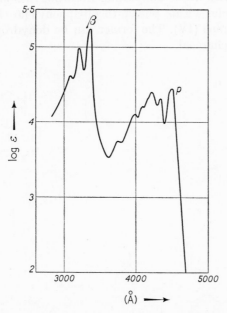

(I)   (III)

(II)

Phenanthreno-(2′.3′:3.4)-pyrene (II) forms deep yellow leaflets from benzene which have m.p. 332–333°. The absorption spectrum is given in Fig. 142.

FIG. 142. Absorption spectrum of phenanthreno-(2′.3′:3.4)-pyrene in benzene: *p*, 4500 (4·45), 4350 (4·31), 4230 (4·40), 4100 (4·20), 4000 (4·10), 3770 (3·75); *β*, 3370 (5·24), 3220 (4·98), 3100 (4·61).

190   POLYCYCLIC HYDROCARBONS

The 5-methylphenanthreno-(2'.3':3.4)-pyrene (m.p. 308°) was obtained by a reaction of phenanthrenopyrene with formylmethylanilide to form the 5-aldehyde which was reduced to the methyl derivative.[2]

REFERENCES

1. Boggiano, B. and Clar, E., *J. chem. Soc.* 2681 (1957).
2. Buu-Hoï, N. G., Lavit, D. and Chalvet, O., *Tetrahedron* 8, 7 (1960).

XXVIII. 1.2-BENZOPHENANTHRENO-(9'.10':6.7)-PYRENE

(*1.2,3.4,5.6,11.12-Tetrabenzotetracene*)

9-Phenanthroyl-propiolic acid (I) can be condensed to the anhydride (II) by boiling with acetic anhydride. Decarboxylation with soda-lime and copper powder yields phenanthryltriphenylene (III) and benzo-phenanthrenopyrene (IV). The former can be dehydrogenated to (IV) with palladium–charcoal.

(I)   (II)

(III)   (IV)

1.2-Benzophenanthreno-(9′.10′:6.7)-pyrene (IV) is separated from the hydrocarbon (III) by chromatography. It forms pale yellow needles (m.p. 289–290°) from xylene. The absorption spectrum is given in Fig. 143.[1]

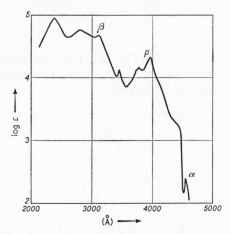

FIG. 143. Absorption spectrum of 1.2-benzo-phenanthreno-(9′.10′:6.7)-pyrene in benzene: α, 4540 (2·40); p, 3980 (4·32), 3780 (4·16); 3450 (4·12); β, 3130 (4·68); in ethanol: 2800 (4·76); 2380 (4·94).[1]

REFERENCE

1. Campbell, A. D., *J. chem. Soc.* 3659 (1954).

XXIX. 1.2,3.4,6.7,12.13-TETRABENZOPENTACENE

Two molecules of triphenylene condense in a sodium chloride–aluminium chloride melt at 140°. The constitution of the resulting hydrocarbon (II) was proved by its infra-red spectrum. The most striking property of this hydrocarbon is its stability and chemical inertness. This is best demonstrated by the fact that it can be formulated as a condensed sexiphenyl, each benzenoid ring being marked by a circle.

1.2,3.4,6.7,12.13-Tetrabenzopentacene (II) crystallizes from trichlorobenzene or 1-methylnaphthalene in almost colourless needles (m.p. 398–399°), which do not dissolve in concentrated sulphuric acid. The

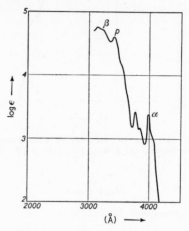

absorption spectrum is given in Fig. 144. The solid solution of the hydrocarbon shows at low temperature phosphorescence bands at 5100, 5190,
5350, 5450, 5545, 5690, 5850, 5990 Å.[1]

FIG. 144. Absorption spectrum of 1.2,3.4,6.7,12.13-tetrabenzopentacene in 1,2,4-
trichlorobenzene: α, 3990 (3·29), 3860 (2·96), 3780 (3·36); p, 3440 (4·64); in dioxane: β,
3100 (4·84); β', 2740 (4·80).[1]

REFERENCE

1. Zander, M., *Chem. Ber.* **92**, 2744 (1959).

XXX. 1.16.4.5-DIBENZOHEXACENE

Benzophenone-tricarboxylic anhydride (I) reacts with hexahydropyrene and aluminium chloride to yield the acid (II). Reduction with
zinc dust and sodium hydroxide solution gives the acid (III). Cyclization

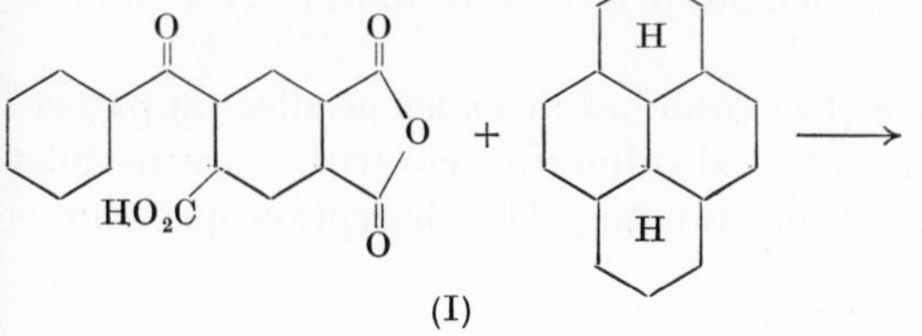

(I)

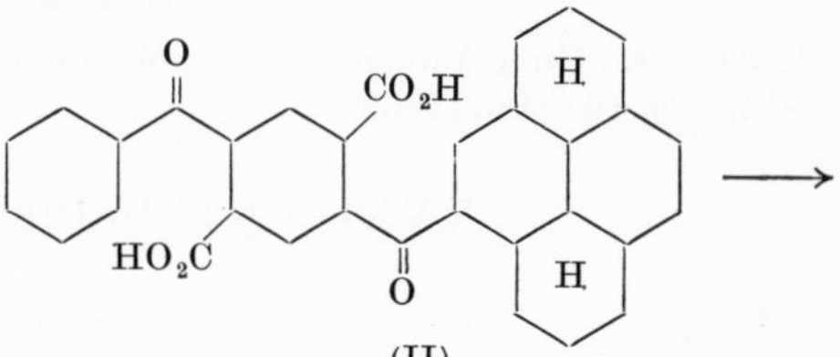

(II)

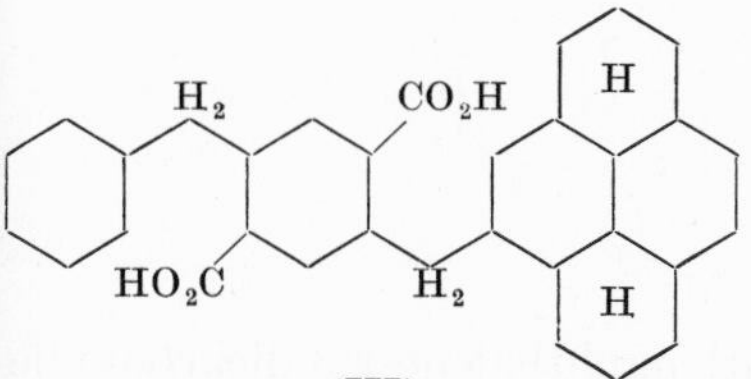

(III)

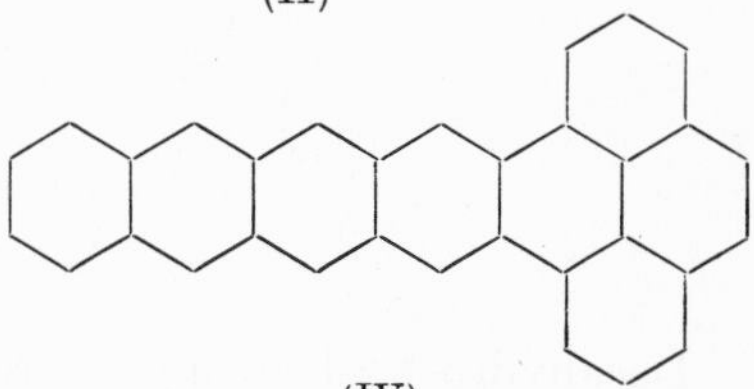

(IV)

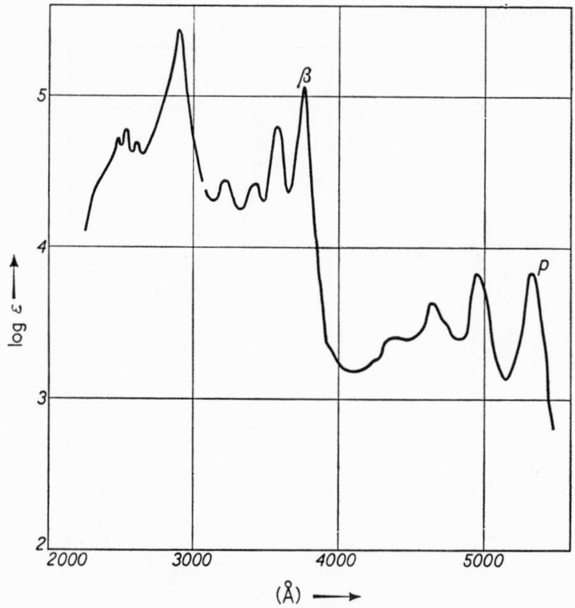

FIG. 145. Absorption spectrum of 1.16,4.5-dibenzohexacene in benzene: p, 5340 (3·85), 4960 (3·85), 4650 (3·65), 4400 (3·42), 4240 (3·27); β, 3770 (5·08), 3580 (4·60), 3430 (4·46); 3220 (4·48); in cyclohexane: β', 2900 (5·45), 2610 (4·72), 2540 (4·78), 2500 (4·76).

II—7

to the hydrocarbon (IV) is carried out in a sodium chloride–zinc chloride melt.

1.16.4.5-Dibenzohexacene (IV) sublimes in violet needles (m.p. 344–345°) which dissolve in concentrated sulphuric acid with a green-violet colour which changes to brown on standing. The absorption spectrum is given in Fig. 145.[1]

REFERENCE

1. Clar, E., Guye-Vuillème, J. F., Macpherson, I. A. and McCallum, A., *Tetrahedron* **19**, 2185 (1963).

XXXI. 5.6,15.16-DIBENZOHEXACENE

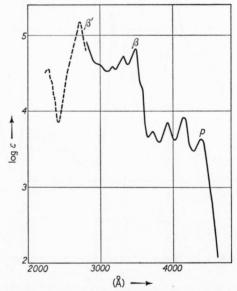

Decahydro-1.2-benzopyrene reacts with naphthalene-2,3-dicarboxylic anhydride to form the keto-acid (I). Cyclization with a sodium chloride–zinc chloride melt followed by dehydrogenation with copper powder yields dibenzohexacene (II).

FIG. 146. Absorption spectrum of 5.6,15.16-dibenzohexacene in benzene: p, 4390 (3·64), 4150 (3·91), 3930 (3·84); 3720 (3·72); β, 3480 (4·82), 3320 (4·71), 3170 (4·59); in cyclohexane (broken line): β', 2720 (5·18), 2280 (4·57).

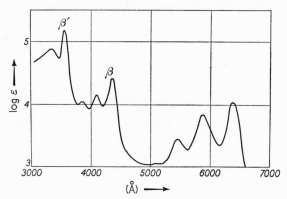

(I)   (II)

5.6,15.16-Dibenzohexacene (II) crystallizes from xylene or trichloro-benzene in orange needles (m.p. 372–373°) which dissolve in concentrated sulphuric acid with a brown colour. The absorption spectrum is given in Fig. 146.[1]

REFERENCE

1. Clar, E., Guye-Vuillème, J. F., Macpherson, I. A. and McCallum, A., *Tetrahedron* **19**, 2185 (1963).

XXXII. NAPHTHO-(1'.7':2.16)-HEXACENE

The reaction of pyrene with anthraquinone-2,3-dicarboxylic anhydride and aluminium chloride leads to the formation of the acid (I). Cyclization

FIG. 147. Absorption spectrum of naphtho-(1'.7':2.16)-hexacene in 1,2,4-trichloro-benzene: *p*, 6390 (4·02), 5860 (3·82), 5460 (3·44); *β*, 4360 (4·40), 4100 (4·14), 3870 (4·04); *β'*, 3580 (5·16), 3360 (4·87).

to the diquinone (II) can be effected in boiling benzoyl chloride with a trace of zinc chloride. Reduction in pyridine with zinc dust and acetic acid yields a dihydro compound which consists of an equilibrium mixture of the isomers (III) and (IV). Dehydrogenation with palladium–charcoal gives naphthohexacene (V).

Naphtho-(1′.7′:2.16)-hexacene (V) sublimes in blue-green leaflets (m.p. 384–386°), which dissolve in concentrated sulphuric acid to form a violet solution which changes to brown, and then to green, on standing. It is a hydrocarbon of high reactivity. Its solutions are readily photo-oxidized and it reacts immediately with maleic anhydride to form the adduct (VI). The absorption spectrum is given in Fig. 147.

Naphtho-(1'.7':2.16)-hexacene-6.15,8.13-diquinone (II) crystallizes from nitrobenzene in red-maroon leaflets (m.p. 418–419°), which give a green colour with concentrated sulphuric acid. A two-stage vat, first a greenish-brown, then a reddish-brown, one is formed with alkaline sodium dithionite solution.[1]

REFERENCE

1. Boggiano, B. and Clar, E., *J. chem. Soc.* 2681 (1957).

XXXIII. 6.7,16.17-DIBENZOHEPTACENE

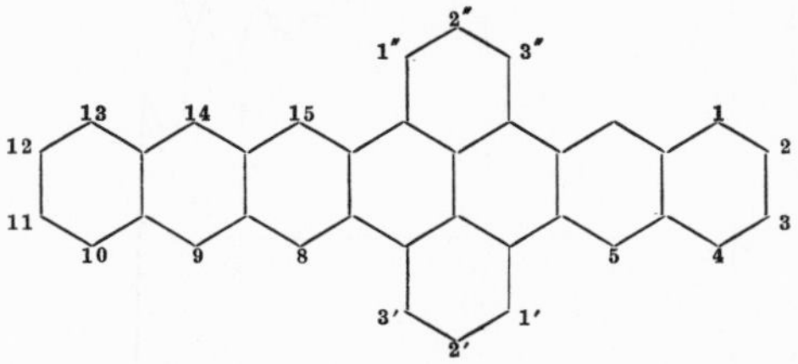

The condensation product of hexahydropyrene and naphthalene-2,3-dicarboxylic anhydride (see p. 186) is reduced to the lactone (I) with zinc dust and sodium hydroxide. It reacts with phthalic anhydride and

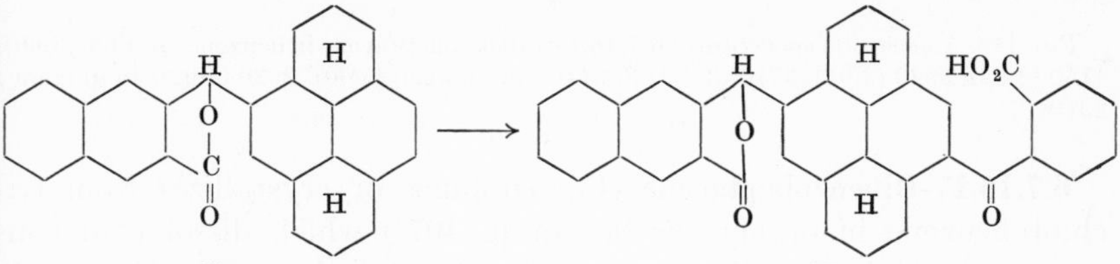

(I)   (II)

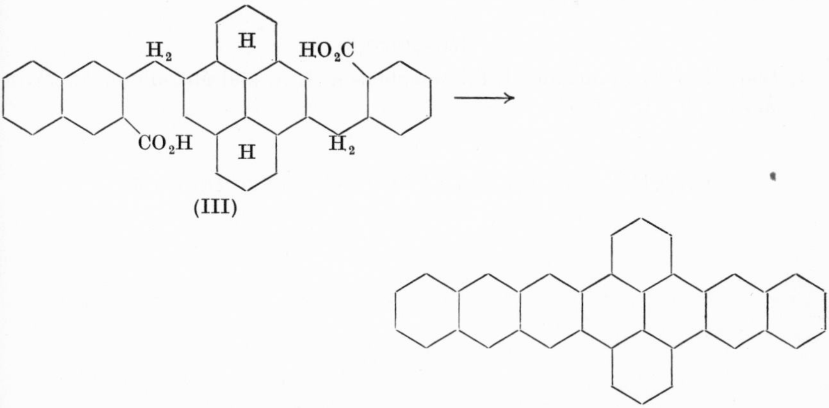

(III)

(IV)

aluminium chloride to give the acid (II). This is reduced to the dicarboxylic acid (III) by prolonged reduction with zinc dust and sodium hydroxide solution. It condenses to dibenzoheptacene (IV) in a melt of sodium chloride and zinc chloride.

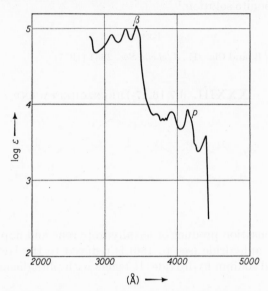

FIG. 148. Absorption spectrum of 6.7,16.17-dibenzoheptacene in benzene: p, 4390 (3·60), 4150 (3·92), 3920 (3·91), 3710 (3·88); β, 3440 (5·05), 3290 (5·00), 3090 (4·92); in dioxane: 2510.

6.7,16.17-Dibenzoheptacene (IV) sublimes or crystallizes from trichlorobenzene in orange needles (m.p. 407°) which dissolve in concentrated sulphuric acid to give a violet solution. The absorption spectrum is given in Fig. 148.[1]

REFERENCE

1. Clar, E., Guye-Vuillème, J. F., Macpherson, I. A. and McCallum, A., *Tetrahedron* **19**, 2185 (1963).

XXXIV. 5.6,8.9,14.15,17.18-TETRABENZOHEPTACENE

7,15-Dihydro-4.5,12.13-dibenzoheptazethrene (I) reacts twice with boiling maleic anhydride to give the dianhydride (II). Cyclization in a zinc chloride–sodium chloride melt yields tetrabenzoheptacene (III). This hydrocarbon is also a condensed polyphenyl and shows the low reactivity which would be expected from the formula (III) which contains only benzenoid rings marked with circles.

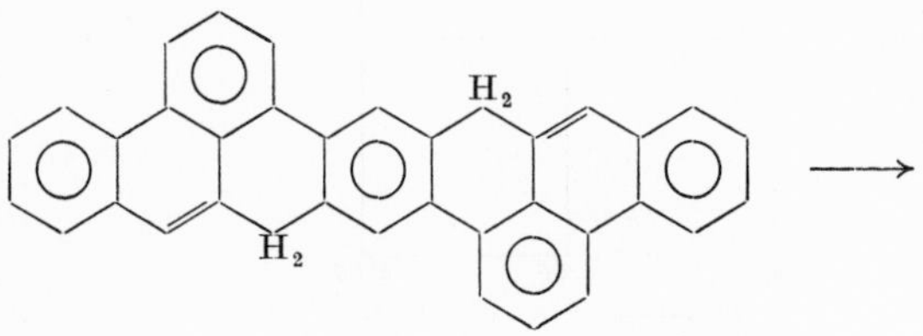

(I)

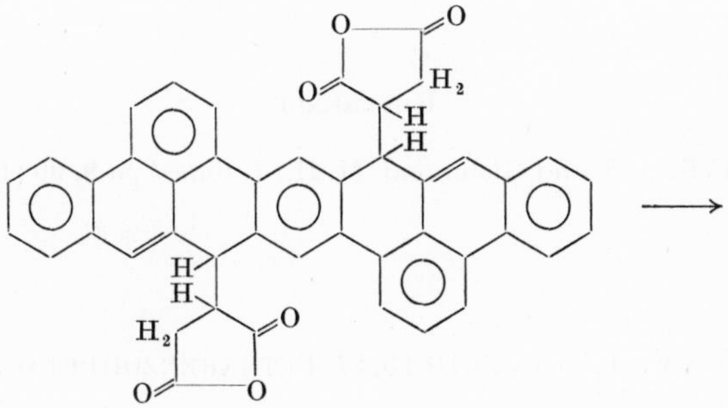

(II)

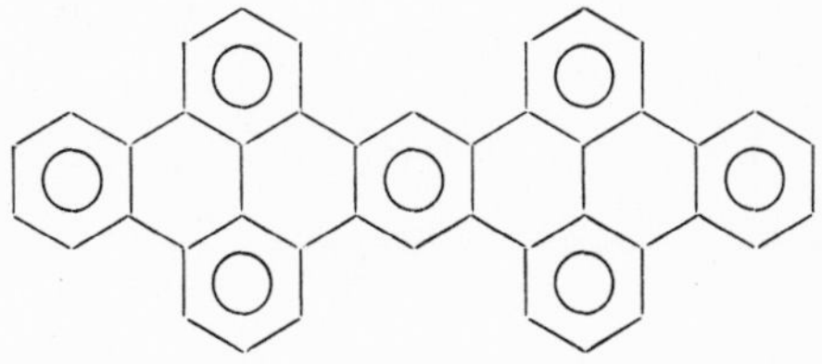

(III)

5.6,8.9,14.15,17.18-Tetrabenzoheptacene (III) forms yellow needles (m.p. 480–490°) from 1-methylnaphthalene or on sublimation *in vacuo*. It does not dissolve in concentrated sulphuric acid and does not react with maleic anhydride. The absorption spectrum is given in Fig. 149. The hydrocarbon shows a long-life phosphorescence in solid ethanolic solution at 77°K with bands at 5215, 5400, 5575, 5685, 5930 Å.[1]

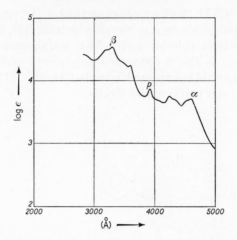

Fig. 149.　Absorption spectrum of 5.6,8.9,14.15,17.18-tetrabenzoheptacene in benzene: α, 4610 (3·70), 4260 (3·75), 3930 (3·86); p, 3700 (4·00); β, 3290 (4·54).

REFERENCE

1.　Clar, E., Fell, G. S. and Richmond, M. H., *Tetrahedron* **9**, 96 (1960).

XXXV.　1.18,4.5,9.10,13.14-TETRABENZOHEPTACENE

Pyromellitic dianhydride and aluminium chloride give a two-fold condensation with hexahydropyrene to form the acid (I). This cyclizes in a sodium chloride–zinc chloride melt and gives, after sublimation over copper powder, tetrabenzoheptacene (II). The hydrocarbon is already obtained as a by-product in the Friedel–Crafts reaction.

1.18,4.5,9.10,13.14-Tetrabenzoheptacene (II) sublimes in red needles (m.p. 570°) which dissolve slowly in concentrated sulphuric acid giving a violet solution. The absorption spectrum is given in Fig. 150.[1]

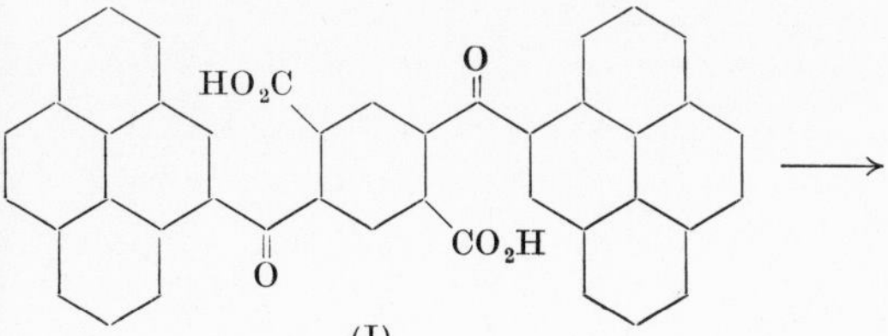

(I)

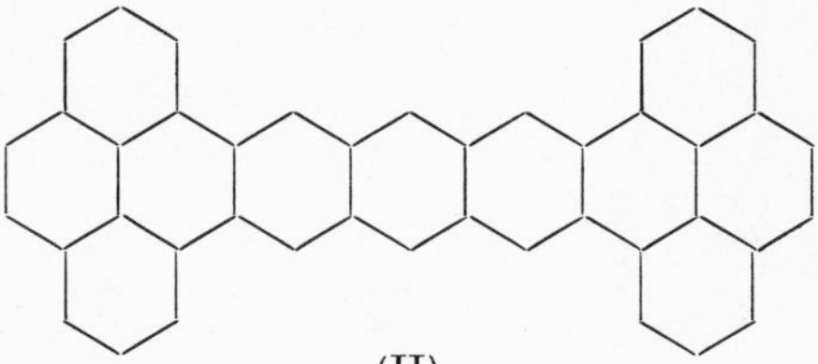

(II)

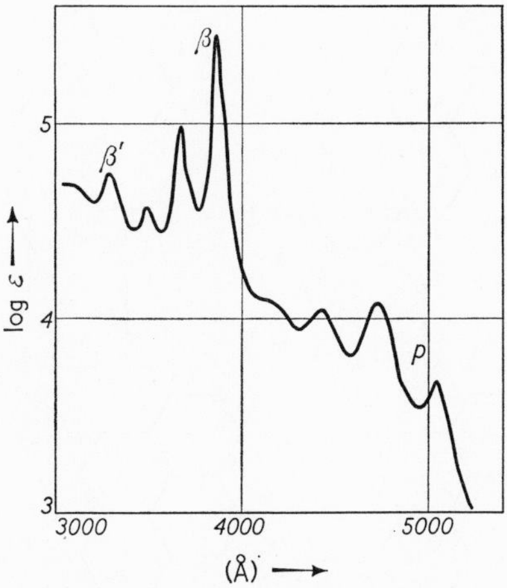

FIG. 150. Absorption spectrum of 1.18,4.5,9.10,13.14-tetrabenzoheptacene in 1,2,4-trichlorobenzene: p, 5060 (3·68), 4730 (4·08), 4420 (4·04), 4170 (4·08); β, 3870 (5·45), 3690 (5·00), 3510 (4·58); β' 3300 (4·76).

REFERENCE

1. Macpherson, I. A., Thesis, Glasgow (1962).

XXXVI. DINAPHTHO-(1′.7′ : 2.18); (7″.1″ ; 9.11)-HEPTACENE

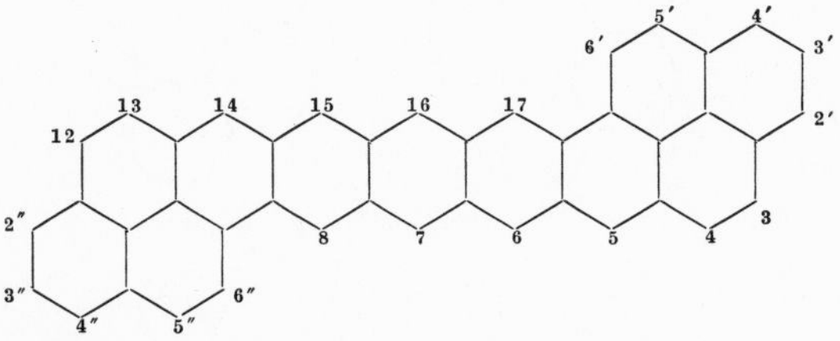

II—7*

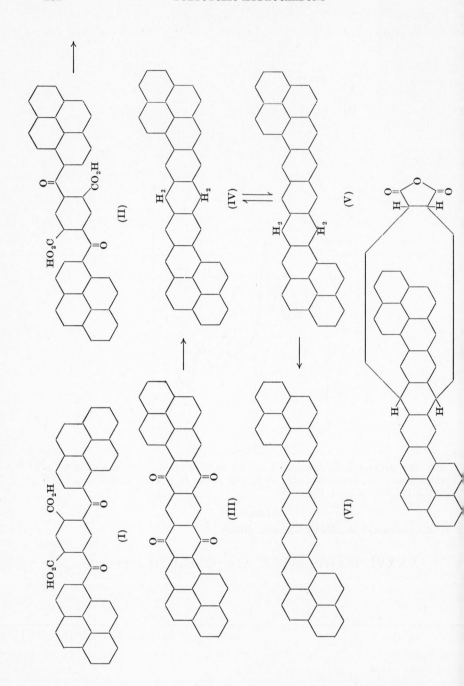

Pyromellitic anhydride condenses twice with pyrene in the presence of aluminium chloride to give an acid which consists possibly of two isomers (I) and (II). Cyclization to the diquinone (III) is effected by boiling with benzoyl chloride containing a trace of zinc chloride. The diquinone (III) can be reduced to an equilibrium mixture of the two dihydro compounds (IV) and (V). Dehydrogenation of these with palladium–charcoal gives the deep green dinaphthoheptacene (VI), which

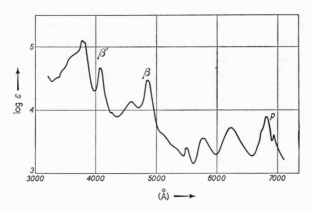

Fig. 151. Absorption spectrum of dinaphtho-(1'.7':2.18);(7".1":9.11)-heptacene in 1,2,4-trichlorobenzene: p, 6830 (3·90), 6240 (3·72), 5770 (3·56), 5500 (3·40); β, 4860 (4·48), 4570 (4·14); β', 4070 (4·66); β'', 3780 (5·10).

is the first benzologue of heptacene to be obtained pure. It reacts immediately with maleic anhydride to form the adduct (VII).

Dinaphtho-(1'.7':2.18);(7".1":9.11)-heptacene (VI) sublimes in deep green-black needles (m.p. 461–462°). It dissolves very slowly in concentrated sulphuric acid with a brown-violet colour. The green solution in 1-methylnaphthalene is photo-oxidizable. The absorption spectrum is given in Fig. 151.

Dinaphtho - (1'.7':2.18);(7".1":9.11) - heptacene - 6.17,8.15 - diquinone (III) sublimes *in vacuo* to give violet-red plates (m.p. 500–502°).[1]

REFERENCE

1. Boggiano, B. and Clar, E., *J. chem. Soc.* 2681 (1957).

XXXVII. 7.8,17.18-Dibenzoctacene

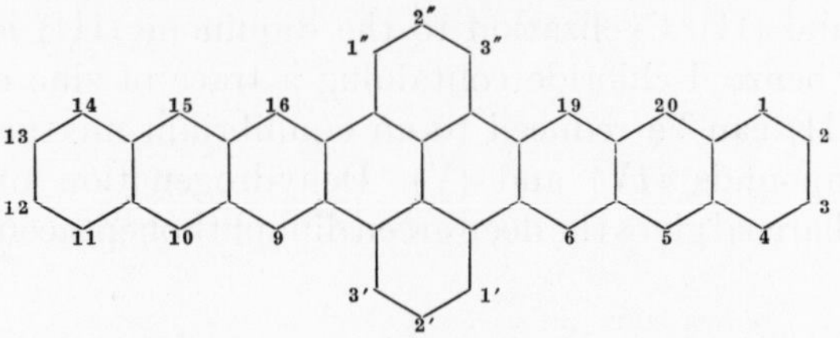

The condensation product of naphthalene-2,3-dicarboxylic anhydride and aluminium chloride (see p. 186) is reduced with zinc dust and sodium hydroxide solution for an extended time to the acid (I). This reacts again with naphthalene-2,3-dicarboxylic anhydride and aluminium chloride

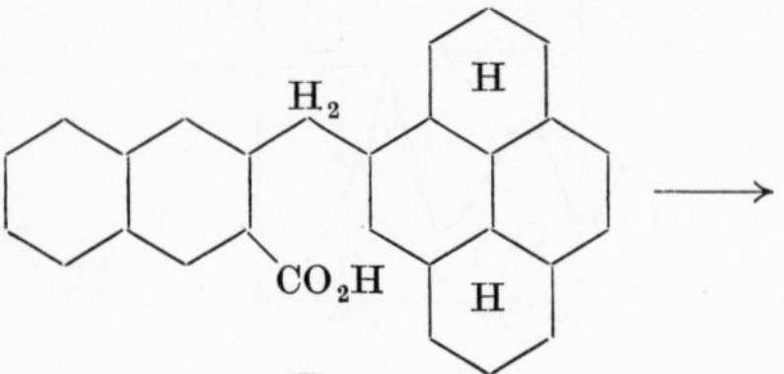

(I)

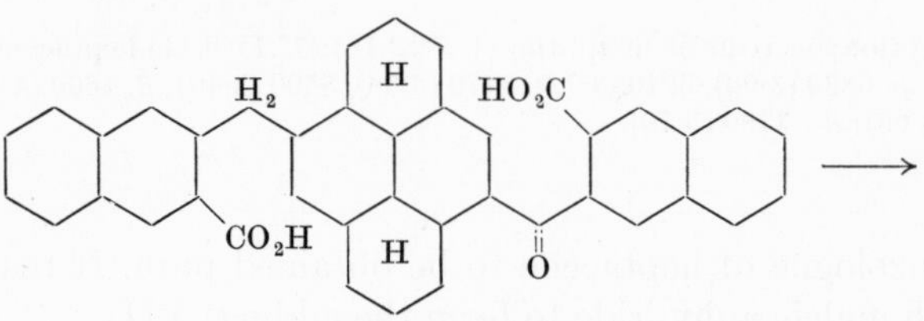

(II)

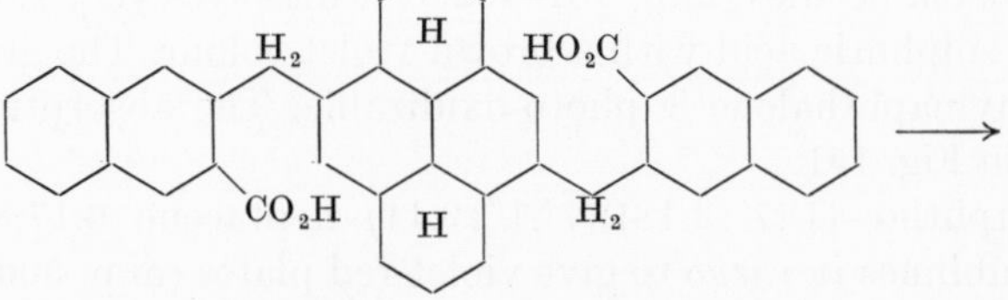

(III)

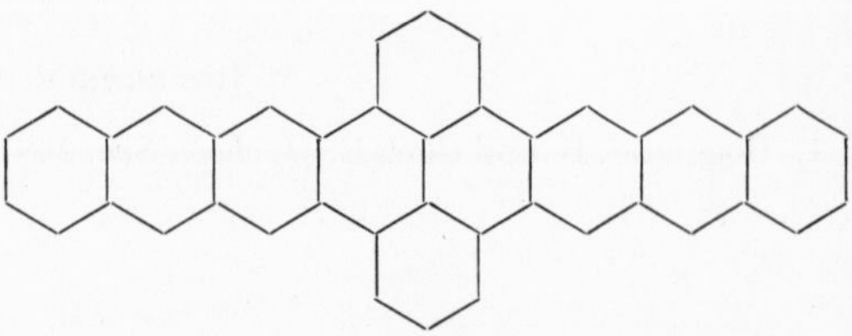

(IV)

to yield the acid (II). Another reduction with zinc dust and sodium hydroxide solution gives the acid (III). Cyclization to the hydrocarbon (IV) is carried out in a sodium chloride–aluminium chloride melt.

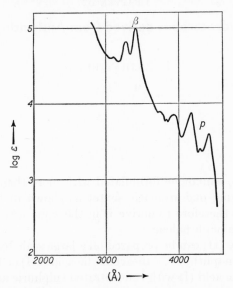

FIG. 152. Absorption spectrum of 7.8,17.18-dibenzoctacene in benzene: p, 44 20 (3·63), 4280 (3·42), 4160 (3·90), 3930 (3·88), 3720 (3·91); β, 3400 (5·00), 3260 (4·82), 3110 (4·62); in dioxane: β', 2780 (5·30).

7.8,17.18-Dibenzoctacene (IV) sublimes or crystallizes from trichlorobenzene in orange needles (m.p. 560°) which assume first a green surface colour with sulphuric acid and give a brownish violet solution on standing. The absorption spectrum is given in Fig. 152.[1]

REFERENCE

1. Clar, E., Guye-Vuillème, J. F., Macpherson, I. A. and McCallum, A., *Tetrahedron* **19**, 2185 (1963).

CHAPTER 32

Hydrocarbons derived from Anthanthrene

I. ANTHANTHRENE

Anthanthrene cannot be formulated with more than two benzenoid rings, each having one aromatic sextet as shown in formula (IV). It appears correct therefore to derive it in the same way from pyrene as anthracene from naphthalene.

Anthanthrone (II) can be prepared on a large scale by a double cyclization of 1,1'-dinaphthyl-8,8'-dicarboxylic acid (III) or 1,1'-dinaphthyl-2,2'-dicarboxylic acid (I) with concentrated sulphuric acid.

(I)   (II)   (III)

(IV)

The esters of both acids can be used for cyclization with sulphuric acid as well as the chloride for cyclization with aluminium chloride.[1]

Anthanthrone (II) can easily be reduced to anthanthrene (IV) by a zinc-dust melt.[2] Reduction with hydriodic acid and red phosphorus gives a hydro-anthanthrene of unknown structure, which is dehydrogenated by subliming over copper at 500°.[3]

Anthanthrene (IV) crystallizes from xylene in golden yellow plates (m.p. 261°), which dissolve in concentrated sulphuric acid to form a brown solution. The absorption spectrum is given in Fig. 153.

Anthanthrene in benzene solution gives a sparingly soluble deep brown compound with bromine.[4] Iodine forms under the same condition an almost black crystalline compound which contains three atoms of iodine.[4]

Sulphuryl chloride gives 6,12-dichloroanthanthrene.[5]

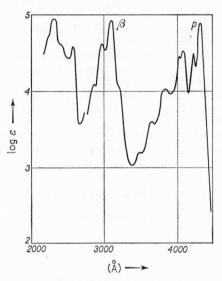

FIG. 153. Absorption spectrum of anthanthrene in benzene: p, 4330 (4·92), 4250 (4·45), 4080 (4·56), 4020 (4·47), 3850 (4·06), 3670 (3·63), 3500 (3·20); β, 3100 (4·95), 2970 (4·65), 2870 (4·10); in ethanol: β', 2570 (4·58), 2400 (4·63); β'', 2310 (4·97).

6-Methylanthanthrene (m.p. 192°) can be prepared via the anthanthrene-6-aldehyde. 6,12-Dimethylanthanthrene (m.p. 281°) was obtained in an analogous way.[5]

Nitration of anthanthrene yields two nitro-compounds of unknown constitution.[6] Anthanthrene is not carcinogenic.[7]

Anthanthrone is an orange-yellow dyestuff of technical importance. The m.p. is 340° and it dissolves in concentrated sulphuric acid to form a green solution. It readily gives a violet-red vat with alkaline sodium dithionite.

Direct bromination of anthanthrone in oleum with bromine gives 4,10-dibromoanthanthrone.[8] A number of other halogen derivatives,[9] nitro-derivatives,[10] and sulphonic acids[11] are known. The synthesis of anthanthrone starting from acenaphthene has been described in detail.[12]

REFERENCES

1. Kalb, L., *Ber. dtsch. chem. Ges.* **47**, 1724 (1914); German Patent 280787 (1913).
2. Clar, E., *Ber. dtsch. chem. Ges.* **72**, 1645 (1939).
3. Scholl, R. and Meyer, K., *Ber. dtsch. chem. Ges.* **67**, 1229 (1934).
4. Brass, K. and Clar, E., *Ber. dtsch. chem. Ges.* **72**, 1882 (1939).
5. Buu-Hoï, N. P. and Lavit, D., *Rec. trav. chim.* **76**, 200 (1957).
6. Dewar, M. J. S., Mole, T., Urch, D. S. and Warford, E. W. T., *J. chem. Soc.* 3572 (1956).
7. Domagk, G., *Medizin und Chemie* **3**, 291 (1936); Cook, J. W. and Kennaway, E. L., *Amer. J. Cancer* **33**, 50 (1938); Rondoni, P., *Chim. e Ind. (Milano)* **17**, 148 (1935).
8. Bradley, J. and Waller, J., *J. chem. Soc.* 3778 (1953).
9. Kalb, L., German Patent 287250 (1913); Casella & Co., Brit. Patents 260998 (1926); 280217 (1927); 295600 (1928); German Patent 507558 (1928); I.G. Farbenindustrie AG, Brit. Patent 286669 (1928); French Patent 678055 (1929); *Chem. Zbl.* **1930 II**, 2968, 3652.
10. Kalb, L., German Patent 287250 (1913); I.G. Farbenindustrie AG, Brit. Patent 327712 (1928); *Chem. Zbl.* **1930 II**, 932; French Patent 669520 (1929); *Chem. Zbl.* **1930 I**, 2172.
11. Casella & Co., Brit. Patent 304613 (1929); *Chem. Zbl.* **1929 I**, 2927.
12. Corbellini, A. and co-workers, *Gior. Chim. ind. appl.* **13**, 109 (1941).

II. 1.2,7.8-DIBENZANTHANTHRENE

(*Pyranthrene*)

1-Chloro- or 1-iodo-2-methylanthraquinone condenses to 2,2'-di-methyl-1,1'-dianthraquinoyl (I) with copper powder in boiling nitro-benzene. Compound (I) can be also obtained by a diazotization and reduction from 1-amino-2-methylanthraquinone. The cyclization of (I) to (II) can be effected in many ways, but best by treatment with alcoholic potassium hydroxide.[1]

3,8-Dibenzoylpyrene (III) can be cyclized with aluminium chloride[2] or better in a sodium chloride–aluminium chloride melt in the presence of molecular oxygen.[3] Even 3,10-dibenzoylpyrene yields pyranthrone (II) under the same conditions.[3] Pyranthrone can also be obtained directly from pyrene with benzoyl chloride in a sodium chloride–aluminium chloride melt.[4]

Pyranthrone (II) is easily reduced to pyranthrene in a zinc-dust melt.[5] The reduction can be carried out also with hydriodic acid and red phosphorus, which yield dihydropyranthrone (V). Dehydrogenation with copper at 400° gives pyranthrene.[6]

1.2,7.8-Dibenzanthanthrene (pyranthrene) sublimes in reddish-brown needles (m.p. 372–373°), which dissolve in concentrated sulphuric acid

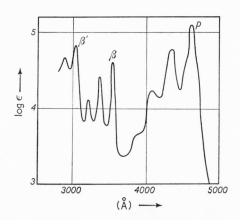

FIG. 154. Absorption spectrum of 1.2,7.8-dibenzanthanthrene in benzene: p, 4620 (5·10), 4340 (4·77), 4075 (4·20), 3860 (3·66); β, 3540 (4·60), 3370 (4·40), 3205 (4·10); β', 3040 (4·82), 2880 (4·64).

to give a violet-blue solution which changes to blue on heating. The solution in benzene gives a deep brown precipitate with bromine. The absorption spectrum is given in Fig. 154. With two molecules of iodine it forms a complex which is paramagnetic.[7]

Pyranthrone (II) is sparingly soluble and forms reddish-brown crystals which dissolve in concentrated sulphuric acid to yield a blue solution. Alkaline sodium dithionite solution gives a purple-red vat which dyes cotton orange-red.

The oxidation of pyranthrone with chromic acid gives 1,1'-dianthraquinonyl-2,2'-dicarboxylic acid (VI). This yields the acid (VII) on reduction with ammonia and zinc dust. Cyclization with zinc chloride or phosphorus pentachloride or heating leads to 1.2,7.8-dibenzanthanthrene-6,12-quinone (amphi-isopyranthrone, VIII). This is a greyish-violet vat dye which gives a blue-green vat which dyes cotton violet.[8] It dissolves in concentrated sulphuric acid to give a red-violet solution. It has no technical importance.

Many derivatives are known of the technically important pyranthrone

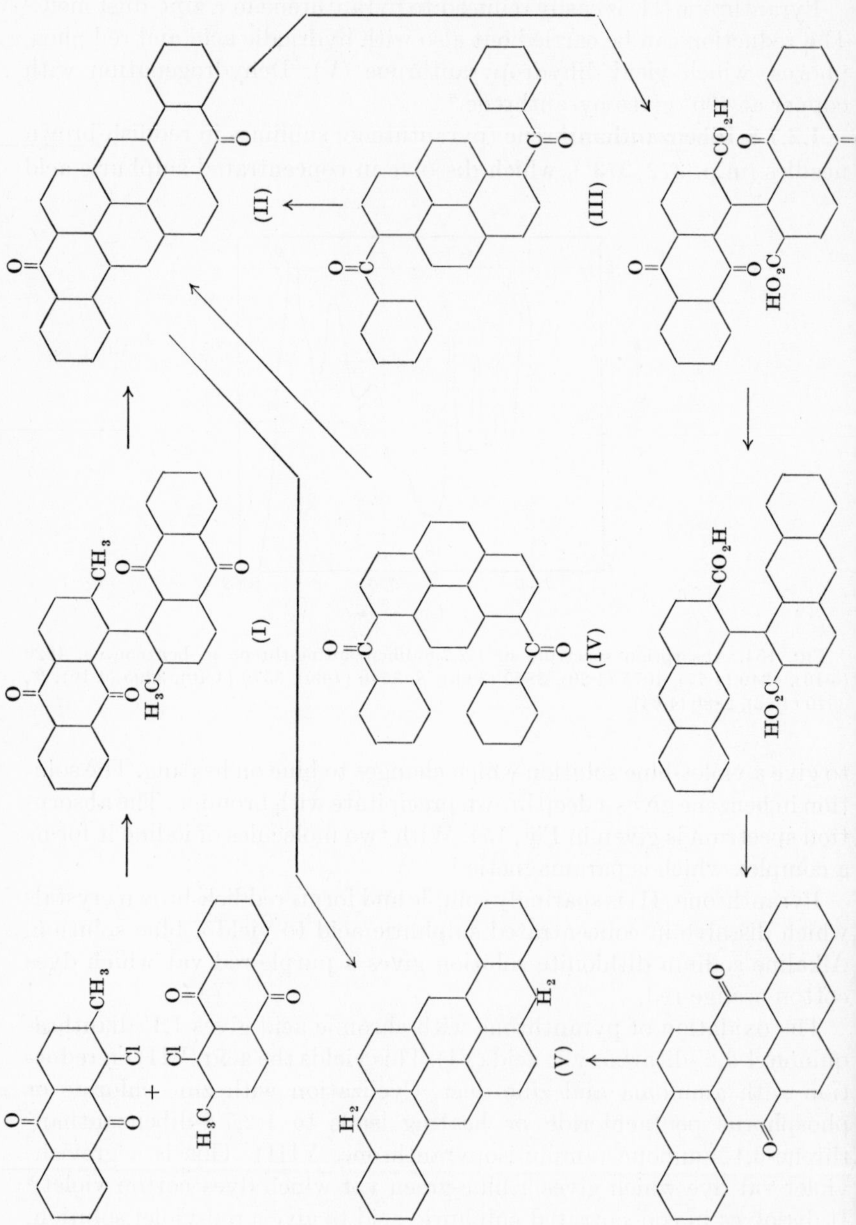
(I)
(II)
(III)
(IV)
(V)

II). Alkyl derivatives can be obtained from the corresponding dianthra-quinonyls.[9] Diaryl-pyranthrones are formed on reduction of 2,2'-bisaroyl-1,1'-dianthraquinonyls. The corresponding dialdehyde gives pyranthrone.[10] Halogen derivatives can be prepared by synthesis[11] or by halogenation.[12] Nitration can be carried out with a mixture of nitric acid and sulphuric acid or with nitric acid in nitrobenzene.[13] Dibenzoylpyranthrone can be prepared from tetrabenzoylpyrene tetrachloride with boiling quinoline and potassium hydroxide.[14]

Both pyranthrone and amphi-isopyranthrone give the same dihydroxy pyranthrone in a melt of potassium hydroxide and magnanese dioxide.[15]

REFERENCES

1. Scholl, R., *Ber. dtsch. chem. Ges.* **43**, 346 (1910); Bad. Anilin und Soda Fabrik, German Patent 175067 (1905); German Patent 212019 (1908); 287270 (1913).
2. Scholl, R., German Patent 239671 (1910); Scholl, R. and Seer, C., *Liebigs Ann.* **394**, 111 (1912); *Mh. Chem.* **33**, 1 (1912).
3. Vollmann, H., Becker, H., Corell, M. and Streeck, H., *Liebigs Ann.* **531**, 38 (1937).
4. I.G. Farbenindustrie AG, Brit. Patent 382877 (1932); *Chem. Zbl.* **1933 I**, 1525.
5. Clar, E., *Ber. dtsch. chem. Ges.* **76**, 332 (1943).
6. Scholl, R. and Meyer, K., *Ber. dtsch. chem. Ges.* **67**, 1229 (1934).
7. Matsunaga, Y., *J. chem. Phys.* **30**, 855 (1959).
8. Scholl, R. and Tänzer, C., *Liebigs Ann.* **433**, 177 (1923).
9. Scholl, R., *Ber. dtsch. chem. Ges.* **43**, 353 (1910); Bad. Anilin and Soda Fabrik, German Patent 175067 (1905); Scholl, R., Potschiwauscheg, J. and Lenko, L., *Mh. Chem.* **32**, 687 (1911).
10. Bad. Anilin und Soda Fabrik, German Patent 238980 (1910); German Patent 278424 (1913).
11. Bad. Anilin und Soda Fabrik, German Patent 211297 (1908).
12. Bad. Anilin und Soda Fabrik, German Patent 186596 (1906).
13. Farbw. Bayer, German Patent 220580 (1909); Bad. Anilin und Soda Fabrik, German Patent 268504 (1912).
14. Scholl, R., Meyer, K. and Donat, J., *Ber. dtsch. chem. Ges.* **70**, 2180 (1937).
15. Backhouse, A. J. and Bradley, W., *J. chem. Soc.* 4506 (1954).

III. 2.3,4.5-DIBENZANTHANTHRENE

The reaction of phthalyl-pyrene (see p. 168) with phenyl magnesium bromide followed by reduction with hydriodic acid in acetic acid yields the diphenyl derivative (I). Cyclization in a sodium chloride–aluminium chloride melt gives dibenzanthanthrene (II), naphthopyrene (III) and the two fluoranthene derivatives (IV) and (V).

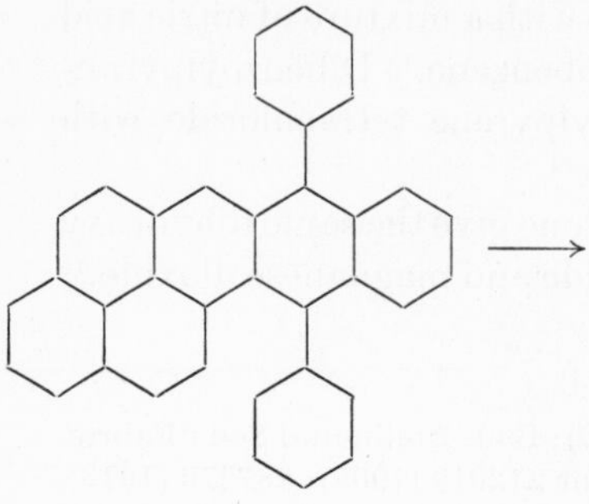

(I)

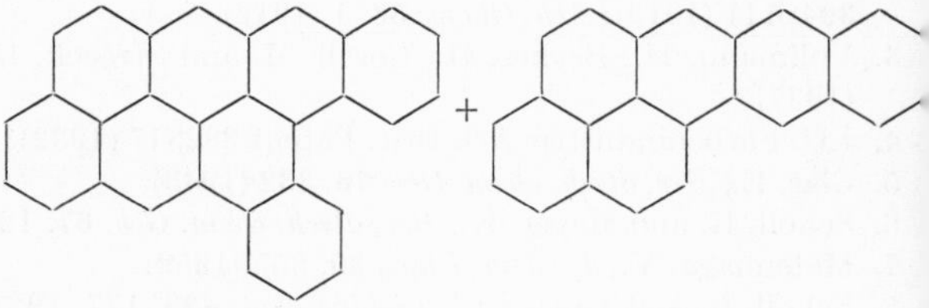

(II)   +   (III)

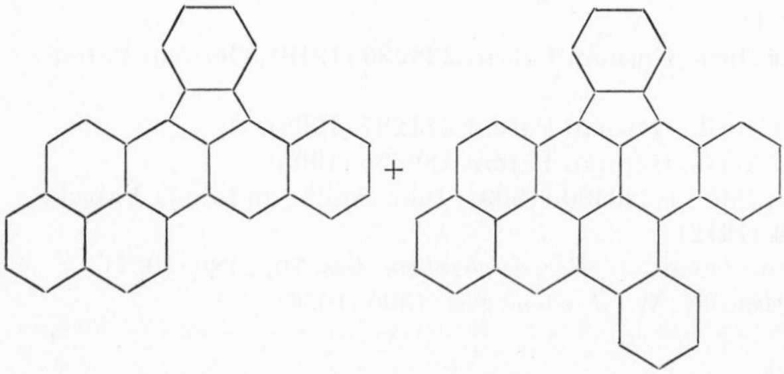

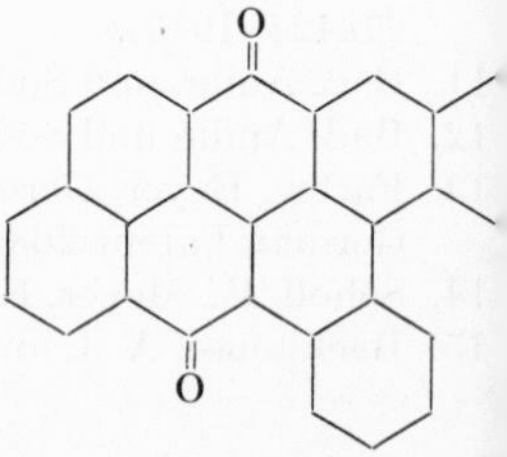

(IV)   +   (V)   (VI)

2.3,4.5-Dibenzanthanthrene (II) crystallizes from xylene in long dark red needles (m.p. 261°), which dissolve in concentrated sulphuric acid to give a blue solution (with a red fluorescence) which turns to green on heating. The absorption spectrum is given in Fig. 155. Oxidation with selenium dioxide in boiling nitrobenzene yields the quinone (VI). This crystallizes from nitrobenzene in violet needles which sublime at about 320° in an evacuated capillary without melting. Concentrated sulphuric acid dissolves the quinone with a green colour. Alkaline sodium dithionite solution yields a violet vat.[1]

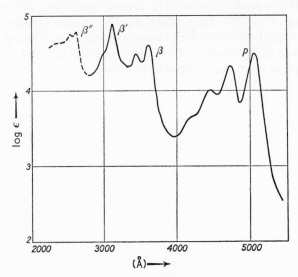

Fig. 155. Absorption spectrum of 2.3,4.5-dibenzanthanthrene in benzene: *p*, 5050 (4·50), 4720 (4·32), 4430 (4·00); *β*, 3600 (4·60), 3430 (4·48); *β'*, 3100 (4·88), in dioxane: *β''*, 2600 (4·78).

REFERENCE

1. Clar, E. and Willicks, W., *Chem. Ber.* **89**, 743 (1956).

IV. 2.3,8.9-DIBENZANTHANTHRENE

Dibenzoylhexahydropyrene (I) can be prepared from hexahydro-pyrene, benzoyl chloride and aluminium chloride.[1] Pyrolysis in the presence of copper powder yields 2.3,8.9-dibenzanthanthrene (II).[2]

2.3,8.9-Dibenzanthanthrene (II) crystallizes from xylene in blue needles (m.p. 382–380° dec.), which dissolve in concentrated sulphuric acid to give a red solution which changes to green on standing. Solutions in benzene or xylene show a red fluorescence and are photo-oxidizable. The absorption spectrum is given in Fig. 156.[2]

(III)   (IV)

(V)

(VI)   (VII)

Dibenzanthanthrenequinone (VII) was synthesized from hexahydropyrene. This yields the dibromo compound (III) on bromination. The bromine atoms can be exchanged with simultaneous dehydrogenation to (IV) by heating with copper cyanide. Hydrolysis yields the dicarboxylic acid (V), the chloride of which gives the diketone (VI). Cyclization in a sodium chloride–aluminium chloride melt results in the formation of dibenzanthanthrenequinone.[1]

2.3,8.9-Dibenzanthanthrene-1,7-quinone (VII) forms dark red needles which have a green surface shine and dissolve in concentrated sulphuric acid to form a blue solution. Alkaline sodium dithionite solution gives a violet vat with a sparingly soluble vat salt which dyes cotton in bluish-red shades.

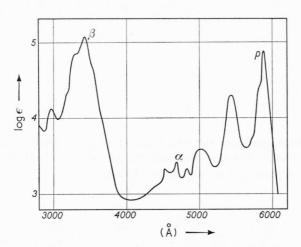

FIG. 156. Absorption spectrum of 2.3,8.9-dibenzanthanthrene in benzene: p, 5890 (4·90), 5450 (4·30), 5020 (3·60); α, 4840 (3·33), 4680 (3·41), 4530 (3·33); β, 3450 (5·08); β', 2980 (4·12).

REFERENCES

1. Vollmann, H., Becker, H., Corell, M. and Streeck, H., *Liebigs Ann.* **531**, 63 (1937).
2. Clar, E., *Ber. dtsch. chem. Ges.* **76**, 331 (1943). Also unpublished results.

V. 1.2-BENZONAPHTHO-(2″.1″ : 7.8)-ANTHANTHRENE, DINAPHTHO-(2′.1′ : 1.2);(2″.1″ : 7.8)-ANTHANTHRENE AND DINAPHTHO-(1′.2′ : 1.2);-(1″.2″ : 7.8)-ANTHANTHRENE

Only three quinones derived from these hydrocarbons have been prepared. Their syntheses follow an analogous course to the synthesis of pyranthrone from pyrene and benzoyl chloride.

(I)   (II)

(III)   (IV)

3-Benzoylpyrene, 1-naphthoyl chloride and aluminium chloride give the ketone (I) and cyclization the benzopyranthrone (II).[1] Pyrene and 1-naphthoyl chloride or 2-naphthoyl chloride yield the ketones (III) and

(V) respectively. These can be cyclized to the dibenzopyranthrones (IV) and (VI) respectively.[2] The benzopyranthrones dye cotton similarly to pyranthrones; however, the shades are more red.

(V)   (VI)

REFERENCES

1. Scholl, R., Meyer, K. and Donat, J., *Ber. dtsch. chem. Ges.* **70**, 2180 (1937).
2. Scholl, R. and Seer, C., *Liebigs Ann.* **394**, 121 (1912).

VI. 1.2-BENZOPHENANTHRENO-(10″.2″ : 8.10)-ANTHANTHRENE

A quinone of this unknown hydrocarbon was synthesized from benzoylnaphthostyrile in a similar way to that of anthanthrone from naphthostyrile. Compound (I) can be obtained from naphthostyrile, benzoyl chloride and aluminium chloride. Treatment of the diazo-compound with cuprous chloride yields (II). A two-fold cyclization with concentrated sulphuric acid gives the diketone (III) and a sodium chloride–aluminium chloride melt in the presence of oxygen gives the diquinone (IV).[1]

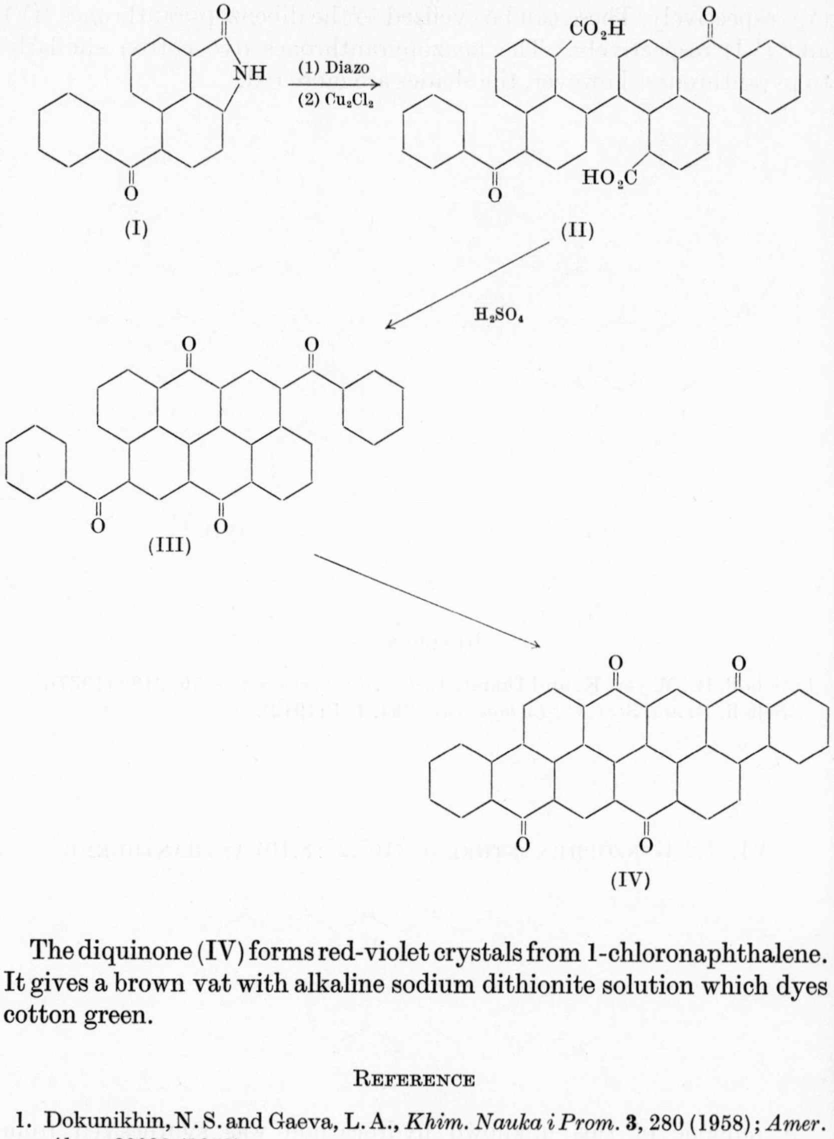

(I) → (1) Diazo / (2) Cu₂Cl₂ → (II)

(II) → H₂SO₄ → (III)

(III) → (IV)

The diquinone (IV) forms red-violet crystals from 1-chloronaphthalene. It gives a brown vat with alkaline sodium dithionite solution which dyes cotton green.

REFERENCE

1. Dokunikhin, N. S. and Gaeva, L. A., *Khim. Nauka i Prom.* **3**, 280 (1958); *Amer. Abstr.* 20098 (1958).

PART IV

peri-Condensed Hydrocarbons consisting only of Six-membered Rings and derived from Fundamental Systems with Three Benzenoid Rings

CHAPTER 33

Hydrocarbons derived from p-Terphenyl

I. p-TERPHENYL

The pyrolysis of benzene yields diphenyl, terphenyl, 1,2-diphenyl-benzene and 1,3-diphenylbenzene. This can be carried out in a glowing iron tube[1] or by an electrically heated wire in benzene vapour.[2] Terphenyl is also obtained from 1,4-dibromobenzene, bromobenzene and sodium in ether[3] or from solid benzenediazonium chloride, fused diphenyl and aluminium chloride.[4] The decomposition of benzenediazonium chloride with copper powder also yields terphenyl.[5]

Terphenyl results from a diene synthesis of diphenylbutadiene (I) and maleic anhydride which gives first the adduct (II). This can be decarboxylated with soda-lime to terphenyl directly or after dehydrogenation to the dicarboxylic acid (III).[6]

Cinnamaldehyde gives terphenyl when reduced with zinc dust.[7]

Phenyl magnesium bromide[8] or phenyl lithium[9] react with cyclo-hexanedione to form the diol (IV), from which terphenyl is obtained by dehydration and dehydrogenation.

(IV)   (V)

A diene synthesis of diphenylcinnamic acid with butadiene and a little picric acid and hydroquinol in an autoclave gives terphenyl.[10]

Terphenyl crystallizes or sublimes in colourless crystals (m.p. 208°), and boils at about 400°. The absorption spectrum is given in Fig. 157. Oxidation with chromic acid in acetic acid gives diphenyl-4-carboxylic acid. Terphenyl yields 4,4"-dibenzoyl terphenyl with benzoyl chloride and aluminium chloride.[11]

A number of alkyl derivatives have been prepared: 4-methylterphenyl

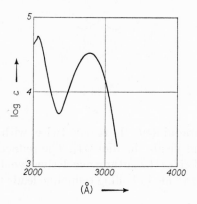

FIG. 157. Absorption spectrum of terphenyl in n-heptane: p, 2780 (4·52); β, 2065 (4·74).

(m.p. 207–208°), 3-methylterphenyl (m.p. 125·5–126°), 2-methylterphenyl (m.p. 93–94°) and 3,4-dimethylterphenyl (m.p. 127°).[10,12] The fluorene derivative (V) can be also considered an alkylterphenyl.[13]

REFERENCES

1. Schultz, G., *Liebigs Ann.* **174**, 230 (1874); Schmidt, H. and Schultz, G., *Liebigs Ann.* **203**, 124 (1880).
2. Löb, W., *Z. elekt. Chem.* **7**, 903 (1901); **8**, 777 (1902); *Ber. dtsch. chem. Ges.* **34**, 917 (1901).
3. Riese, F., *Liebigs Ann.* **164**, 172 (1872).
4. Möhlau R. and Berger, R., *Ber. dtsch. chem. Ges.* **26**, 1998 (1893).
5. Gerngross, O., Schachnow, C. and Jonas, R., *Ber. dtsch. chem. Ges.* **57**, 749 (1924); Gerngross, O. and Dunkel, M., *Ber. dtsch. chem. Ges.* **57**, 742 (1924).
6. Diels, O. and Alder, K., *Ber. dtsch. chem. Ges.* **62**, 2081 (1929); Kuhn, R. and Wagner-Jauregg, T., *Ber. dtsch. chem. Ges.* **63**, 2662 (1930).
7. Kuhn, R. and Winterstein, A., *Ber. dtsch. chem. Ges.* **60**, 432 (1927).
8. Meyer, F., *Ber. dtsch. chem. Ges.* **65**, 1337 (1932).
9. Müller, E. and Sok, G., *Ber. dtsch. chem. Ges.* **70**, 1992 (1937).
10. Skarchenko, V. P., Tsybikova, D. T. and Lavina, R. Y., *J. gen. Chem. U.S.S.R.* **30**, 3477 (orig. p. 3504) (1960).
11. Müller, E. and Pfanz, H., *Ber. dtsch. chem. Ges.* **74**, 1069 (1941).
12. Gilman, H. and Weipert, E. A., *J. org. Chem.* **22**, 446 (1957).
13. Nierenstein, M. and Webster, C. W., *J. Amer. chem. Soc.* **67**, 691 (1945).

II. 1.9,5.10-Di-(*PERI*-NAPHTHYLENE-)—ANTHRACENE

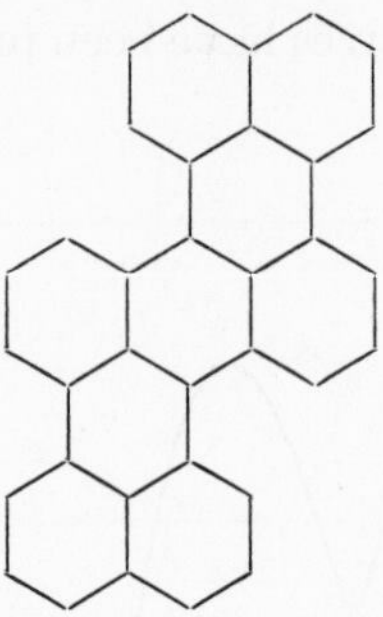

1,5-Dichloroanthraquinone (I) reacts twice with 1-naphthyl magnesium bromide and yields the diol (II). The reduction with hydrogen iodide in acetic acid gives the anthracene derivative (III) and cyclization with potassium hydroxide in boiling quinoline leads to the hydrocarbon (IV).

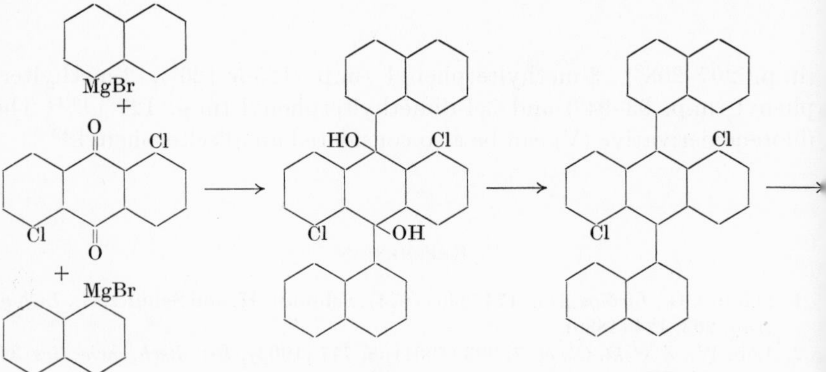

(II)   (III)

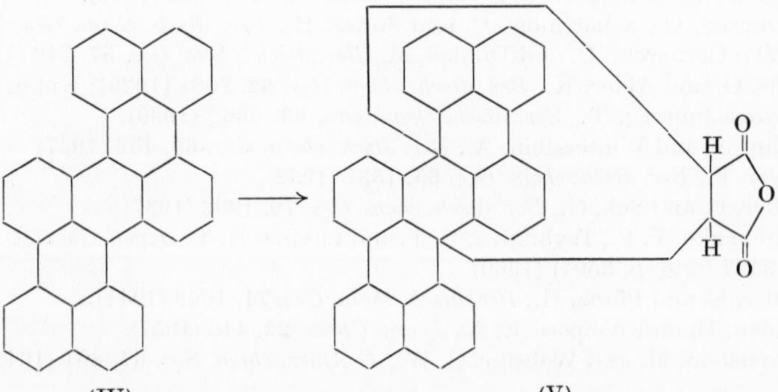

(IV)   (V)

1.9,5.10-Di-(*peri*-naphthylene)-anthracene (IV) sublimes or crystallizes from xylene in deep blue prisms with a coppery sheen (m.p. 333–334°), which dissolve in concentrated sulphuric acid to give a green colour

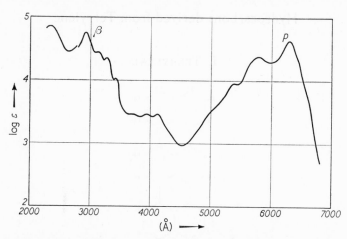

Fig. 158. Absorption spectrum of 1.9,5.10-di-(*peri*-naphthylene)-anthracene in benzene: p, 6300 (4·64), 5790 (4·40), 5360 (3·96); α, 4120 (3·47), 3920 (3·47), 3720 (3·47); 3420 (4·02), 3280 (4·36), 3120 (4·44); β, 2920 (4·76); in ethanol: β', 2360 (4·88).

which quickly becomes pinkish-brown. The solution in xylene shows a red fluorescence. The absorption spectrum is given in Fig. 158. The hydrocarbon easily adds maleic anhydride to form the endocyclic adduct (V), the absorption spectrum of which is characteristic for a benzanthrene derivative.[1]

REFERENCE

1. Clar, E., Kelly, W. and Wright, J. W., *J. chem. Soc.* 1108 (1954).

CHAPTER 34

Hydrocarbons derived from Terrylene

I. TERRYLENE

1-Naphthyl magnesium bromide reacts with 2,3-dichloro-1,4-naphthoquinone (I) to yield the diol (II). This is reduced to dinaphthyldichloronaphthalene (III) in boiling acetic acid with hydriodic acid. Cyclization in a sodium chloride–aluminium chloride melt gives dichloroterrylene (IV). The chlorine atoms can be removed by hydrogenation with hydriodic acid and red phosphorus under pressure, which leads to the picene derivative (V). Lower hydrogenated derivatives and some terrylene are formed in the same reduction. The dehydrogenation of (V) to terrylene (VI) is carried out with palladium–charcoal.[1]

In a similar synthesis 1-naphthyl magnesium bromide reacts with decalindione (VII) to give the diol (VIII). Heating with $KHSO_4$ at 280° dehydrates the diol to hexahydrodinaphthylnaphthalene (IX). Dehydrogenation with sulphur to (X) followed by cyclization in a sodium chloride–aluminium chloride melt yields terrylene (VI) and another hydrocarbon (m.p. 308–310°), which is believed to be 1-naphthylperylene (XI).

Derivatives of terrylene can be prepared from the reactive isobenzofuran derivative (XII) by diene synthesis. Acrylic acid gives the acid (XIII) from which terrylene is obtained by a sodium chloride–aluminium chloride melt. Addition of acrylonitrile leads to (XIV). This compound can be cyclized directly to terrylene-nitrile (XVI) or, after preceding dehydration, to (XV).[2]

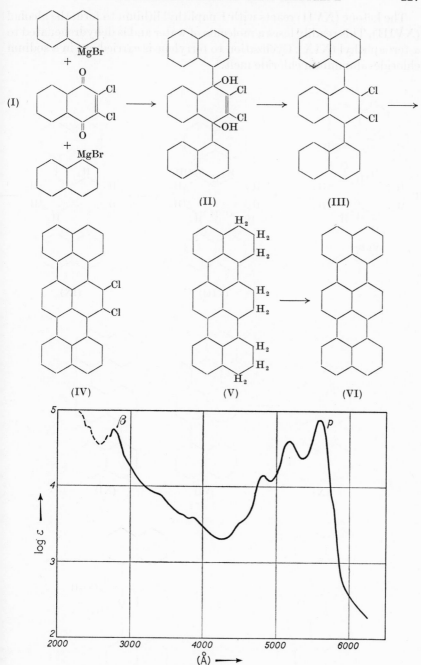

Fig. 159. Absorption spectrum of terrylene in benzene: p, 5600 (4·90), 5190 (4·60), 4830 (4·14); β, 2770 (4·74); in dioxane: 2650 (4·64); β', 2440 (4·74).

The ketone (XVII) reacts with 1-naphthyl lithium to form the alcohol (XVIII). This readily loses a molecule of water and is dehydrogenated to α-ternaphthyl (XIX). Cyclization to terrylene is carried out in a sodium chloride–aluminium chloride melt.[2]

(VII)   (VIII)   (IX)

(X)   (VI)   +   (XI)

(XII)   (XIII)

Terrylene sublimes *in vacuo* or crystallizes from trichlorobenzene in deep red-violet plates (m.p. 510–511°), which dissolve in concentrated sulphuric acid to form a blue solution with a red fluorescence. The pink

(XIV)   (XV)   (XVI)

(XVII)   (XVIII)   (XIX)

solution in benzene or xylene shows an orange fluorescence. The absorption spectrum is given in Fig. 159.[1] The crystal structure has been investigated by X-rays.[3]

REFERENCES

1. Clar, E., Kelly, W. and Laird, R. M., *Mh. Chem.* **87**, 391 (1956).
2. Buchta, E., Vates, H. and Knopp, H., *Chem. Ber.* **91**, 228 (1958); Buchta, E. and Bösche, J., *Liebigs Ann.* **660**, 33 (1962).
3. Clar, E. and Speakman, J. C., *J. chem. Soc.* 2492 (1958).

II. 7.8-Benzoterrylene

1,4-Dichloroanthraquinone (I) and two molecules of 1-naphthyl-magnesium bromide give the diol (II). Reduction with hydrogen iodide in acetic acid yields the anthracene derivative (III) and cyclization with potassium hydroxide in boiling quinoline yields 7.8-benzoterrylene (IV).

7.8-Benzoterrylene (IV) can also be prepared from the diol (VI), which is obtained from anthraquinone and 1-naphthyl magnesium bromide.

Cyclization by a sodium chloride–aluminium chloride melt yields 7.8-benzoterrylene (IV) and no 1.9,5.10-di-(*peri*-naphthylene)-anthracene (see p. 224).[1] The same result is obtained if the dichloro-diol is submitted to the melt.

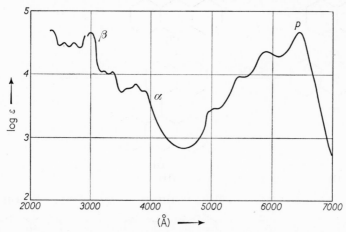

(VI)   (IV)

7.8-Benzoterrylene (IV) crystallizes from xylene in dark green-blue prisms or needles (m.p. 348–350°). It dissolves in concentrated sulphuric acid to give a blue-green solution. The solution in xylene shows a red

FIG. 160. Absorption spectrum of 7.8-benzoterrylene in benzene: *p*, 6435 (4.67), 5890 (4·36), 5440 (3·96), 5030 (3·46); α, 3920 (3·73), 3740 (3·84), 3360 (4·04), 3220 (4·05); β, 2980 (4·66); in ethanol: 2720 (4·54), 2540 (4·52), 2360 (4·74).

fluorescence. The absorption spectrum is given in Fig. 160. 7.8-Benzoterrylene readily adds maleic anhydride to form a colourless adduct whose absorption spectrum is not related to benzanthrene.[1]

REFERENCE

1. Clar, E., Kelly, W. and Wright, J. W., *J. chem. Soc.* 1108 (1954); Clar, E. and Guzzi, A., *Ber. dtsch. chem. Ges.* **65**, 1521 (1932).

III. 1.2,13.14-DIBENZOTERRYLENE

Dichloroanthrone (I) reacts two-fold with naphthalene and aluminium chloride in benzene solution. The first reaction gives the 3-hydroxy-1.2-benzoperylene (II) (see p. 40) and the second condensation either (III) or (IV). The latter constitution is the more likely one.

The dihydroxy compound is oxidized to the quinone (V) by boiling with nitrobenzene. The reduction to the hydrocarbon (VI) can be carried out in pyridine with zinc dust and acetic acid.

1.2,13.14-Dibenzoterrylene (VI) crystallizes from nitrobenzene or 1-methylnaphthalene in deep blue-green crystals. It decomposes very readily in solution as indicated by a shift of the first absorption bands to the violet. Freshly prepared solutions in xylene show absorption bands at 6200 and 5700 Å and in 1-methylnaphthalene at 6360 and 5820 Å.

(VI)   (V)

1.2,13.14-Dibenzoterrylene-3,12-quinone (V) forms deep blue crystals from nitrobenzene which dissolve in nitrobenzene to give a violet solution. Alkaline sodium dithionite solution produces an insoluble green vat salt. A further reduction to a violet product takes place in the presence of pyridine.[1]

REFERENCE

1. Clar, E., *Chem. Ber.* **82**, 52 (1949).

IV. 7.8,15.16-DIBENZOTERRYLENE

A double reaction of 1-naphthyl lithium with tetracenequinone (I) yields the diol (II). A double cyclization can be achieved in a sodium chloride–aluminium chloride melt at 120°. Besides dibenzoterrylene (III), another hydrocarbon is obtained, which has absorption bands at 6480, 5890 and 5500 Å. This is probably the tetrahydro derivative (IV) of benzoterrylene (III).

7.8,15.16-Dibenzoterrylene (IV) crystallizes from xylene or sublimes *in vacuo* in deep green needles (m.p. 460°). Its solutions show a red fluorescence. The hydrocarbon dissolves in concentrated sulphuric acid

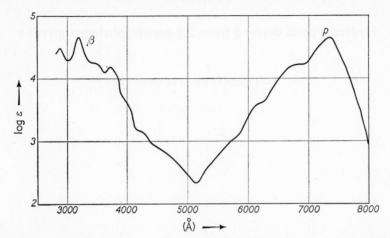

FIG. 161. Absorption spectrum of 7.8,15.16-dibenzoterrylene in benzene: *p*, 7375 (4·62) 6800 (4·20), 6100 (3·58); α, 4250 (3·12), 3960 (3·60), 3725 (4·16), 3460 (4·22); β, 3200 (4·66) 2875 (4·50).

with a blue colour and a red fluorescence. The solution in xylene, which is relatively stable, reacts with maleic anhydride to form the yellow adduct (V). The absorption spectrum is given in Fig. 161.[1]

REFERENCE

1. Clar, E. and Willicks, W., *Chem. Ber.* **88**, 1205 (1955).

Chapter 35

Hydrocarbons derived from 2.3-*peri*-Naphthylenepyrene

I. 2.3-*PERI*-NAPHTHYLENEPYRENE

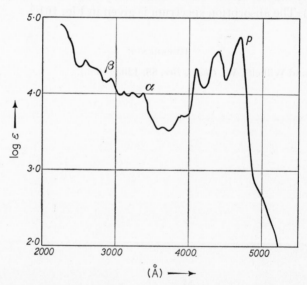

The condensation of 1-bromonaphthalene with pyrene and aluminium chloride yields perinaphthylenepyrene (I) besides a condensation product of pyrene with two molecules 1-bromonaphthalene (see p. 286). *peri*-Naphthylenepyrene is related to terrylene in the same way as pyrene is to

Fig. 162. Absorption spectrum of 2.3-*peri*-naphthylenepyrene in dioxane: *p*, 4700 (4·76), 4400 (4·56), 4100 (4·33); α, 3380 (4·00); β, 2940 (4·19); β′, 2580 (4·42).

perylene. It can be considered a benzologue of *m*-terphenyl just as terrylene is a benzologue of *p*-terphenyl.

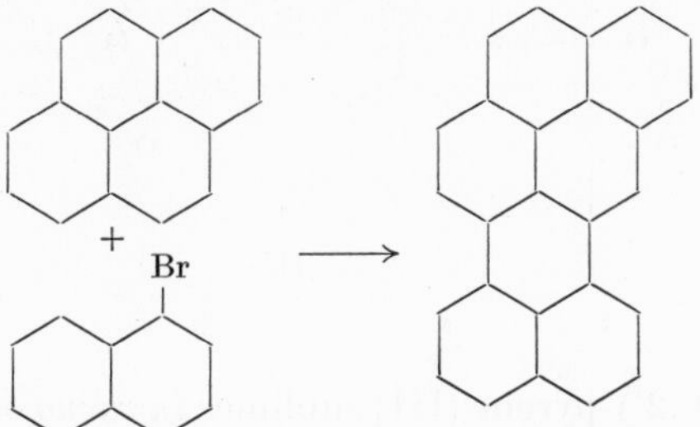

(I)

2.3-Perinaphthylenepyrene crystallizes from xylene in orange yellow
needles (m.p. 310–311°), which dissolve in concentrated sulphuric acid
to give a violet solution with a red fluorescence. The solution in benzene
is yellow and shows a yellowish-green fluorescence. The absorption
spectrum is given in Fig. 162.[1]

REFERENCE

1. Clar, E. and Kühn, O., *Liebigs Ann.* **601**, 181 (1956).

II. PYRENO-(1.3:10'.2')-PYRENE

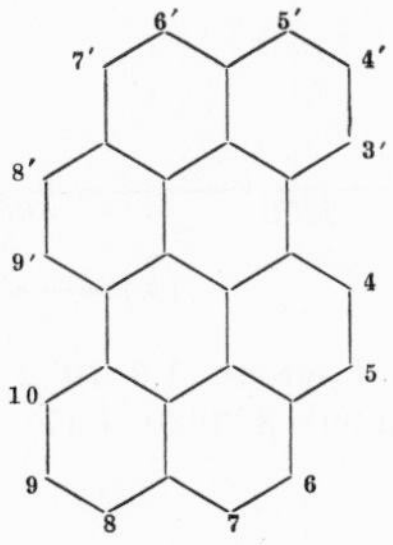

2.3-Perinaphthylenepyrene (I) condenses readily with boiling maleic
anhydride and chloranil as a dehydrogenating agent to give the anhydride (II). This is decarboxylated by boiling with quinoline and
copper powder.

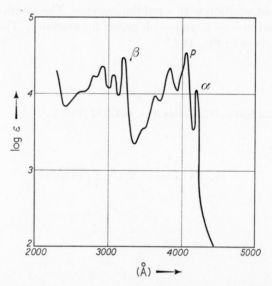

(I)   (II)   (III)

Pyreno-(1.3:10′.2′)-pyrene (III) sublimes *in vacuo* or crystallizes from xylene in pale yellow prisms (m.p. 396°), which are sparingly soluble in concentrated sulphuric acid. The solution in benzene is pale yellow and shows a blue fluorescence. The absorption spectrum is given in Fig. 163.[1]

FIG. 163. Absorption spectrum of pyreno-(1.3:10′.2′)-pyrene in dioxane: α, 4200 (4·06); *p*, 4060 (4·55), 3850 (4·36), 3640 (3·99); β, 3220 (4·47), 3080 (4·26), 2930 (4·37).

REFERENCE

1. Clar, E. and Kühn, O., *Liebigs Ann.* **601**, 181 (1956).

III. 1.12,2.3,6.7,8.9-TETRABENZANTHANTHRENE

If the ketone (I)[1] is reduced with amalgamated aluminium and ethanol, two molecules condense to the compound (II). This is dehydrated with acetic anhydride to the hydrocarbon (III) which cyclizes on dehydrogenation with copper powder to the hydrocarbon (IV).

1.12,2.3,6.7,8.9-Tetrabenzanthanthrene sublimes in pale yellow plates (m.p. 530°) which do not dissolve in concentrated sulphuric acid. A solid solution of the hydrocarbon in 1,2,4-trichlorobenzene shows an orange phosphorescence of long life at $-170°$. The stability of the hydrocarbon can be explained by formula (IV) which shows the aromatic sextets. The absorption spectrum is given in Fig. 164.[2]

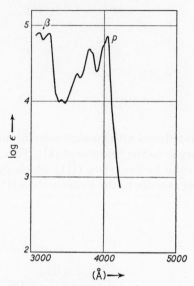

FIG. 164. Absorption spectrum of 1.12,2.3,6.7,8.9-tetrabenzanthanthrene in 1,2,4-trichlorobenzene: p, 4040 (4·86), 3800 (4·69), 3620 (4·35), 3440 (4·00); β, 3240 (4·89), 3090 (4·88).

REFERENCES

1. van de Kamp, J., Burger, A. and Mossetig, E., *J. Amer. chem. Soc.* **60**, 1321 (1938).
2. Clar, E. and McCallum, A., *Tetrahedron*, in press.

IV.   9.10,3′.4′-DIBENZOPYRENO-(1.3:10′.2′)-PYRENE

Tetraphenequinone gives 1-nitrotetraphenequinone by direct nitration.[1] The nitro group can be exchanged for a chlorine atom with chlorine in trichlorobenzene. An Ullmann synthesis with copper powder

in nitrobenzene yields 1,1'-di-(tetraphene-7,12-quinonyl) (II). Cyclization to (III) is effected in concentrated sulphuric acid with copper
powder.[2]

(I)   (II)

(III)

9.10,3'.4'-Dibenzopyreno-(1.3:10'.2')-pyrene-5',8-quinone (III) crystallizes from trichlorobenzene in violet needles which dissolve in
concentrated sulphuric acid to form a green solution. Alkaline sodium
dithionite gives a vat which dyes cotton violet.

Chlorine-containing derivatives of the quinone (III) are obtained if
the cyclization is carried out in a melt of aluminium chloride and pyridine.
Halogen derivatives of (III) can be also synthesized.[3] The chlorination
of the quinone (III) is achieved in nitrobenzene with sulphuryl chloride.
Oxidation of the quinone in sulphuric acid with manganese dioxide
yields a hydroxy compound which can be methylated to a green methoxy
compound. The nitro derivative of the quinone (III) dyes cotton grey.[3]

REFERENCES

1. Scholl, R., *Ber. dtsch. chem. Ges.* **44**, 2370 (1911).
2. I.G. Farbenindustrie AG, German Patent 553000 (1930); 576131 (1931);
   Chem. Zbl. **1932 II**, 2245; **1933 II**, 288.
3. I.G. Farbenindustrie AG, German Patent 551447, 553000 (1930); 549206;
   Brit. Patent 362965 (1930); *Chem. Zbl.* **1932 II**, 2245; **1933 II**, 288.

CHAPTER 36

Hydrocarbons derived from Peropyrene

I. PEROPYRENE

A zinc-dust melt of perinaphthone (I) yields trimethylenenaphthalene and peropyrene in low yields. Its production can be explained by the formation of an intermediate product (II) which results from a reductive condensation as observed in unsaturated ketones[1]. Better results are obtained if perinaphthone (I) is first reduced with zinc dust in sodium

hydroxide to the diketone (IV). This gives peropyrene very readily in a sodium chloride–zinc chloride melt.[2] Peropyrene (III) is formed in small yield during the decarboxylation of trimethylenenaphthalenecarboxylic acid.[3]

Peropyrene (III) crystallizes in golden yellow leaflets (m.p. 374–375°), which dissolve in concentrated sulphuric acid to give a greenish-blue solution. The solution in xylene shows a strong blue fluorescence. The absorption spectrum is given in Fig. 165. Peropyrene does not react with maleic anhydride. However, it yields a chloroperopyrene if boiled with maleic anhydride and chloranil. Peropyrene gives peropyrenequinone when oxidized with chromic acid in acetic acid. Further oxidation leads to perylene-3,4,9,10-tetracarboxylic acid. A phenylperopyrene can be prepared from peropyrene, benzene and aluminium chloride.

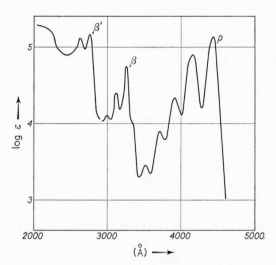

FIG. 165. Absorption spectrum of peropyrene in benzene: p, 4435 (5·14), 4155 (4·90), 3920 (4·33), 3710 (3·89), 3520 (3·45); β, 3260 (4·74), 3120 (4·39), 2990 (4·10), in ethanol: β', 2770 (5·16), 2640 (5·10).

Peropyrenequinone is obtained from a fusion of perinaphthone (I) with alcoholic potassium hydroxide.[4] It could have the structure (V) or (VI). The formation of peropyrene (III) via (IV) indicates that the primary condensation takes place in the position 3 of perinaphthone-(9). Peropyrenequinone must have the carbonyls in the positions 1- and 10- accordingly. Peropyrene-1,10-quinone (V), which only recently has been described as a pure and uniform compound, forms deep violet crystals (dec. > 450°) from trichlorobenzene or nitrobenzene, which dissolve in concentrated sulphuric acid to give a blue solution. The violet solution in trichlorobenzene is readily decolourized by the addition of maleic anhydride. The brownish-yellow adduct dissociates on heating or during reduction.[2]

(I)   (V)   (VI)

(VII)   (VIII)   (IX)

(X)   (XI)

Perinaphthindandione (VII) condenses also with alcoholic potassium hydroxide to form 1,2,3,8,9,10-hexahydro-1,3,8,10-tetraketoperopyrene (VIII).[5] This gives perylenetetracarboxylic acid (IX) on oxidation.[6]

| (XII) | (XIII) | (XIV) |

Similar systems (XI) can be built up from perylenetetracarboxylic dianhydride (X), malonic ester or similar compound with reactive methylene groups.[7] Diaminoperopyrenequinone (XIV) can be prepared from 4,10-diacetyl-3,9-dichloroperylene (XII) which gives the dinitrile (XIII) with cuprous cyanide. This cannot be isolated but re-arranges immediately to (XIV).[8] Substituted peropyrenequinones can be synthesized from substituted perinaphthones.[9]

REFERENCES

1. Clar, E., *Ber. dtsch. chem. Ges.* **76**, 458 (1943).
2. Clar, E., Fell, G. S., Ironside, C. T. and Balsillie, A., *Tetrahedron* **10**, 26 (1960).
3. Alder, K. and Wolff, O., *Liebigs Ann.* **576**, 182 (1952).
4. Bad. Anilin- und Soda-Fabrik, German Patent 283066 (1913).
5. Bad. Anilin- und Soda-Fabrik, German Patent 283365 (1913).
6. Kalle & Co. AG, German Patent 408513 (1922).
7. Kalle & Co. AG, German Patent 413942 (1923).
8. Pongratz, A., *Mh. Chem.* **50**, 87 (1928).
9. I.G. Farbenindustrie AG, French Patent 823261 (1937); *Chem. Zbl.* **1938 I**, 3539.

II. 1.2,8.9-Dibenzoperopyrene
(*Isoviolanthrene*)

1.2,8.9-Dibenzoperopyrene-3,10-quinone (II, isoviolanthrone, isodibenzanthrone) is obtained besides violanthrone (see p. 251) by a fusion of benzanthrone with alcoholic potassium hydroxide.[1] The best yield is achieved at 170–175°, whilst at lower or higher temperatures the percentage of violanthrone increases.[2]

(I)   (II)   (III)

Isoviolanthrone is exclusively formed by the application of chloro- or bromobenzanthrone (III) in the fusion reaction at 120–140°.[3] It can be prepared also from a mixture of benzanthrone and chlorobenzanthrone.[4] Dibenzanthronyl (IV) must be assumed as an intermediate product, since it can be prepared from the same mixture with sodium–aniline at 0–5°.[2] Dibenzanthronyl smoothly yields isoviolanthrone in an alcoholic potassium hydroxide melt. The thioether (V) or (VI) also gives isoviolanthrone under similar conditions.[5]

(IV)   (V)   (VI)

It has been assumed that the diradical (VII) is an intermediate product in the condensation of benzanthrone to the compound (VIII).[6] However, an addition of potassium hydroxide to benzanthrone, forming the adducts (IX) and (X) respectively, appears a possibility. Splitting out two molecules of water would lead to (VIII) and (XI) respectively. The oxidation

(VII)   (VIII)   (IX)

of these compounds and their further condensation in an analogous way could explain the formation of violanthrone and isoviolanthrone.

Isoviolanthrone is preferably formed at low temperature if the condensation with potassium hydroxide is carried out in the presence of a solvent like benzene or trichlorobenzene.[7] The alkali anilides are powerful condensing agents.[8]

(X)   (XI)   (IV)

Isoviolanthrone has been obtained by synthesis from 3,9-dibenzoylperylene (XII) which cyclizes to isoviolanthrone (II) by heating with aluminium chloride.[9] Oxidizing agents like manganese dioxide improve

(XII)   (II)   (XIII)

the yield.[10] The cyclization of 4,10-dibromo-3,9-dibenzoylperylene (XIII) proceeds particularly smoothly.[9] This condensation can also be carried out in boiling quinoline with potassium hydroxide.[10]

The reduction of isoviolanthrone (II) to 1.2,8.9-dibenzoperopyrene (XIV) is best carried out by a zinc-dust melt.[11] Reduction with hydrogen iodide and red phosphorus yields a tetrahydrodibenzoperopyrene of unknown constitution which can be dehydrogenated by sublimation over copper at 460°.[12]

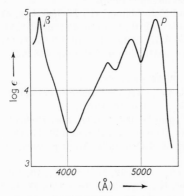

(XIV)   (XV)   (XVI)

1.2,8.9-Dibenzoperopyrene (XIV, isoviolanthrene) sublimes *in vacuo* or crystallizes from 1-methylnaphthalene in dark red plates (m.p. 510°), which dissolve in concentrated sulphuric acid to give a violet solution.

FIG. 166. Absorption spectrum of 1.2,8.9-dibenzoperopyrene in 1-methylnaphthalene: *p*, 5230 (4·90), 4880 (4·65), 4590 (4·34); *β*, 3640 (4·96).

It is very sparingly soluble and the solutions in organic solvents show a green fluorescence. The hydrocarbon and its quinone are semiconductors.[13] 1.2,8.9-Dibenzoperopyrene forms with two molecules of I_2 an addition compound which is paramagnetic.[14] The absorption spectrum is given in Fig. 166.

Isoviolanthrone gives dark violet coppery shining crystals from nitrobenzene, which dissolve in concentrated sulphuric acid with a green colour. Alkaline sodium dithionite solution produces a blue vat which dyes cotton reddish violet. The vat salt is sparingly soluble. This makes it possible to separate mixtures of violanthrone and isoviolanthrone.[15] Oxidation with chromic acid gives first the triquinone (XVI)[16] and then 1.2,5.6-diphthalylanthraquinone (XV).[17]

Isoviolanthrone (isodibenzanthrone) is a technically important vat dyestuff. Numerous derivatives have been prepared. Methyl derivatives can be obtained from diaroyl-perylenes,[18] or from methylbenzanthrones.[19] Chlorine or sulphuryl chloride in nitrobenzene give chloroisoviolanthrones, and bromine in nitrobenzene gives bromoisoviolanthrones.[20] Halogen derivatives can also be prepared from halogenbenzanthrones[21] or halogen-diaroylbenzanthrones.[22] Nitro and amino derivatives are obtained by nitration and reduction.[23] Hydroxy derivatives are synthesized from hydroxy benzanthrones[24] or by direct oxidation of isoviolanthrone with manganese dioxide in concentrated sulphuric acid and boric acid.[25] Reaction of halogen-isoviolanthrones with phenolates yields ethers.[26]

REFERENCES

1. Bad. Anilin- und Soda-Fabrik, German Patent 185221 (1904); Bohn, R., Ber. dtsch. chem. Ges. **28**, 195 (1905).
2. Lüttringhaus, A. and Neresheimer, H., Liebigs Ann. **473**, 259 (1929).
3. Bad. Anilin- und Soda-Fabrik, German Patent 194252 (1906).
4. I.G. Farbenindustrie AG, German Patent 426888 (1924).
5. I.G. Farbenindustrie AG, German Patent 448262 (1924); 445889 (1925); 453134 (1925).
6. Schwenk, E., Chem. Z. **52**, 62 (1928).
7. I.G. Farbenindustrie AG, German Patent 431775 (1924).
8. I.G. Farbenindustrie AG, 436533 (1925).
9. Zinke, A., Linner, F. and Wolfbauer, O., Ber. dtsch. chem. Ges. **58**, 323 (1925); I.G. Farbenindustrie AG, German Patent 436077 (1924).
10. Zinke, A., Funke, K. and Pongratz, A., Ber. dtsch. chem. Ges. **58**, 799, 2222 (1925).
11. Clar, E., Ber. dtsch. chem. Ges. **72**, 1649 (1939); **76**, 458 (1943).
12. Scholl, R. and Meyer, K., Ber. dtsch. chem. Ges. **67**, 1229 (1934).
13. Akamatu, H. and Inokuchi, M., J. chem. Phys. **18**, 810 (1950); Inokuchi, H., Bull. chem. Soc. Japan **24**, 222 (1951).
14. Matsunaga, Y., J. chem. Phys. **30**, 855 (1959).
15. Lüttringhaus, A. and Neresheimer, H., Liebigs Ann. **473**, 259 (1929).
16. Maki, T. and Nagai, Y., Ber. dtsch. chem. Ges. **70**, 1867 (1937).
17. I.G. Farbenindustrie AG, German Patent 487725 (1926); Graselli Dyestuff Corp., Amer. Patent 1706493 (1927); Scholl, R. and Meyer, K., Ber. dtsch. chem. Ges. **61**, 2550 (1928); **65**, 1396 (1932).
18. Zinke, A. and Funke, K., Ber. dtsch. chem. Ges. **58**, 2222 (1925).

19. Bad. Anilin- und Soda-Fabrik, German Patent 188193 (1905); Hey, D. H., Nicholls, R. J. and Prichett, C. W., *J. chem. Soc.* 97 (1944).
20. Bad. Anilin- und Soda-Fabrik, German Patent 217570 (1909); I.G. Farbenindustrie AG, German Patent 436828 (1922).
21. Bad. Anilin- und Soda-Fabrik, German Patent 188193 (1905); I.G. Farbenindustrie AG, German Patent 435533 (1925).
22. Zinke, A., Funke, K. and Pongratz, A., *Ber. dtsch. chem. Ges.* 58, 799 (1925).
23. Bad. Anilin- und Soda-Fabrik, German Patent 185222 (1904); 234749 (1910).
24. Farbwerke Höchst, German Patent 414203; 414924 (1923).
25. Bad. Anilin- und Soda-Fabrik, German Patent 259370; 260020 (1912); 280710 (1913); Scottish Dyes Ltd., German Patent 416208; 418639 (1921).
26. Kalle and Co. AG, German Patent 424881 (1923).

III. 1.2,9.10-DIBENZOPEROPYRENE

(*Violanthrene*)

Violanthrone (III) was first obtained by a fusion of benzanthrone (I) with alcoholic potassium hydroxide.[1] The intermediate product is dibenzanthronyl (II) which can be isolated if the reaction is carried out at lower temperatures.[2] Violanthrone (III) can be synthesized from 1,1'-dinaphthyl (V). A double reaction with benzoyl chloride and aluminium chloride gives dibenzoyl-dinaphthyl (IV) and cyclization with aluminium chloride yields violanthrone.[3]

The reduction of violanthrone to 1.2,9.10-dibenzoperopyrene (VI) is carried out in a zinc-dust melt.[4] Reduction with hydrogen iodide and red phosphorus at 220° gives a tetrahydroviolanthrene of unknown constitution which is dehydrogenated by copper at 450°.[5]

1.2,9.10-Dibenzoperopyrene (violanthrene, VI) sublimes in bright red plates (m.p. 478°), which dissolve in concentrated sulphuric acid to give a blue colour. The solution in trichlorobenzene shows a green fluorescence. Dibenzoperopyrene and its quinone are semiconductors.[6] 1.2,9.10-Dibenzoperopyrene gives with two molecules of I_2 a molecular

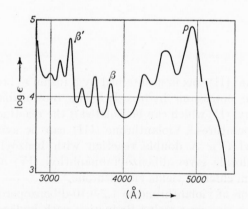

compound which is paramagnetic.[7] The absorption spectrum is given in Fig. 167.

Violanthrone (1.2,9.10-Dibenzoperopyrene-3,8-quinone, III) is very sparingly soluble and forms dark violet crystals from nitrobenzene which

FIG. 167. Absorption spectrum of 1.2,9.10-dibenzoperopyrene in benzene: p, 4920 (4·91), 4580 (4·60), 4280 (4·28); β, 3820 (4·16), 3610 (4·26), 3430 (4·10); β', 3275 (4·76), 3140 (4·47), 3000 (4·30); from 5000 Å in methylnaphthalene.

dissolve in concentrated sulphuric acid with a violet colour. Alkaline sodium dithionite gives a reddish-violet vat which dyes cotton violet.

Violanthrone (dibenzanthrone) is a vat dye of great technical importance. Derivatives can be obtained by synthesis or substitution.

(VI)   (VII)   (VIII)

(IX)   (X)   (XI)

Alkyl-violanthrones,[8] halogen-violanthrones,[8] hydro and alkoxy derivatives[9] have been prepared from the corresponding benzanthrone derivatives. Other halogen derivatives[10] and nitro compounds are formed by substitution from violanthrone.[11] The vat of the nitro compound yields a green amino compound which can be oxidized on the fibre to a valuable black dye.[12] The formula (VII) has been attributed to this compound.[13] However, if the nitration takes place in the positions 3'- and 2''- then the structure (VII) cannot be correct.[14]

Of technical importance is the oxidation of violanthrone to violanthrone-quinone (IX) which is achieved in concentrated sulphuric acid with manganese dioxide and boric acid.[15] Reduction gives dihydroxyviolanthrone (VIII) from which the corresponding dimethoxy compound is obtained. This is a valuable green vat dye.[16] Further oxidation leads from (IX) to the pyrene derivative (X).[17] The oxidation with chromic acid of violanthrone suspended in dilute sulphuric acid yields 2,2'-dianthraquinonyl-1,1'-dicarboxylic acid (XI). This can also be obtained from dibenzanthonyl.[18]

REFERENCES

1. Bad. Anilin- und Soda-Fabrik, German Patent 185221 (1904); Bohn, R., *Ber. dtsch. chem. Ges.* **28**, 195 (1905).
2. Bad. Anilin- und Soda-Fabrik, German Patent 407838 (1922); Lüttringhaus, A. and Neresheimer, H., *Liebigs Ann.* **473**, 259 (1929).
3. Scholl, R. and Seer, C., *Liebigs Ann.* **394**, 126 (1912); Scholl, R., German Patent 239671 (1910).
4. Clar, E., *Ber. dtsch. chem. Ges.* **72**, 1648 (1939); **76**, 458 (1943).
5. Scholl, R. and Meyer, K., *Ber. dtsch. chem. Ges.* **67**, 1229 (1934).
6. Akamatu, H. and Inokuchi, H., *J. chem. Phys.* **18**, 810 (1950); Inokuchi, H., *Bull. chem. Soc. Japan* **24**, 222 (1951).
7. Matsunaga, Y., *J. chem. Phys.* **30**, 855 (1959).
8. Bad. Anilin- und Soda-Fabrik, German Patent 188193 (1905); I.G. Farbenindustrie AG, German Patent 435533 (1925).
9. Farbwerke Höchst, German Patent 414203, 414924 (1923); I.G. Farbenindustrie AG, German Patent 436887 (1924); Farbwerke Höchst, German Patent 413738 (1923); 442511 (1924).
10. Bad. Anilin- und Soda-Fabrik, German Patent 217570 (1909); 402640 (1922); I.G. Farbenindustrie AG, German Patent 436828 (1922).
11. Bad. Anilin- und Soda-Fabrik, German Patent 185222 (1904); 234749 (1910).
12. Bad. Anilin- und Soda-Fabrik, German Patent 226215 (1909).
13. Maki, T., Nagai, Y. and Hayashi, Y., *J. Soc. chem. Ind. Japan* (Suppl.) **38**, 710B (1935); *Chem. Zbl.* **1936 II**, 470.
14. Bennet, D. J., Pritchard, R. R. and Simonsen, J. L., *J. chem. Soc.* 31 (1943).
15. Bad. Anilin- und Soda-Fabrik, German Patent 259370, 260020 (1912); 280710 (1913); 411013 (1922); Scottish Dyes Ltd., German Patent 416208, 418639 (1921); Bad. Anilin- und Soda-Fabrik, German Patent 395691 (1922); 403394 (1923); Farbwerke Höchst, German Patent 420146 (1923); I.G. Farbenindustrie AG, German Patent 436829, 438478 (1922).
16. Scottish Dyes Ltd., German Patent 417068 (1921); Bad. Anilin- und Soda-Fabrik, German Patent 398485 (1922); Farbwerke Höchst, German Patent 420147 (1923); I.G. Farbenindustrie AG, German Patent 443610 (1923); 436887 (1924); 451122, 452449 (1922).
17. I.G. Farbenindustrie AG, Brit. Patent 480882 (1936); *Chem. Zbl.* **1938 II**, 1134.
18. Scholl, R., Müller, E. and Böttger, O., *Ber. dtsch. chem. Ges.* **68**, 45 (1935).

IV. 1.2,6.7-DIBENZOPEROPYRENE AND 1.2,11.12-DIBENZOPEROPYRENE

These two hydrocarbons are formed besides isomers if benzanthrone (I) is boiled with phosphorus oxychloride.[1] Although the hydrocarbons have been obtained in a pure state it is not certain which structure belongs to each of them.

Dibenzoperopyrene (II) or (III) (m.p. 334–335°) is separated from the mixture of its isomers by chromatography and crystallizes from xylene in orange needles. It dissolves in concentrated sulphuric acid to give a blue colour. The absorption spectrum is given in Fig. 168.

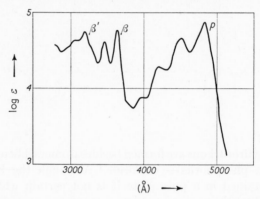

FIG. 168. Absorption spectrum of dibenzoperopyrene (m.p. 334–335°) in benzene: p, 4820 (4·87), 4530 (4·66), 4200 (4·28), 3960 (3·89); β, 3630 (4·78), 3460 (4·60); β', 3185 (4·75), 3060 (4·63).

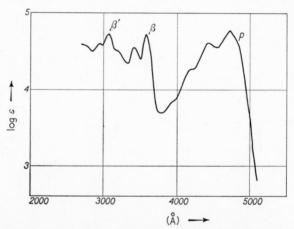

FIG. 169. Absorption spectrum of dibenzoperopyrene (m.p. 279°) in benzene: p, 4720 (4·78), 4450 (4·62), 4180 (4·27); β, 3580 (4·72), 3415 (4·55); β', 3070 (4·73), 2950 (4·59).

Dibenzoperopyrene (III) or (II) (m.p. 279°) crystallizes in golden brown needles and dissolves in concentrated sulphuric acid to form a blue solution. The absorption spectrum is given in Fig. 169.[1]

As by-products in the production of violanthrone (see p. 251) and isoviolanthrone (see p. 246) two compounds have been observed and

termed "violanthrone B" and "isoviolanthrone B". The structures
(IV) and (V) have been proposed for these compounds.[2] They may be
reduced to "violanthrene B" and "isoviolanthrene B" respectively.[3]

REFERENCES

1. Clar, E., Fell, G. S., Ironside, C. T. and Balsillie, A., *Tetrahedron* **10**, 26 (1960).
2. Lüttringhaus, A. and Neresheimer, H. *Liebigs Ann.* **473**, 259 (1929); Maki, T., *J. Soc. chem. Ind. Japan* (Suppl.) **35**, 577B (1932); **36**, 99B (1933); **37**, 213B (1934); **38**, 487B (1935); *Chem. Zbl.* **1933 I**, 1778; **1933 II**, 60; **1934 II**, 1300; **1936 I**, 4904; *Ber. dtsch. chem. Ges.* **71**, 2036 (1938).
3. Aoki, J., *Bull. chem. Soc. Japan* **12**, 1817, 1820 (1961).

V. 4.5,11.12-DIBENZOPEROPYRENE

Benzanthrone (I) condenses under the influence of aluminium chloride
and a reducing agent like zinc dust, activated magnesium, or aluminium.
Aluminium chloride can be applied as such in benzene solution or as
a compound with alkali chloride or pyridine. Besides the 4.5,11.12-
dibenzoperopyrene (II) which is the main product, a number of isomers
are formed (see p. 255).[1]

(I)

(II)   (III)

II—9

Dibenzoperopyrene (II) is also obtained as the main product if benz-anthrone is boiled with phosphorus oxychloride. The constitution of (II) is proved by the fact that it cannot be further cyclized in an aluminium chloride–sodium chloride melt as would be the case with its unknown

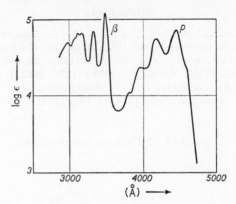

FIG. 170. Absorption spectrum of 4.5,11.12-dibenzoperopyrene in benzene: *p*, 4450 (4·86), 4180 (4·73), 3980 (4·36); *β*, 3480 (5·10), 3320 (4·85), 3165 (4·82), 3110 (4·82) 2960 (4·70).

isomer (III). The other combinations of two benzanthrene complexes are all known.[2]

4.5,11.12-Dibenzoperopyrene (II) crystallizes from xylene in long yellow needles (m.p. 343–345°), which dissolve with a blue colour in concentrated sulphuric acid. The absorption spectrum is given in Fig. 170.

REFERENCES

1. Clar, E., German Patent 621861 (1933); *Chem. Zbl.* **1936 II**, 3601; *Ber. dtsch. chem. Ges.* **76**, 458 (1943).
2. Clar, E., Fell, G. S., Ironside, C. T. and Balsillie, A., *Tetrahedron* **10**, 26 (1960); Campbell, N. and Woodham, A. A. *J. chem. Soc.* 843 (1952).

VI. 4.5,6.7,11.12,13.14-TETRABENZOPEROPYRENE

Tetrabenzoperopyrene can be synthesized in an analogous way to dibenzoperopyrene described above. 2.3,7.8-Dibenzoperinaphthene (I) in benzene solution adds three atoms of bromine to form a deep brown adduct. This decomposes when heated and gives tetrabenzoperopyrene (II).[1]

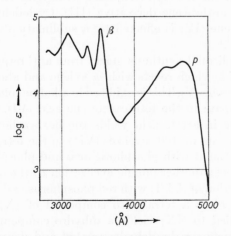

(I)   (II)   (III)

Tetrabenzoperopyrene (II) together with an isomer and hexabenzo-coronene are formed in a zinc-dust melt of 2.3,7.8-dibenzoperinaphthone (III).[2]

4.5,6.7,11.12,13.14-Tetrabenzoperopyrene (II) sublimes or crystal-lizes from xylene in orange prisms. It does not dissolve in concentrated sulphuric acid and it melts at 481–482° with the evolution of hydrogen and

FIG. 171. Absorption spectrum of 4.5,6.7,11.12,13.14-tetrabenzoperopyrene in benzene: p, 4670 (4·40), 4420 (4·34); β, 3530 (4·83), 3375 (4·61); β', 3090 (4·78).

the formation of hexabenzocoronene (see p. 95). The absorption spectrum is given in Fig. 171.[1] The hydrocarbon cannot be uniplanar and the resulting loss of aromatic (resonance) energy has been calculated to be 36·3 cal.[3]

REFERENCES

1. Clar, E. and Ironside, C. T., *Proc. chem. Soc.* 150 (1958); Clar, E., Ironside, C. T. and Zander, M., *J. chem. Soc.* 142 (1959).
2. Halleux, A., Martin, R. H. and King, G. S. D., *Helv. chim. Acta* **41**, 1177 (1958).
3. Ali, M. A. and Coulson, C. A., *J. chem. Soc.* 1558 (1959).

VII. 5.6,12.13-Dibenzoperopyrene

(*2.3,8.9-Dibenzocoronene*)

The reaction of *o*-tolyl magnesium bromide with 1,4-dimethylanthraquinone (I) gives the diol (II). Reduction with hydrogen iodide in acetic acid yields the anthracene derivative (III). Cyclodehydrogenation to dibenzoperopyrene (IV) is effected by a sublimation over palladium–charcoal at 500°.[1]

A more complicated synthesis starts from anthraquinone-1,5-dicarboxylic dichloride which reacts with *m*-xylene and aluminium chloride to give the dilactone (V). This is oxidized in alkaline solution with potassium permanganate to the tetracarboxylic acid (VI). Reduction with hydrogen iodide in acetic acid yields the hexacarboxylic acid (VII). Heating with oleum at 100° cyclizes (VII) to the tetracarboxylic acid (VIII) and treatment with phosphoric acid and phosphorus pentoxide at 340–350° effects another double cyclization to the dicarboxylic acid (IX). The reduction of (VIII) with red phosphorus and hydrogen iodide under pressure gives a tetrahydro compound of (X) and the same treatment applied to (IX) yields a dihydro compound of (X). Both reduction products can be dehydrogenated and decarboxylated with copper powder and soda-lime to dibenzoperopyrene (XI).[2]

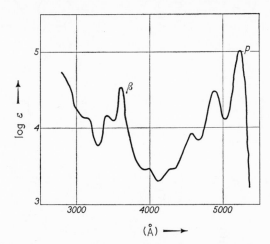

(I)   (II)

(III)   (IV)

5.6,12.13-Dibenzoperopyrene (IV) sublimes in green shining needles which dissolve in concentrated sulphuric acid to give a violet-blue solution which changes to red on standing. The solutions in 1-methylnaphthalene or trichlorobenzene are red with a green fluorescence. They

Fig. 172. Absorption spectrum of 5.6,12.13-dibenzoperopyrene in 1-methylnaphthalene: p, 5240 (5·02), 4880 (4·50), 4580 (3·94); β, 3620 (4·54), 3440 (4·16); from 3400 Å in benzene.

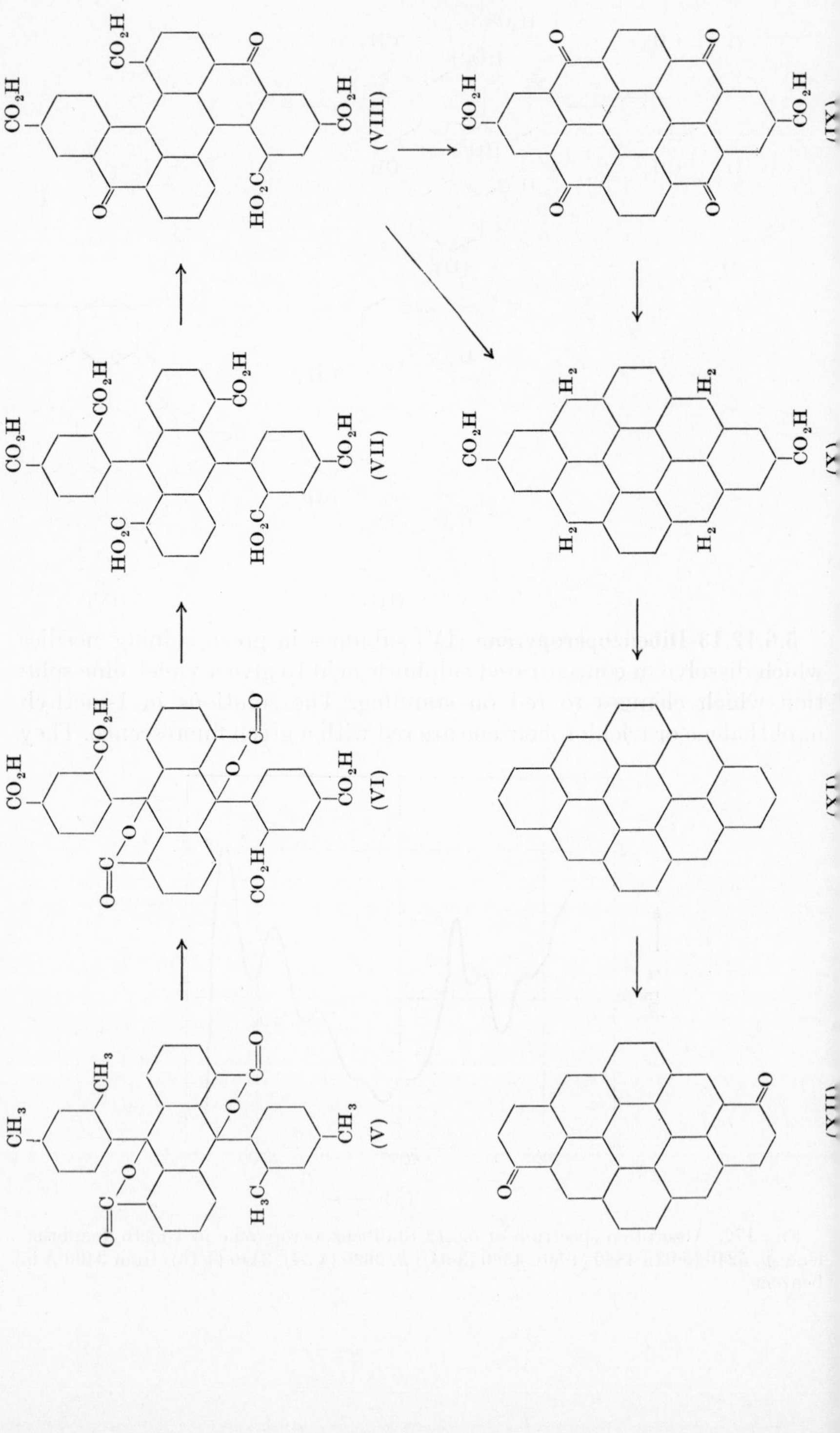

CO₂H CO₂H (VIII) CO₂H HO₂C

CO₂H CO₂H (VII) CO₂H HO₂C HO₂C

CO₂H CO₂H (VI) CO₂H CO₂H

CH₃ CH₃ (V) CH₃ H₃C

CO₂H CO₂H (XI) CO₂H

CO₂H H₂ H₂ (X) CO₂H H₂ H₂

(IX)

(XII)

3,6,12,15-Tetraketoperylene (IX) separates in greenish-yellow needles which dissolve in concentrated sulphuric acid to give a violet-blue solution which changes to red on standing. The oxidation is limited. Benzil, however, is not oxidized under similar conditions.

are photo-oxidizable. The solution in trichlorobenzene gives a dark blue adduct with bromine. The absorption spectrum is given in Fig. 172.

Dibenzoperopyrenequinone can be prepared from the hydrocarbon in concentrated sulphuric acid or with dilute nitric acid or with chromic acid in acetic acid. It crystallizes from trichlorobenzene in red needles which give a blue vat with alkaline sodium dithionite solution. The structure (XII) is assumed for the quinone which yields coronene-tetracarboxylic acid on further oxidation.

REFERENCES

1. Clar, E., Fell, G. S., Ironside, C. T. and Balsillie, A., *Tetrahedron* **10**, 26 (1960).
2. Scholl, R. and Meyer, K., *Ber. dtsch. chem. Ges.* **65**, 902 (1932); Scholl, R., Meyer, K. and Winkler, W., *Liebigs Ann.* **494**, 201 (1932).

VIII. 2.3,5.6,8.9-TRIBENZOPEROPYRENE

A melt of methylbenzanthrone (I) with potassium hydroxide and glucose or with naphthalene, potassium hydroxide and manganese dioxide yields dimethylviolanthrone (II). Cyclization to (III) is carried out in boiling nitrobenzene with barium oxide.[1]

A quinone with the properties of (III) can be prepared from methylene-anthrone (IV), which is submitted to a diene synthesis with cyclohexa-diene to give the compound (V). Cyclization to (VI) is carried out in an alkali melt, which may contain sodium nitrite as an oxidizing agent.[2]

A diphenyl derivative of the quinone (III) is obtained if benzoyl-benzanthrone (VII) is submitted to a fusion with alcoholic potassium hydroxide.[3]

(I)   (II)   (III)

(IV)   (V)   (VI)

(VII)   (VIII)

2.3,5.6,8.9-Tribenzoperopyrene-1,10-quinone (III) is red-brown and dissolves in concentrated sulphuric acid to give a violet solution. Alkaline sodium dithionite forms a blue vat which dyes cotton bordeaux red. The diphenyl derivative (VIII) has similar properties but dyes cotton bright red.

REFERENCES

1. Hey, D. H., Nicholls, R. J. and Pritchett, C. W., *J. chem. Soc.* 97 (1944).
2. Straly, J. M. (to Eastman Kodak Co.), Amer. Patent 2637733, 2659735 (1953); *Amer. Abstr.* 7788 (1953); 3037 (1954).
3. I.G. Farbenindustrie AG, German Patent 718704 (1939); *Chem. Zbl.* **1942 II**, 101.

IX. 1.14,7.8-DIBENZOPEROPYRENE

Two molecules of pyrene or 3-chloropyrene or 3-bromopyrene can be condensed in a sodium chloride–aluminium chloride melt.[1,2] The resulting two dibenzoperopyrenes (II) and (III) can be separated by

chromatography or by their very different reactivity against maleic anhydride.[2] 1.14,7.8-Dibenzoperopyrene (II) reacts in boiling xylene with maleic anhydride without the use of chloranil. The adduct can be extracted with alkali. The different reactivities of these two hydrocarbons can be compared with the reactivities of 2.3,8.9- and 2.3,9.10-dibenzoperylene (see pp. 53, 56).

II—9*

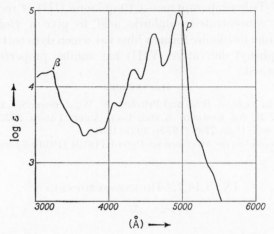

FIG. 173. Absorption spectrum of 1.14,7.8-dibenzoperopyrene in 1,2,4-trichloro-benzene: p, 4950 (4·97), 4620 (4·69), 4350 (4·23), 4075 (3·79), 3750 (3·44); β, 3230 (4·21).

1.14,7.8-Dibenzoperopyrene (II) forms orange crystals from trichloro-benzene or 1-methylnaphthalene which decompose above 400°. The solution in concentrated sulphuric acid is violet. The absorption spectrum is given in Fig. 173. The two hydrocarbons are also obtained from the pyrolysis of pyrene.[3]

REFERENCES

1. Ammerer, L. and Zinke, A., *Mh. Chem.* **84**, 25 (1953).
2. Clar, E. and Kühn, O., *Liebigs Ann.* **601**, 181 (1956).
3. Lang, K. F. and Buffleb, H., *Ber. dtsch. chem. Ges.* **90**, 2894 (1957).

X. 1.14,10.11-DIBENZOPEROPYRENE

This hydrocarbon can be obtained free of its isomer by a short sodium chloride–aluminium chloride melt of 3,3'-dipyrenyl (I).[1] The latter is prepared from the Grignard compound of 3-iodopyrene and cuprous chloride[2] or from 3-bromopyrene and copper powder.[1,3]

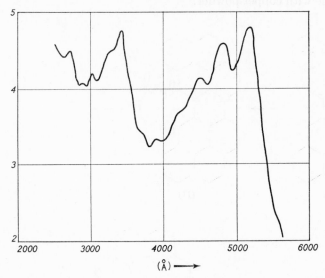

1.14,10.11-Dibenzoperopyrene (II) forms red needles (m.p. 350°) from xylene which dissolve in concentrated sulphuric acid to give a bluish-green solution. The absorption spectrum is given in Fig. 174.

Fig. 174. Absorption spectrum of 1.14,10.11-dibenzoperopyrene in benzene: p, 5200 (4·81), 4820 (4·59), 4500 (4·14); 3900 (3·35); β, 3425 (4·77), 3280 (4·51), 3020 (4·21), in dioxane: β', 2740 (4·52).

REFERENCES

1. Clar, E. and Kühn, O., *Liebigs Ann.* **601**, 181 (1956).
2. Lund, H. and Berg, A., *Kgl. danske Vidensk. Selsk. mat.-fysiske Medd.* No. 15 (1946); *Amer. Abstr.* 6072 (1946).
3. Ammerer, L. and Zinke, A., *Mh. Chem.* **84**, 25 (1953).

XI. 3.4,5.6,7.8-Tribenzoperopyrene

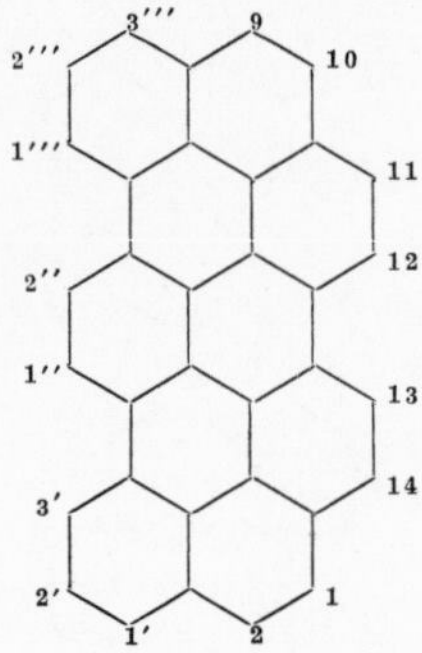

Dibenzoperopyrene (I) reacts readily with maleic anhydride to form an adduct which probably has the structure (II). This is immediately dehydrogenated in the presence of chloranil and gives the anhydride (III). The decarboxylation to the hydrocarbon (IV) takes place in boiling quinoline with copper powder.[1]

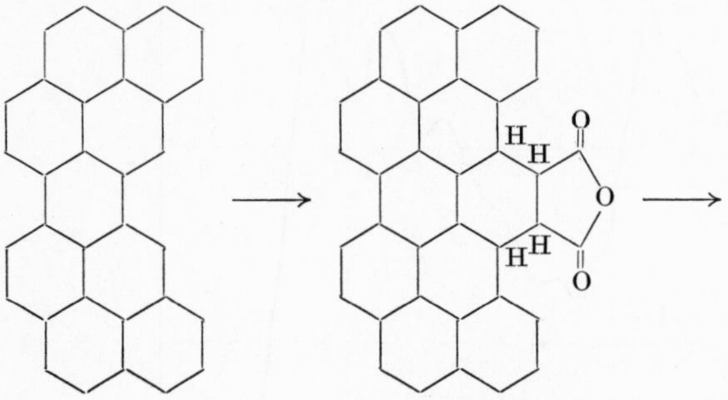

(I)   (II)

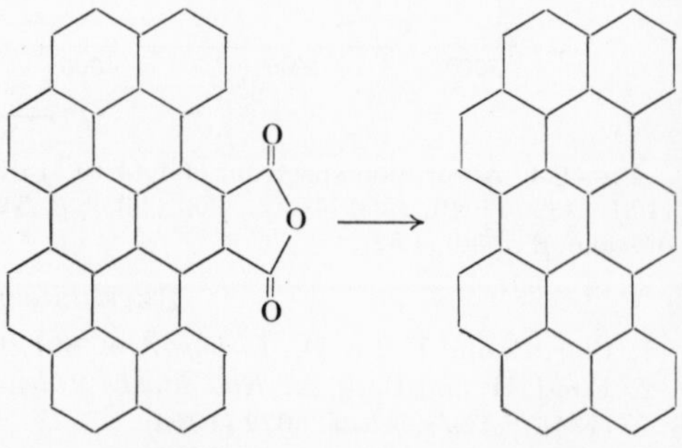

(III)   (IV)

3.4,5.6,7.8-Tribenzoperopyrene (III) sublimes or crystallizes from trichlorobenzene in golden yellow leaflets, which do not melt below

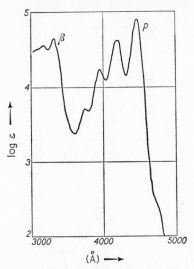

FIG. 175. Absorption spectrum of 3.4,5.6,7.8-tribenzoperopyrene in 1,2,4-trichlorobenzene: p, 4460 (4·89), 4200 (4·60), 3950 (4·23), 3750 (3·70); β, 3310 (4·65).

510°. They are insoluble in concentrated sulphuric acid. The absorption spectrum is given in Fig. 175. The yellow solution in trichlorobenzene shows a blue fluorescence.[1]

REFERENCE
1. Clar, E. and Kühn, O., *Liebigs Ann.* **601**, 181 (1956).

XII. 3.4,5.6,10.11,12.13-TETRABENZOPEROPYRENE

1,5-Dichloroanthroquinone reacts with 2-methyl-1-naphthyl magnesium bromide to give the diol (I) which is reduced by hydriodic acid to the

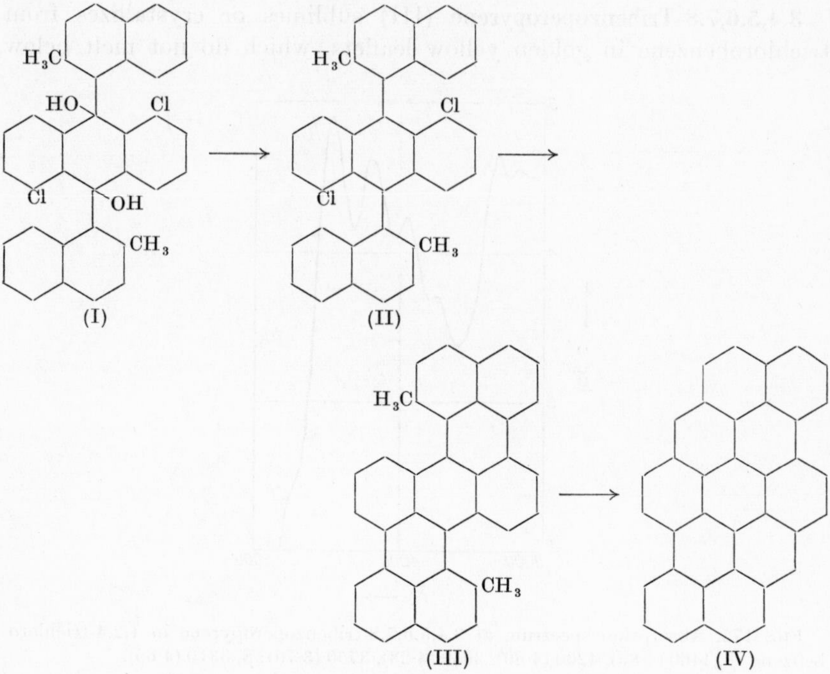

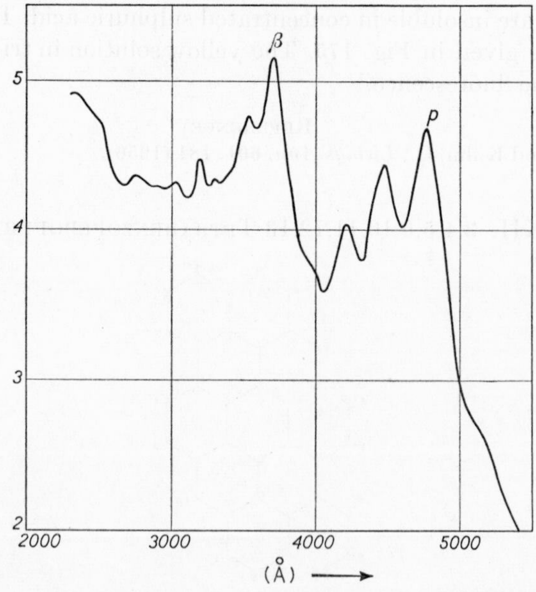

FIG. 176. Absorption spectrum of 3.4,5.6,10.11,12.13-tetrabenzoperopyrene in 1-methylnaphthalene: *p*, 4780 (4·68), 4490 (4·44), 4220 (4·04); *β*, 3715 (5·14), 3540 (4·76); in dioxane: 3200 (4·48), 3020 (4·32), 2750 (4·36).

anthracene derivative (II). A short treatment of this with potassium hydroxide in boiling quinoline yields the blue 7,7'-dimethyl-1.9,5.10-di-(*peri*-naphthylene)-anthracene (III). A longer treatment in the presence of molecular oxygen leads to a further double cyclization involving the methyl groups and yielding tetrabenzoperopyrene (IV).[1]

3.4,5.6,10.11,12.13-Tetrabenzoperopyrene (IV) crystallizes from trichlorobenzene in feathery orange needles (m.p. 487–488°), which dissolve in concentrated sulphuric acid to give a green solution. The yellow solution in trichlorobenzene shows a strong green fluorescence. The absorption spectrum is given in Fig. 176.

REFERENCE

1. Clark, E. and Kelly, W., *J. chem. Soc.* 3875 (1956).

XIII. DINAPHTHO-(7'.1':1.13); (1".7":6.8)-PEROPYRENE

Di-(*peri*-naphthylene)-anthracene (I) condenses twice with boiling maleic anhydride and chloranil as a dehydrogenating agent to give the dianhydride (II). Decarboxylation in boiling quinoline with copper powder yields dinaphthoperopyrene (III). If the decarboxylation is carried out by sublimation with soda-lime, circumanthracene (see p. 108) is obtained in addition to dinaphthoperopyrene.[1]

Dinaphthoperopyrene (III) is the main condensation product if naphthanthrone (IV) is reduced with zinc dust in a sodium chloride–aluminium chloride melt.[2]

Dinaphtho-(7'.1':1.13); (1".7":6.8)-peropyrene (III) crystallizes from xylene in orange-red needles (m.p. 338–339°), which show a green fluorescence in solution. It dissolves in warm concentrated sulphuric acid to give a magenta solution. The absorption spectrum is given in Fig. 177.

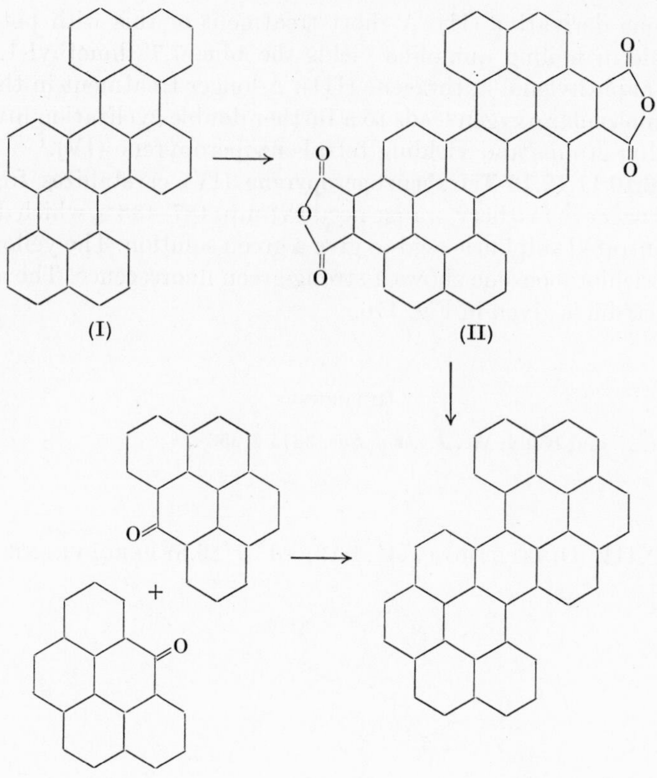

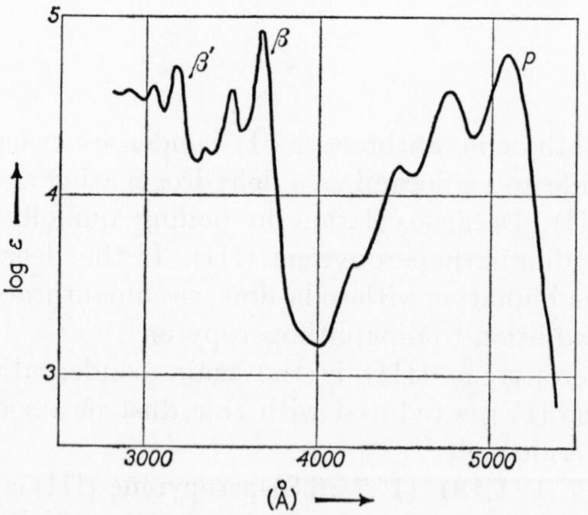

FIG. 177. Absorption spectrum of dinaphtho-(7′.1′ : 1.13); (1″.7″ : 6.8)-pyrene in benzene : p, 5100 (4·80), 4760 (4·59), 4470 (4·16); β, 3670 (4·92), 3490 (4·58), 3340 (4·26); β′, 3170 (4·72), 3040 (4·61), 2900 (4·59).

REFERENCES

1. Clar, E., Kelly, W., Monteath Robertson, J. and Rossmann, M. G., *J. chem. Soc.* 3878 (1956).
2. Clar, E., Fell, G. S., Ironside, C. T. and Balsillie, A., *Tetrahedron* **10**, 26 (1960).

XIV. DINAPHTHO-$(7'.1':1.13)$; $(1''.7'':9.11)$-PEROPYRENE

The reduction and condensation of naphthanthrone (I) in a sodium chloride–zinc chloride melt with zinc dust yields besides the dinaphtho-$(7'.1':1.13)$; $(1''.7'':6.8)$-peropyrene described above, another hydrocarbon which was given the structure (II). However, the formula (III) cannot be excluded.[1]

(I)   (II)   (III)

The course of the reaction is assumed from a comparison with the analogous condensation of benzanthrone (see pp. 255, 257).

Dinaphtho-$(7'.1':1.13)$; $(1''.7'':9.11)$-peropyrene (II) forms reddish-brown crystals from xylene (m.p. 358–360°), which dissolve in concentrated sulphuric acid to form a dark green solution. The absorption spectrum is given in Fig. 178.

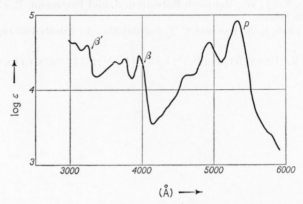

Fig. 178. Absorption spectrum of dinaphtho-(7′.1′:1.13); (1″.7″:9.11)-peropyrene in benzene: p, 5330 (4·93), 4950 (4·64), 4650 (4·20); β, 3960 (4·48), 3760 (4·42), 3630 (4·37); β', 3240 (4·60).

REFERENCE

1. Clar, E., Fell, G. S., Ironside, C. T. and Balsillie, A., *Tetrahedron* **10**, 26 (1960).

XV. DINAPHTHO-(1′.7′:2.4); (1″.7″:9.11)-PEROPYRENE AND DINAPHTHO-(1′.7′:2.4); (2″.8″:7.9)-PEROPYRENE

The quinone (II) derived from the first mentioned hydrocarbon is obtained if bromonaphthanthrone (I) is fused with alcoholic potassium hydroxide at 115–120°. The quinone (IV) can be prepared from naphthanthrone in a melt with potassium hydroxide and potassium acetate at 240–250°. The quinone (II) is purified through the vat and the quinone (IV) by chromatography in trichlorobenzene.

(I)   (II)   (III)   (IV)

Dinaphtho-(1′.7′:2.4);(1″.7″:9.11)-peropyrene-1,8-quinone (II) forms a violet-black powder, which dissolves in concentrated sulphuric acid to give a bluish-green solution. A blue-green vat is produced with alkaline sodium dithionite solution.

Dinaphtho-(1′.7′:2.4); (2″.8″:7.9)-peropyrene-1,10-quinone (IV) is a bluish-black powder which dissolves in concentrated sulphuric acid to give a violet solution with absorption bands at 5320 and 7400 Å. Alkaline sodium dithionite gives a bluish-green vat.[1]

REFERENCE

1. Bradley, W. and Sutcliffe, F., *J. chem. Soc.* 2118 (1951).

XVI. DINAPHTHOPEROPYRENES

Naphtho-(1'.2':7.8)-perinaphthone (I) condenses in a melt of potassium hydroxide, potassium acetate and ethanol to form dibenzoviolanthrone (II) and dibenzoisoviolanthrone (III). The parent hydrocarbons (IV) and (V) of these quinones are obtained by a zinc-dust melt. The hydrocarbon (V) can also be prepared from a tetrahydroxy derivative of (III) which is formed if a tribromo derivative of (I) is submitted to a melt with potassium hydroxide in glycol.

(I)   (II)   (III)

Dinaphtho-(1'.2':1.2); (2".1":9.10)-peropyrene (IV) forms red needles (m.p. 374–376°) which have the following absorption bands: 5090, 4750, 4440, 4180, 3880, 3670, 3440 and 3280Å.

Dinaphtho-(2'.1':2.3); (2".1":9.10)-peropyrene (V) crystallizes in dark red needles (m.p. 440–444°) which have the following absorption bands: 5200, 4860, 4550, 4500, 3840, 3660, 3370 and 3200Å.

Dibenzoviolanthrone (II) forms bluish black crystals and has absorption bands at 7300, 6500 and 3700Å.

Dibenzoisoviolanthrone (III) is bluish green and has absorption bands at 6500 and 3650 Å.

The two hydrocarbons (VI) and (VII) are formed as by-products if naphthoperinaphthone (I) is submitted to a melt of potassium hydroxide,

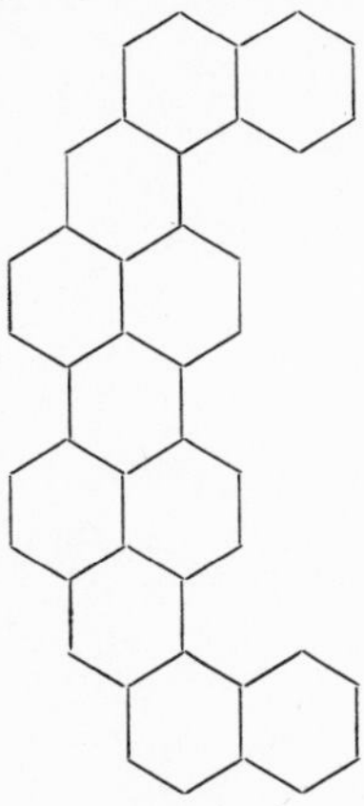

(IV)

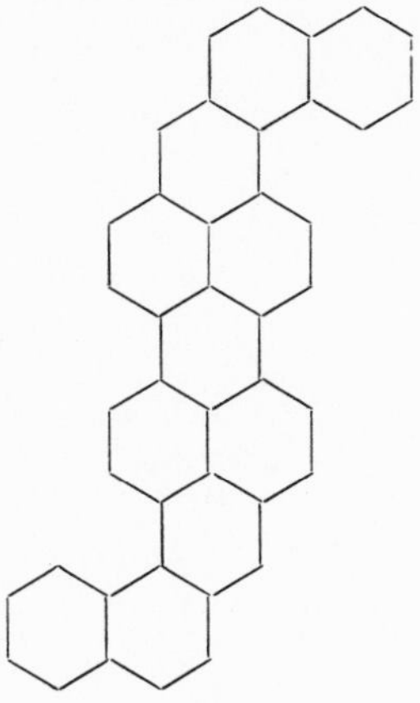

(V)

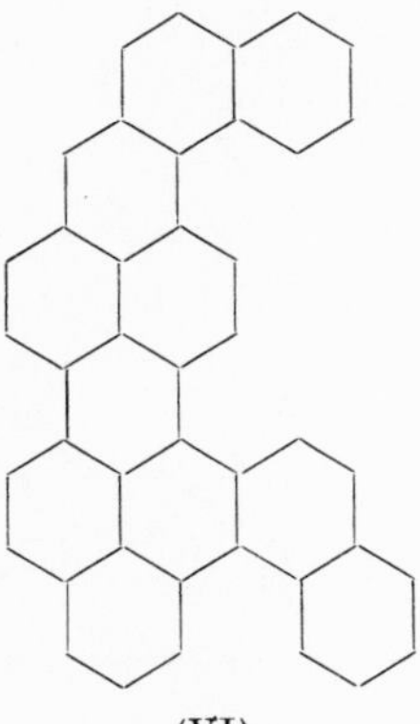

(VI)

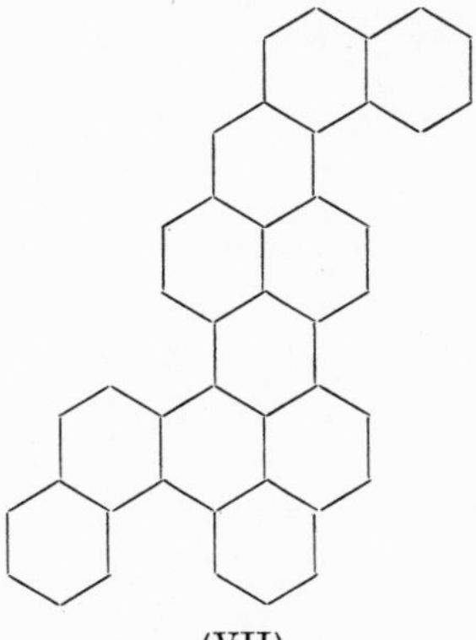

(VII)

potassium acetate and manganese dioxide. The hydrocarbon (m.p. 332–334°) forms orange needles, does not dissolve in concentrated sulphuric acid and has absorption bands at: 4950, 4630, 4100, 3800, 3620, 3300 and 3150Å. The hydrocarbon (m.p. 344–346°) crystallizes in golden yellow needles and has absorption bands at 4780, 4650, 4500, 3650 and 3500Å.[1]

REFERENCE

1. Stephenson, M. and Sutcliffe, F. K., *J. chem. Soc.* 3516 (1962).

PART V

peri-Condensed Hydrocarbons consisting only of Six-membered Rings and derived from Fundamental Systems with Four Benzenoid Rings

CHAPTER 37

Hydrocarbons derived from Quaterphenyl

QUATERPHENYL

Quaterphenyl is formed by pyrolysis if benzene is distilled through a glowing iron tube[1] or over an electrically heated wire.[2] 4-Bromodiphenyl and sodium yield quaterphenyl[3] as well as 4-iododiphenyl with copper powder at $250-270°$[4] or with magnesium.[5] 4-Bromo- or iododophenyl, hydrazine and methanolic potassium hydroxide give quaterphenyl.[6] It is also obtained from dibenzoylperoxide and benzene[7] or by reduction of diazotized 4-aminodiphenyl.[8] 1,8-Diphenyloctatetraene (I) reacts with maleic anhydride to form the adduct (II). Dehydrogenation with potassium ferricyanide and decarboxylation with soda-lime yield quaterphenyl.[9]

(II)

Quaterphenyl is obtained by pyrolysis of the diol (III) with a catalyst consisting of chromium oxide, magnesium oxide and aluminium oxide at $550°$.[10]

Quaterphenyl is formed by oxidation of lithium diphenyl with molecular oxygen.[11]

Quaterphenyl sublimes in colourless crystals (m.p. 318°), which dissolve without colour in concentrated sulphuric acid. The absorption spectrum is given in Fig. 179.

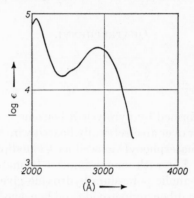

Fig. 179. Absorption spectrum of quaterphenyl in n-heptane: p, 2900 (4·56); β, 2060 (4·94).

A number of alkyl-quaterphenyls have been synthesized: 2-methyl- (m.p. 172–173°), 3-methyl- (m.p. 245–266°), 4-methylquaterphenyl (m.p. 328–330°), 2,2″-dimethyl- (m.p. 150–151°), 3,3″-dimethyl- (m.p. 214–215°), and 4,4″-dimethylquaterphenyl (m.p. 338–340°).[12] Quaterphenyl reacts with benzoyl chloride and aluminium chloride to give 4,4″-dibenzoylquaterphenyl.[13]

REFERENCES

1. Schmidt, H. and Schultz, G., *Liebigs Ann.* **203**, 134 (1880).
2. Meyer, H. and Hofmann, A., *Mh. Chem.* **37**, 711 (1916).
3. Noyes, A. A. and Ellis, R. M., *J. Amer. chem. Soc.* **17**, 620 (1895).
4. Ullmann, F. and Meyer, G. M., *Liebigs Ann.* **332**, 52 (1904); Pummerer, R., and Seligsberger, L., *Ber. dtsch. chem. Ges.* **67**, 2477 (1931).
5. Rupe, H. and Iselin, M., *Ber. dtsch. chem. Ges.* **49**, 45 (1916).
6. Busch, M. and Schmidt, W., *Ber. dtsch. chem. Ges.* **62**, 2618 (1929).
7. Gelissen, H. and Hermans, P. H., *Ber. dtsch. chem. Ges.* **58**, 290, 293, 764 (1925).
8. Gerngross, O., Schachnow, C., and Jonas, R., *Ber. dtsch. chem. Ges.* **57**, 749 (1924).
9. Kuhn, R., *Liebigs Ann.* **705**, 132 (1929); Kuhn, R. and Wagner-Jauregg, T., *Ber. dtsch. chem. Ges.* **63**, 2662 (1930).
10. Shvartsberg, M. S., Vasilev, E. K. and Kotlyarevskii, I. L., *J. gen. Chem. U.S.S.R.* (translation) **31**, 1186 (1961).
11. Müller, E. and Töpel, T., *Ber. dtsch. chem. Ges.* **72**, 282 (1939).
12. Gilmont, H. and Weipert, E. A., *J. Amer. chem. Soc.* **79**, 2281 (1957); Pummerer, R. and Seligsberger, L., *Ber. dtsch. chem. Ges.* **64**, 2477 (1931).
13. Müller, E. and Pfanz, H., *Ber. dtsch. chem. Ges.* **74**, 1075 (1941).

CHAPTER 38

Hydrocarbons derived from Quaterrylene

I. QUATERRYLENE

Two molecules of perylene (I) condense in a sodium chloride–aluminium chloride melt at 150° to form quaterrylene (II) and a more readily soluble hydrocarbon as by-product.[1]

(I)   (II)

Quaterrylene sublimes *in vacuo* or crystallizes from boiling pyrene in green shining plates (m.p. > 570°), which dissolve in concentrated sulphuric acid to give a green-blue solution. The absorption spectrum is given in Fig. 180.

The crystal structure of quaterrylene has been determined by X-rays[2] and the C—C distances measured.[3]

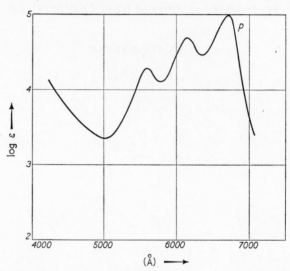

FIG. 180. Absorption spectrum of quaterrylene in l-methylnaphthalene: at 150°: p, 6700 (5·00), 6100 (4·70), 5580 (4·30). (Intensities $\log(\epsilon + x)$ at 18°: 6730, 6150, 5630.)

REFERENCES

1. Clar, E., Kelly, W. and Laird, R. M., *Mh. Chem.* **80**, 391 (1956).
2. Clar, E. and Speakman, J. C., *J. chem. Soc.* 2492 (1958).
3. Shrivastava, H. N. and Speakman, J. C., *Proc. roy. Soc.* **A257**, 477 (1960).

II. 1.20,16.17-DIBENZOQUATERRYLENE

The decarboxylation of benzoperylene-dicarboxylic acid (III) with aqueous potassium hydroxide at 350° under pressure yields, besides 1.12-benzoperylene, a violet hydrocarbon which is probably formed via the tetracarboxylic acid (IV). The condensation appears to be similar to the formation of perylene-tetracarboxylic di-imide from naphthalimide (see p. 30). The structure (V) is more likely than an isomeric structure because the hydrocarbon reacts readily with maleic anhydride, with or without the addition of chloranil.

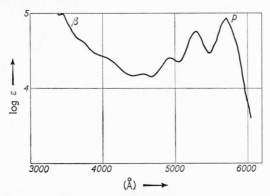

1.20,16.17-Dibenzoquaterrylene (V) sublimes *in vacuo* in violet leaflets which do not dissolve in concentrated sulphuric acid. The absorption spectrum is given in Fig. 181. The red-violet solution in trichlorobenzene is photo-oxidizable.[1]

FIG. 181. Absorption spectrum of 1.20,16.17-dibenzoquaterrylene in 1-methylnaphthalene: p, 5770 (4·93), 5300 (4·76), 4940 (4·40); β, 3440 (5·00).

REFERENCE

1. McCallum, A., Thesis, Glasgow (1963).

CHAPTER 39

Hydrocarbons derived from 2.3,7.8-Di-(peri-naphthylene)-pyrene

I. 2.3,7.8-Di-(peri-NAPHTHYLENE)-PYRENE

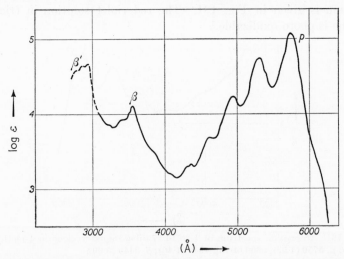

Pyrene (I) can be condensed twice with 1-bromonaphthalene in a sodium chloride–aluminium chloride melt to give 2.3,7.8-di-(peri-naphthylene)-pyrene which is separated from by-products by sublimation.[1]

FIG. 182. Absorption spectrum of 2.3,7.8-di-(peri-naphthylene)-pyrene in 1,2,4-trichlorobenzene: p, 5750 (5·07), 5300 (4·75), 4930 (4·24), 4625 (3·70); β, 3550 (4·11), in benzene: β′, 2930 (4·67).

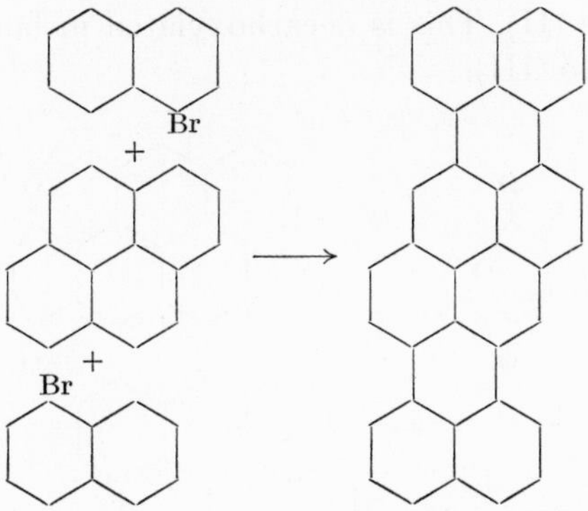

(I)   (II)

2.3,7.8-Di-(*peri*-naphthylene)-pyrene (II) crystallizes from trichlorobenzene in dark violet crystals (m.p. > 520°), which dissolve in concentrated sulphuric acid to give a blue solution. The reddish-violet solution
in trichlorobenzene shows an orange fluorescence. The absorption
spectrum is given in Fig. 182.[1]

REFERENCE

1. Clar, E. and Kühn, O., *Liebigs Ann.* **601**, 181 (1956).

II. DIPYRENO-(1′.3′ : 10.2) ; (1″.3″ : 5.7)-PYRENE

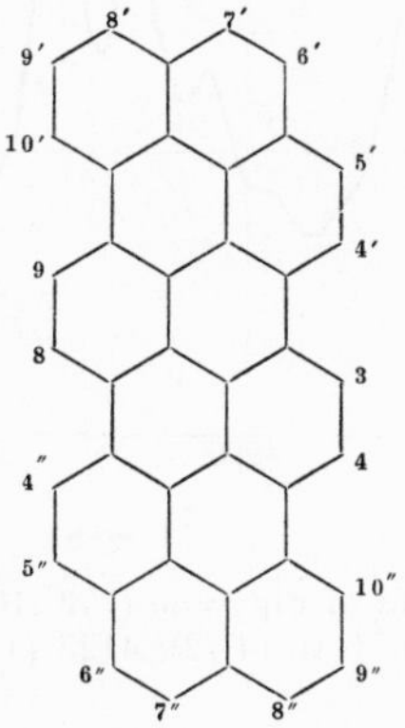

The violet di-(*peri*-naphthylene)-pyrene (I) reacts readily with boiling
maleic anhydride and chloranil as a dehydrogenating agent and yields

the dianhydride (II). This is decarboxylated in boiling quinoline with copper powder to (III).

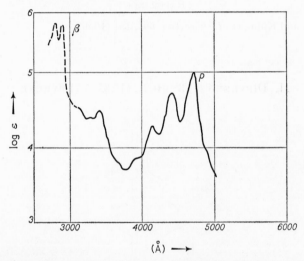

(I)   (II)   (III)

Dipyreno-(1′.3′:10.2); (1″.3″:5.7)-pyrene (III) forms yellow crystals from 1-methylnaphthalene or trichlorobenzene which do not melt below 510°. They are insoluble in cold concentrated sulphuric acid. The absorption spectrum is given in Fig. 183.[1]

Fig. 183. Absorption spectrum of dipyreno-(1′.3′:10:2); (1″.3″:5.7)-pyrene in 1,2,4-trichlorobenzene: p, 4700 (4·99), 4410 (4·72), 4125 (4·27), 3400 (4·48), in benzene: $β$, 2880 (5·63), 2790 (5·66).

REFERENCE

1. Clar, E. and Kühn, O., *Liebigs Ann.* **601**, 181 (1956).

PART VI

peri-Condensed Hydrocarbons consisting only of Six-membered
Rings and derived from Fundamental Systems with Five and
Six Benzenoid Rings

CHAPTER 40:

Quinquiphenyl and Sexiphenyl

QUINQUIPHENYL

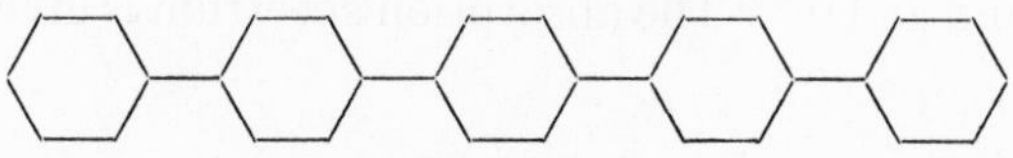

Quinquiphenyl and other polyphenyls are formed by reduction of benzenediazonium sulphate in concentrated sulphuric acid and acetic

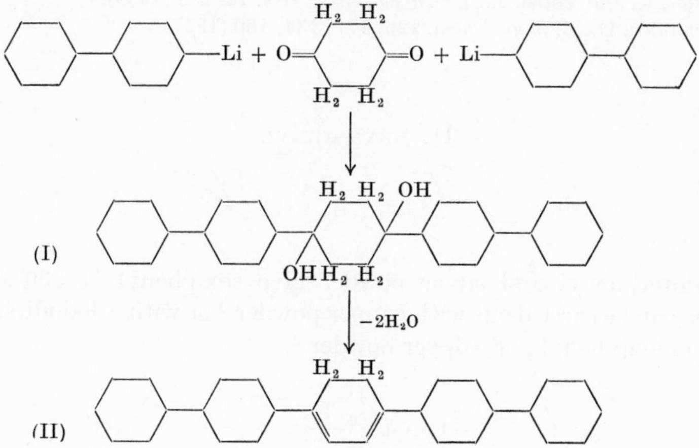

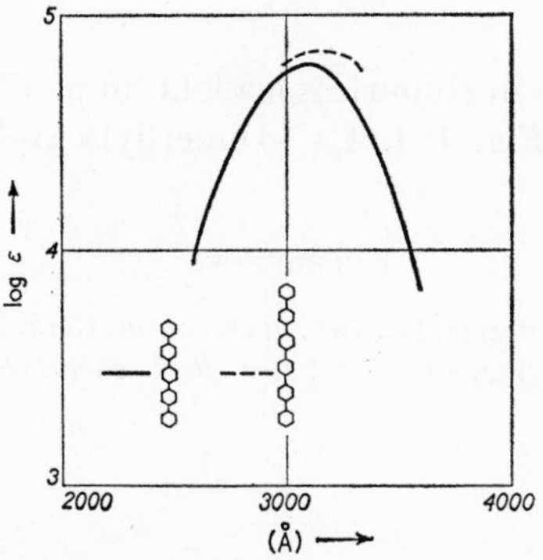

(I)

$-2H_2O$

(II)

FIG. 184. Absorption spectra of: quinquiphenyl in chloroform (full line): p, 3100 (4·79) and sexiphenyl in chloroform (broken line): p, 3180 (4·83) (Gillam, A. E. and Hey, D. H., *J. chem. Soc.* 1170 (1939)).

acid with formic acid and copper powder.[1] A mixture of 4-iododiphenyl, 4-iodoterphenyl and silver powder gives quinquiphenyl.[1] 4-Diphenyl lithium and cyclohexanedione yield the diol (I). This is easily dehydrated to the dihydro compound (II) which is dehydrogenated to quinquiphenyl by heating with selenium. Even contact with air achieves dehydrogenation.[2]

Quinquiphenyl crystallizes from quinoline in colourless needles, which sinter at 365°, melt to a crystalline liquid at 380°, and to an amorphous liquid at 410°.[3] The absorption spectrum is given in Fig. 184.

REFERENCES

1. Gerngross, O. and Dunkel, M., *Ber. dtsch. chem. Ges.* **57**, 730 (1924); Gerngross, O., Schachnow, C. and Jonas, R., *Ber. dtsch. chem. Ges.* **57**, 749 (1924).
2. Müller, E. and Töpel, T., *Ber. dtsch. chem. Ges.* **72**, 282 (1939).
3. Vorländer, D., *Z. phys. Chem.* **126**, 471; **134**, 160 (1927).

II. Sexiphenyl

4-Iodoterphenyl and silver powder give sexiphenyl at 330°.[1] The reaction can be carried out with copper powder,[2] or with 4-iododiphenyl, 4,4'-di-iododiphenyl and copper powder.[2]

Sexiphenyl

Sexiphenyl sublimes in colourless leaflets (m.p. 475°). The absorption spectrum is given in Fig. 184. 4,4''''-Dimethylsexiphenyl has a m.p. of 469°.[2]

REFERENCES

1. Pummerer, R. and Bittner, K., *Ber. dtsch. chem. Gers.* **57**, 84 (1924).
2. Pummerer, R. and Seligsberger, L., *Ber. dtsch. chem. Ges.* **64**, 2477 (1931).

PART VII

peri-Condensed Hydrocarbons consisting of Six- and Five-membered Rings in which no Carbon Atom Is Linked with more than One Hydrogen Atom

Chapter 41

Hydrocarbons Containing One Five-membered Ring

I. Fluoranthene

Fluoranthene is abundantly present in coal-tar, where it was discovered long ago.[1] Almost simultaneously it was isolated from "Stupp", a by-product in the production of mercury, in Idria.[2] Fluoranthene was assigned the wrong formula (I), which remained unchallenged for many years.

The correct structure of fluoranthene was established by synthesis. The sodium compound of fluoro-9-carboxylic ester (II) reacts with 2-chloropropionic ester to form the ester (III). Hydrolysis and decarboxylation give the fluorenyl-propionic acid (IV), the chloride of which can be cyclized with aluminium chloride to (V). Clemmensen reduction leads to tetrahydrofluoranthene (VI), and dehydrogenation by distillation over heated lead oxide gives fluoranthene (VII).[3] The fluorenyl-propionic acid (IV) is more easily obtainable by the addition of acrylonitrile to fluorenecarboxylic ester.[4]

2-Methylcyclohexanone reacts with 1-naphthyl magnesium bromide (VIII) to give the carbinol (IX). Dehydration with KHSO$_4$ yields (X) and cyclization with aluminium chloride leads to (XI). Dehydrogenation with selenium also removes the methyl group, which is essential for the preceding reaction.[5]

Cyclodehydrogenation with palladium–charcoal at 450°, or with a chromium oxide–aluminium oxide catalyst at 500°, yields fluoranthene from 1-phenylnaphthalene (XII), its tetrahydro derivative (XIII), or from tetrahydrofluoranthene (XIV). The latter compound is obtained from (XV) with hydrobromic acid.[6]

Fluorene adds maleic anhydride to form the adduct (XVI). Cyclization with aluminium chloride in nitrobenzene gives the acid (XVII) and Clemmensen reduction (XVIII). Dehydrogenation with sulphur leads to the acid (XIX) and decarboxylation to fluoranthene (VII).[7]

(XVI)   (XVII)

(XVIII)   (XIX)   (VII)

Acenaphthenequinone reacts with methyl magnesium iodide to give the diol (XX). Splitting out two molecules of water and addition of maleic anhydride take place in one reaction. The resulting anhydride (XXI) is dehydrogenated to (XXII) and decarboxylated to fluoranthene (VII).[8]

(XX)

(XXI)   (XXII)   (VII)

The carbinol (XXIII) reacts in an analogous way with maleic anhydride and gives fluoranthene-dicarboxylic anhydride (XXIV).[9] Decarboxylation yields fluoranthene (VII).

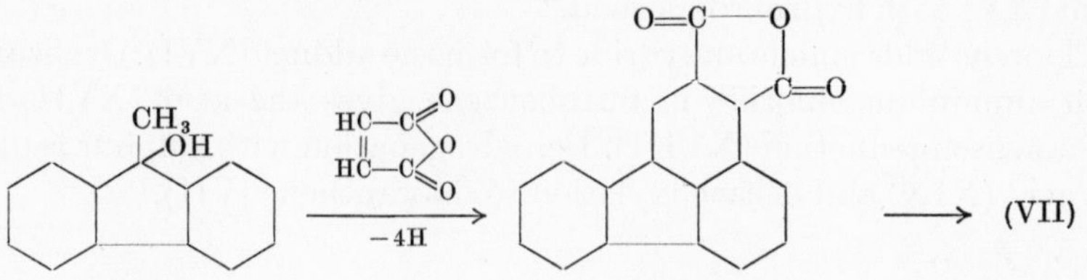

(XXIII)   (XXIV)   (VII)

The condensation of 1-iodonaphthalene and *o*-bromonitrobenzene with copper powder at 240–250° gives nitrophenylnaphthalene (XXV). The reduction of the nitro group with stannic chloride or with hydrogen and palladium yields the corresponding amine. Diazotization effects cyclization to fluoranthene in 48% yield.[10]

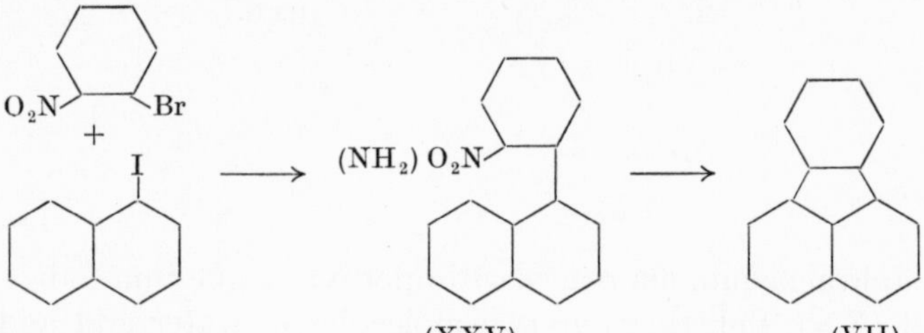

(XXV)   (VII)

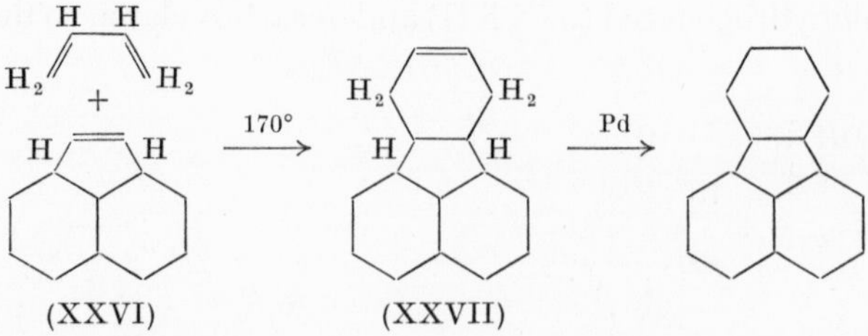

(XXVI)   (XXVII)

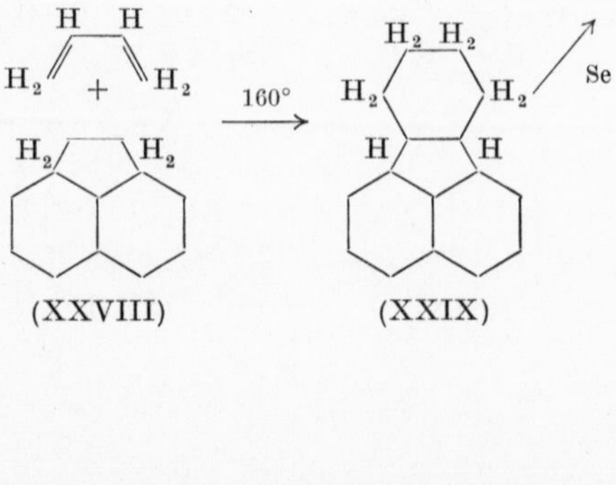

(XXVIII)   (XXIX)

Fluoranthene can be synthesized also from acenaphthylene (XXVI) and butadiene which give the tetrahydro compound (XXVII). Dehydrogenation with palladium yields fluoranthene.[11] Acenaphthene (XXVIII) also condenses with butadiene to form the hexahydrofluoranthene (XXIX) which is dehydrogenated to fluoranthene with selenium.[12]

Fluoranthene, which is in the coal-tar fraction preceding pyrene, can be separated by its compound with sodium which hydrolyses to tetrahydrofluoranthene.[13] However, careful distillation alone is sufficient to

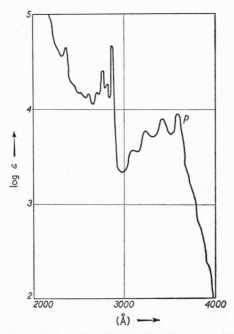

FIG. 185. Absorption spectrum of fluoranthene in ethanol: p, 3585 (3·95), 3420 (3·90), 3230 (3·76), 3090 (3·56): β, 2870 (4·66), 2820 (4·26), 2760 (4·40), 2715 (4·17), 2615 (4·16), 2525 (4·17); β' 2360 (4·66).

yield fluoranthene which can be purified by crystallization. Fluoranthene has also been obtained by destructive hydrogenation of coal.[14] Fluoranthene has been isolated from the soot of polluted air.[15]

Fluoranthene crystallizes from alcohol in colourless needles or plates (m.p. 110°). It dissolves slowly in concentrated sulphuric acid to give an almost colourless solution. It forms a yellow picrate (m.p. 184–185°). The absorption spectrum is given in Fig. 185. Fluoranthene in solid solution at low temperature shows phosphorescence bands at: 18510, 17920, 17020, 16860, 16440, 15870 cm^{-1}.[16]

The hydrogenation of fluoranthene with sodium in alcohol gives tetrahydrofluoranthene (XXX). This can be oxidized to fluorenone-propionic acid (XXXI).[17] Reduction with sodium in ammonia and methanol yields a dihydro compound which dimerizes.[18] Further hydrogenation with hydrogen and nickel yields decahydrofluoranthene (XXXII), which can be oxidized to benzene-1,2,3-tricarboxylic acid (XXXIII). Further hydrogenation leads to perhydrofluoranthene.[19]

(XXX)   (XXXI)   (XXXII)   (XXXIII)

Fluoranthene has reactive atoms in positions 4- and 11-, whilst 1-phenylnaphthalene reacts exclusively in the position 4- of the naphthalene system.[20] It appears that there is a reduced conjugation between the phenylene group and the naphthalene complex.[21]

Fluoranthene in chloroform reacts with chlorine to yield trichlorofluoranthene.[22] In carbon disulphide solution and under radiation the main products of the bromination are 4-bromo- and 11-bromofluoranthene.[23] The application of four atoms of bromine gives a dibromofluoranthene [22, 23] which is the 4,11-compound.[24] Bromine in acetic acid forms a tribromofluoranthene,[22] which is 4,11,12-tribromofluoranthene as has been established by synthesis.[25]

Bromination in nitrobenzene yields tribromofluoranthene and a tetrabromofluoranthene.[26] CuCN replaces the bromine atoms in 4-bromo- and 4,11-dibromofluoranthene to give the corresponding nitriles.[27]

The nitration of fluoranthene in acetic acid with nitric acid leads to 4-nitro- and 11-nitrofluoranthene.[28] Fuming nitric acid forms trinitrofluoranthene.[29] Concentrated sulphuric acid gives a mono- and a disulphonic acid.[27, 30] The latter is fluoranthene-4,12-disulphonic acid.[31] A melt with potassium hydroxide gives 4,12-dihydroxyfluoranthene.[30] Chlorosulphonic acid in chloroform yields a mixture of sulphonic acids from which fluoranthene-4-sulphonic acid may be obtained in a pure state.[28] The reduction of 4-nitrofluoranthene gives 4-aminofluoranthene, the amino group can be exchanged against the hydroxy group.[28]

Numerous Friedel–Crafts reactions have been carried out with fluoranthene. Acetyl chloride and aluminium chloride give 4- and 11-acetylfluoranthene and 4,12-diacetylfluoranthene. Oxalyl chloride in carbon disulphide yields fluoranthene-11-carboxylic acid and some fluoranthene-4-carboxylic acid and fluoranthene-4,12-dicarboxylic acid. The mixture can be separated through the esters or hydrazides.[32] Dyestuffs have been obtained from fluoranthene carboxylic chloride and aminoanthraquinones.[33] Benzoyl chloride gives mainly 11-benzoylfluoranthene and less 4-benzoylfluoranthene. The two compounds can be separated through the oximes.[34]

Phthalic anhydride and aluminium chloride in carbon disulphide lead to a mixture of 4- and 11-fluoranthenoylbenzoic acid, which can be separated by crystallization from chloroform.[32, 34] Cyclization of the acids yields phthaloyl-fluoranthenes which can also be obtained in one reaction.[7, 9]

TABLE I. *Alkyl and Aryl Derivatives of Fluoranthene*

Derivative	M.P. (°C)	References
2-Methyl-	72–75	Campbell and Wang, *J. chem. Soc.* 1513 (1949); Tucker, *J. chem. Soc.* 2182 (1949).
3-Methyl-	78–80	Tucker, *J. chem. Soc.* 803 (1952).
4-Methyl-	66	von Braun and Manz, *Ber. dtsch. chem. Ges.* **70**, 1603; Stubbs and Tucker, *J. chem. Soc.* 3288 (1950).
10-Methyl-	132–135	Tucker and Whalley, *J. chem. Soc.* 3213 (1949); 3187 (1952).
	135	Kloetzel and Mertel, *J. Amer. chem. Soc.* **72**, 4786 (1950).
11-Methyl-	88–90	Tucker and Whalley, *J. chem. Soc.* 3213 (1949); 3187 (1952).
	91	Kloetzel and Mertel, *J. Amer. chem. Soc.* **72**, 4786 (1950).
2,4-Dimethyl-	113–115	Forrest and Tucker, *J. chem. Soc.* 1137 (1948); Tucker and Whalley, *J. chem. Soc.* 632 (1949); Tucker, *J. chem. Soc.* 2182 (1949).
3,4-Dimethyl-	83–85	Stubbs and Tucker, *J. chem. Soc.* 227 (1954).
11,12-Dimethyl-	144–145	Kloetzel and Mertel, *J. Amer. chem. Soc.* **72**, 4786 (1950).
2,3,4-Trimethyl-	133–134	France, Maitland and Tucker, *J. chem. Soc.* 1739 (1937); Forrest and Tucker, *J. chem. Soc.* 1137 (1948); Tucker and Whalley, *J. chem. Soc.* 632 (1949).
4-Phenyl-	144	von Braun and Manz, *Ber. dtsch. chem. Ges.* **70**, 1603 (1937).
	141–143	Stubbs and Tucker, *J. chem. Soc.* 3288 (1950).
2,4-Diphenyl-	158–160	Tucker and Whalley, *J. chem. Soc.* 50 (1949).
2-Phenyl-4-methyl-	150–153	Tucker and Whalley, *J. chem. Soc.* 50 (1949).

In suspension in dilute sulphuric acid, fluoranthene can be oxidized with potassium bichromate to fluoranthene-3,4-quinone (XXXIV). This crystallizes in red needles (m.p. 188°). Further oxidation leads to fluorenone-1-carboxylic acid (XXXV).[35]

In acetic acid suspension fluoranthene gives an ozonide with ozone. The decomposition of this yields a mixture of fluorenone-1-carboxylic acid (XXXV) and fluorenone-1-aldehyde (XXXVI). These two products can be separated with sodium bisulphite solution.[36]

A number of fluoranthene derivatives can be prepared by the condensation of substituted acetone derivatives with acenaphthenequinone (XXXVII). Diene synthesis with maleic anhydride or other compounds capable of reacting with the diene (XXXVIII) gives the dihydro-fluoranthene-dicarboxylic anhydride (XXXIX), from which fluoranthene derivatives (XL) can be obtained.[37]

(XXXIV)   (XXXV)   (XXXVI)

(XXXVII)   (XXXVIII)   (XXXIX)   (XL)

Fluoranthene shows no carcinogenic activity[38] and does not inhibit the growth of tumours.[39]

REFERENCES

1. Fittig, R. and Gebhard, F., *Ber. dtsch. chem. Ges.* **10**, 2141 (1877); *Liebigs Ann.* **193**, 142 (1878); Fittig, R. and Liepmann, H., *Liebigs Ann.* **200**, 3 (1880).
2. Goldschmiedt, G., *Ber. dtsch. chem. Ges.* **10**, 2028, 2141 (1877); *Mh. Chem.* **1**, 221 (1880); Goldschmiedt, G. and Schmidt, von M., *Mh. Chem.* **2**, 7 (1881).
3. von Braun, J. and Anton, E., *Ber. dtsch. chem. Ges.* **62**, 145 (1929).
4. Campbell, A. and Tucker, S. H., *J. chem. Soc.* 2623 (1949).
5. Cook, J. W. and Lawrence, C. H., *J. chem. Soc.* 1431 (1936).
6. Orchin, M. and Reggel, L., *J. Amer. chem. Soc.* **69**, 505 (1947); **73**, 2955 (1951).
7. Bergmann, E. D. and Orchin, M., *J. Amer. chem. Soc.* **71**, 1917 (1949).
8. Campbell, N. and Gow, R. S., *J. chem. Soc.* 1555 (1949).
9. Campbell, N. and Wang, H., *J. chem. Soc.* 1513 (1949).
10. Forrest, J. and Tucker, S. H., *J. chem. Soc.* 1137 (1948).
11. Kloetzel, M. C. and Mertel, H. E., *J. Amer. chem. Soc.* **72**, 4786 (1950).
12. Bergmann, E. D., Brit. Patent 646214 (1950); *Amer. Abstr.* 6222 (1951).
13. Kruber, O., *Ber. dtsch. chem. Ges.* **64**, 84 (1931).
14. I. G. Farbenindustrie AG, Brit. Patent 435254 (1934); French Patent 781543, 45561 (1934); *Chem. Zbl.* **1936 II**, 3618.
15. Cooper, R. L. and Lindsey, A. J., *Chem. & Ind.* (*Rev.*) 1205 (1953).
16. Clar, E. and Zander, M., *Ber. dtsch. chem. Ges.* **89**, 749 (1956).
17. Kruber, O., *Ber. dtsch. chem. Ges.* **64**, 84 (1931).

18. Streitwieser, A. Jr. and Suzuki, S., *Tetrahedron* **16**, 153 (1962).

19. von Braun, J. and Manz, G., *Ber. dtsch. chem. Ges.* **63**, 2608 (1930).

20. von Braun, J. and Anton, E., *Ber. dtsch. chem. Ges.* **67**, 1051 (1934).

21. Geuskens, G. and Nasielky, J., *Spectrochimica Acta* **16**, 1416 (1960).

22. Goldschmiedt, G., *Mh. Chem.* **1**, 222 (1880).

23. von Braun, J. and Manz, G., *Liebigs Ann.* **488**, 111 (1931); **496**, 170 (1932).

24. Tobler, R., Holbro, T., Sutter, P. and Kern, W., *Helv. chim. Acta* **24**, 100E (1941).

25. Campbell, N., Leadill, W. K. and Wilshire, J. F. K., *J. chem. Soc.* 4615 (1952).

26. Tobler, R., Holbro, T., Sutter, P. and Kern, W., *Helv. chim. Acta* **24**, 100E (1941).

27. Gesellschaft für Chemische Industrie in Basel, French Patent 859394; German Patent 729492 (1939); *Chem. Zbl.* **1941 I**, 2861; **1943 I**, 1619; Campbell, N., Easton, W. W., Rayment, J. L. and Wilshire, J. F. K. *J. chem. Soc.* 2784 (1950).

28. von Braun, J. and Manz, G., *Liebigs Ann.* **488**, 111 (1931); **496**, 170 (1932); Kloetzel, M. C., King, W. and Menkes, J. H., *J. Amer. chem. Soc.* **78**, 1165 (1956).

29. Fittig, R. and Gebhard, F., *Liebigs Ann.* **193**, 147 (1878).

30. I.G. Farbenindustrie AG, German Patent 575953 (1931); *Chem. Zbl.* **1933 II**, 134; Campbell, N. and Keir, N. H., *J. chem. Soc.* 1233 (1955).

31. Holbro, Th., and Campbell, N., *J. chem. Soc.* 2652 (1957).

32. Braun, J. von, and Manz, G., *Liebigs Ann.* **496**, 170 (1932); Campbell, N. and Easton, W., *J. chem. Soc.* 341 (1949); Campbell, N., Leadill and Wilshire, *J. chem. Soc.* 1404 (1951).

33. Gesellschaft für Chemische Industrie in Basel, French Patent 859494 (1939); *Chem. Zbl.* **1941 II**, 3125.

34. I. G. Farbenindustrie AG, German Patent 624918 (1932); C. **1936 I**, 3914; *Chem. Zbl.* **1937 II**, 2597; Gesellschaft für Chemische Industrie in Basel, Brit. Patent 468648 (1936); French Patent 816853 (1937); *Chem. Zbl.* **1938 I**, 738.

35. Braun, J. von and Anton, E., *Ber. dtsch. chem. Ges.* **62**, 145 (1929); Fittig, R. and Gebhard, F., *Liebigs Ann.* **193**, 148 (1878); Fittig, R. and Liepmann, H., *Liebigs Ann.* **200**, 1 (1880).

36. I. G. Farbenindustrie AG, French Patent 817584 (1937); Brit. Patent 472167 (1936); *Chem. Zbl.* **1938 I**, 728; Vollmann, H., *Liebigs Ann.* **531**, 65 (1937); Callighan, R. H., Tarker, M. F. Jr. and Wilt, M. H., *J. org. Chem.* **25**, 820 (1960).

37. Allen, C. F. H. and Van Allan, J. A., *J. org. Chem.* **17**, 845 (1953).

38. Domagk, G., *Medizin und Chemie* **3**, 274 (1934).

39. Haddow, A., Scott, C. M. and Scott, J. D., *Proc. roy. Soc.* **B122**, 477 (1937).

II. 2.3-BENZOFLUORANTHENE

Fluorenone reacts with *o*-tolyl magnesium bromide to give the carbinol (I). This can be oxidized to the phthalide (II) with alkaline potassium permanganate. Reduction yields the acid (III) and cyclization with phosphorus pentoxide the anthrone derivative (IV). The latter does not show any tendency to enolize.[1] A zinc-dust melt of (II) yields directly 2.3-benzofluoranthene (VIII). Reduction with hydrogen iodide gives the dihydro compound (VII) which is easily dehydrogenated to (VIII) with palladium–charcoal.[2]

(I)   (II)

(III)   (IV)

Condensation of the Grignard compound of *o*-chlorobromobenzene with fluorenone gives the carbinol (V). After the reduction of the hydroxyl the Cl atom is exchanged against the CN group with CuCN. Hydrolysis

(V)   (VI)   ⟶ (III) ⟶ (IV) ⟶

(VII)   (VIII)

leads to the acid (III) and cyclization with phosphorus pentachloride and stannic chloride to (IV). Reduction yields the dihydro compound (VII) and dehydrogenation with chloranil gives 2.3-benzofluoranthene (VIII).[3]

2.3-Benzofluoranthene is also formed by the pyrolysis of a mixture of anthracene and benzene,[4] and by the reaction of phenyl radicals with anthracene.[5]

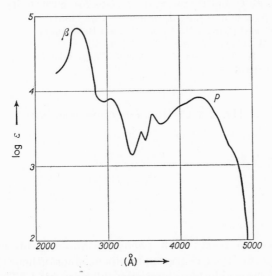

FIG. 186. Absorption spectrum of 2.3-benzofluoranthene in ethanol: p, 4280 (3·91), 3630 (3·68), 3460 (3·45); 3080 (3·90); β, 2560 (4·84).

2.3-Benzofluoranthene crystallizes from light petroleum in orange-yellow needles (m.p. 144–145°), which dissolve in concentrated sulphuric acid to give a yellow solution, which changes to violet on standing. Solutions in organic solvents show a green fluorescence. The absorption spectrum is given in Fig. 186. 2.3-Benzofluoranthene forms a colourless photo-oxide and with maleic anhydride a colourless adduct.

Aceanthrenequinone (IX) and dibenzylketone condense to form the reactive diene (X), from which a number of benzofluoranthene-derivatives (XI) can be obtained by a diene synthesis with compounds with reactive double bonds.[6]

REFERENCES

1. Weisz, R. and Knapp, E., *Mh. Chem.* **61**, 61 (1932).
2. Stubbs, H. W. D. and Tucker, S. H., *J. chem. Soc.* 2939 (1951).
3. Campbell, N. and Marks, A., *J. chem. Soc.* 2941 (1951).
4. Lang, K. F. and Buffleb, H., *Chem. Ber.* **94**, 1075 (1961).
5. Taylor, G. W., *Canad. J. Chem.* **35**, 41 (1957).
6. Abramov, V. S., *Bull. Acad. Sci. U.R.S.S., Classe Sci. Chim.* 330 (1945); *Amer. Abstr.* 5024 (1946).

III. 2.3,6.7-DIBENZOFLUORANTHENE

Tetracenone (I) reacts with phenyl magnesium bromide to give 5-phenyltetracene (II). Cyclization to dibenzofluoranthene (III) is easily effected in a sodium chloride–aluminium chloride melt.[1, 2] The tetrahydro compound (IV) is obtained as a by-product. It can be readily dehydrogenated to (III) with palladium–charcoal.[2] Interesting is the unusual re-arrangement of phenyltetraphene (VI) under the influence of aluminium chloride in benzene. The cyclization yields not only the expected 1.2,3.4-dibenzopyrene (see p. 142) but also dibenzofluoranthene (III).[2]

The Grignard compound of *o*-chlorobromobenzene reacts with 3.4-benzofluorenone (VII) to form the carbinol (VIII). The Cl atom can be exchanged against a CN group. Hydrolysis to the acid and its transformation into the chloride (IX) precede the cyclization, which is carried out with stannic chloride. Dibenzofluoranthene is thus obtained, besides an oxygen-containing compound.[3] Dibenzofluoranthene is also formed by the reaction of phenyl radicals with tetracene.[4]

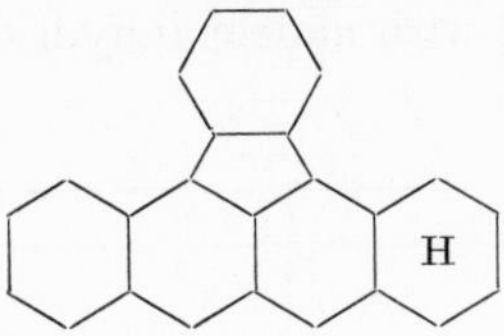

(IV)

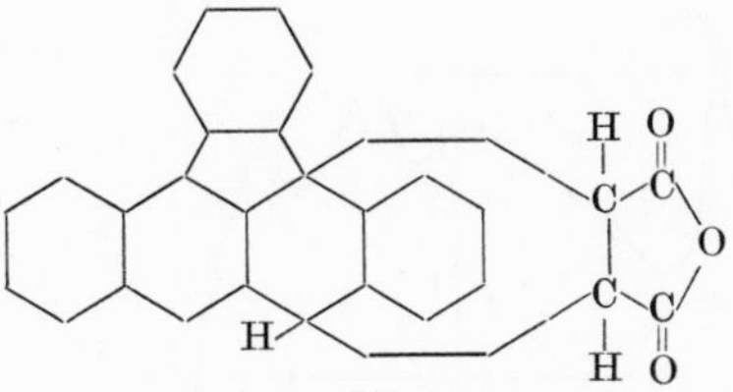

(V)

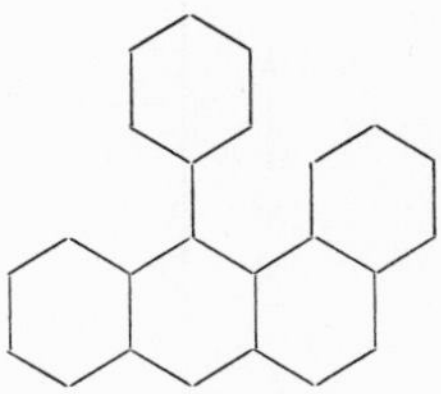

(VI)

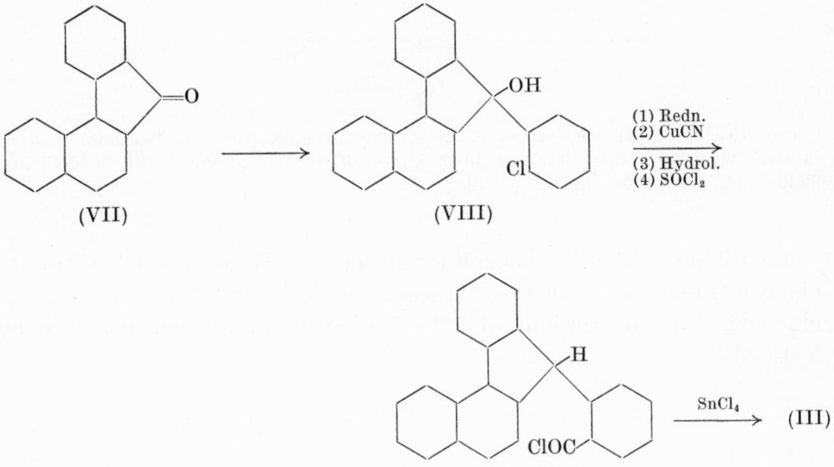

(VII)   (VIII)

(1) Redn.
(2) CuCN
(3) Hydrol.
(4) SOCl$_2$

(IX) $\xrightarrow{\text{SnCl}_4}$ (III)

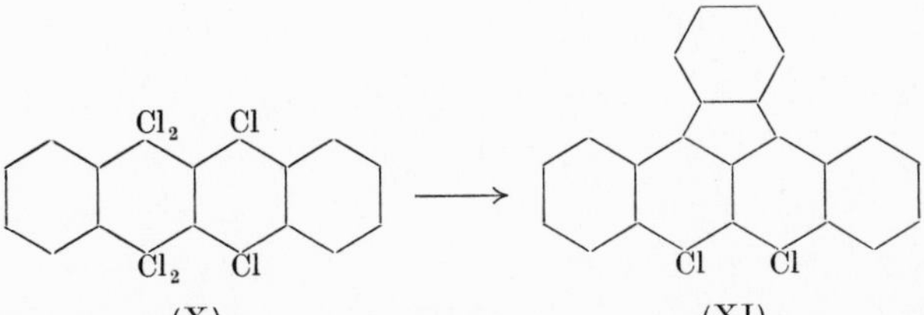

(X)   (XI)

2.3,6.7-Dibenzofluoranthene crystallizes from benzene in red needles (m.p. 216·5–217°), which dissolve in concentrated sulphuric acid to give a red-brown solution which on storage changes to violet. The absorption spectrum is given in Fig. 187. Dibenzofluoranthene is photo-oxidizable and gives the adduct (V) with maleic anhydride.[5]

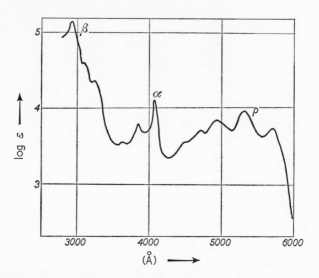

FIG. 187. Absorption spectrum of 2.3,6.7-dibenzofluoranthene in benzene: p, 5710 (3·74), 5330 (3·98), 4940 (3·85), 4630 (3·72); α, 4080 (4·10), 3850 (3·78), 3630 (3·56); 3230 (4·36), 3090 (4·60); β, 2925 (5·16).

4,5-Dichloro-2.3,6.7-dibenzofluoranthene (XI) is formed if tetra-chlorotetracene dichloride (X) reacts with benzene and aluminium chloride. A small amount of 2.3,6.7-dibenzofluoranthene can also be isolated.[6]

Heating dichlorodiphenyltetracene (XII) to 200° yields chlorophenyldibenzofluoranthene (XIII). A second cyclization to (XIV) can be effected by heating with potassium hydroxide at 330°.[7]

Iodotriphenyltetracene (XV) cyclizes to diphenyldibenzofluoranthene (XVI) on heating to 160° or on irradiation.[8]

(XV)   (XVI)

REFERENCES

1. Dufraisse, C., Etienne, A. and Bucourt, R., *C. R. Acad. Sci., Paris* **233**, 1401 (1951).
2. Clar, E. and Stewart, D. G., *J. chem. Soc.* 4783 (1952); 687 (1951).
3. Campbell, N., Marks, A. and McHattie, G. V., *J. chem. Soc.* 1190 (1955).
4. Taylor, G. W., *Canad. J. Chem.* **35**, 41 (1957).
5. Clar, E. and Stewart, D. G., *J. chem. Soc.* 4783 (1952).
6. Lang, K. F. and Theiling, E. A., *Ber. dtsch. chem. Ges.* **89**, 2734 (1956).
7. Dufraisse, C., Buret, R. and Girard, R., *Bull. Soc. chim. Fr.* (4) **53**, 782 (1933).
8. Badoche, M., *Bull. Soc. chim. Fr.* (5) **9**, 393 (1942).

IV. 3.4-BENZOFLUORANTHENE

Fluorene can be condensed with o-chlorobenzaldehyde to form the compound (I). Cyclization to 3.4-benzofluoranthene (II) takes place with potassium hydroxide in boiling quinoline.[1]

2.3-Benzofluorene (III) reacts with maleic anhydride and gives the anhydride (IV) which cyclizes in a sodium chloride–zinc chloride melt.[2]

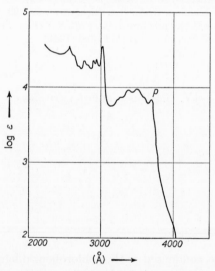

(I)   (II)

(IV)   (III)

4-Fluoranthenoylsuccinic acid (V), which is obtained from fluoranthene, succinic anhydride and aluminium chloride (besides isomers), is reduced to the acid (VI) with hydrazine and potassium hydroxide.

Fig. 188. Absorption spectrum of 3.4-benzofluoranthene in ethanol: p, 3690 (3·84), 3500 (3·98), 3380 (3·96); β, 3010 (4·54), 2930 (4·36), 2890 (4·36), 2760 (4·36); β', 2560 (4·54).

Cyclization to (VII), reduction and dehydrogenation give 3.4-benzo-fluoranthene.[3]

(V)   (VI)   (VII)

3.4-Benzofluoranthene can be isolated from coal-tar.[4]

3.4-Benzofluoranthene crystallizes in colourless needles (m.p. 168°). It forms a picrate (m.p. 156°). The absorption spectrum is given in Fig. 188. 5-Bromo-3.4-benzofluoranthene has been obtained by synthesis.[5] 3.4-Benzofluoranthene-1',4'-quinone (IX) can be prepared by the condensation of the carbinol (VIII) with benzoquinone. It forms orange needles (m.p. 245–246°), which dissolve in concentrated sulphuric acid to give a red solution. Alkaline sodium dithionite solution produces a red vat.[6]

(VIII)   (IX)   (X)

The oxidation of 3.4-benzofluoranthene yields phenylfluorenone-carboxylic acid (X).[7]

3.4-Benzofluoranthene shows no carcinogenic activity.[8]

REFERENCES

1. I. G. Farbenindustrie AG, Brit. Patent 459108 (1936); *Chem. Zbl.* **1937 II**, 2262; French Patent 807704 (1936); *Chem. Zbl.* **1937 I**, 5053.
2. Clar, E., unpublished results.
3. Buu-Hoï, N. and Lamy, J., *J. chem. Soc.* 1845 (1959).
4. Kruber, O., *Ber. dtsch. chem. Ges.* **85**, 433.
5. Tobler, R., Holbro, T., Sutter, P. and Kern, W., *Helv. chim. Acta* **24**, 100E (1941).
6. Campbell, N. and Wang, H., *J. chem. Soc.* 1513 (1949).
7. Kruber, O., *Ber. dtsch. chem. Ges.* **85**, 433 (1952).
8. Domagk, G., *Medizin und Chemie* **3**, 274 (1936).

V. 10.11-Benzofluoranthene

The Grignard compound from β-bromoethylbenzene reacts with acenaphthenone (I) to give the carbinol (II). Its cyclization yields the tetrahydro compound (III), which is dehydrogenated to benzofluoranthene with palladium–charcoal.

1-Naphthyl magnesium bromide and 1-tetralone (V) form the carbinol (VI) which, after cyclization and dehydrogenation, gives also benzofluoranthene (IV). The same result is obtained from a reaction between tetralyl magnesium iodide and 2-tetralone (VII). Cyclization and dehydrogenation yield again 3.4-benzofluoranthene (IV).[1]

Octahydro-10.11-benzofluoranthene is obtained from tetralin and aluminium chloride. It can be prepared by hydrogenation of benzo-

fluoranthene. The reaction of tetralyl magnesium bromide and 1-tetral-
one (X) gives a carbinol (XI) which cyclizes with P_2O_5 to (IX).[1, 2]

Another octahydro compound is obtained from dialin (XII) and
sulphuric acid. It is dehydrogenated to benzofluoranthene (IV) with lead

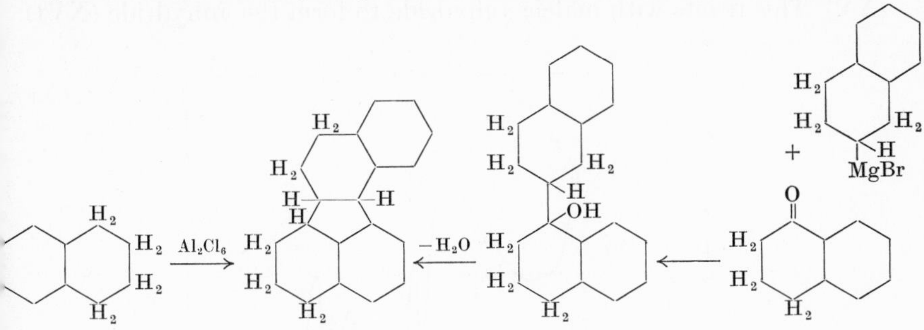

(IX)   (XI)   (X)

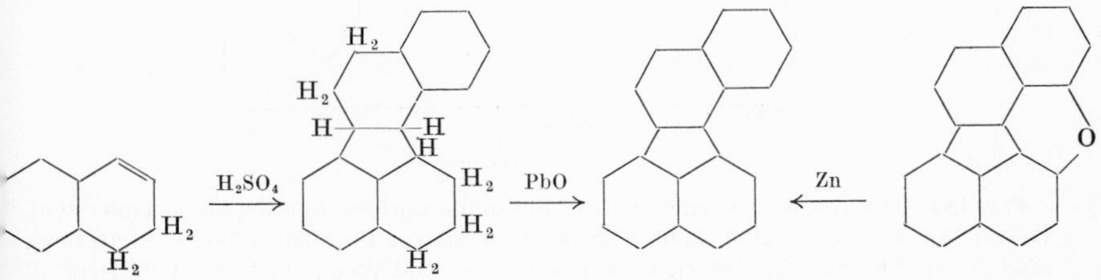

(XII)   (XIII)   (IV)   (XIV)

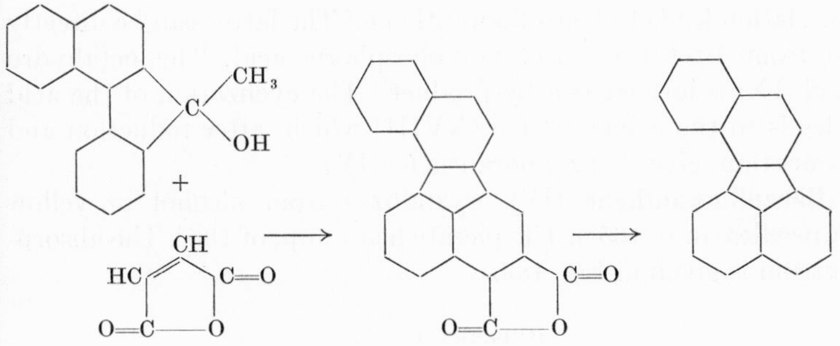

(XV)   (XVI)   (IV)

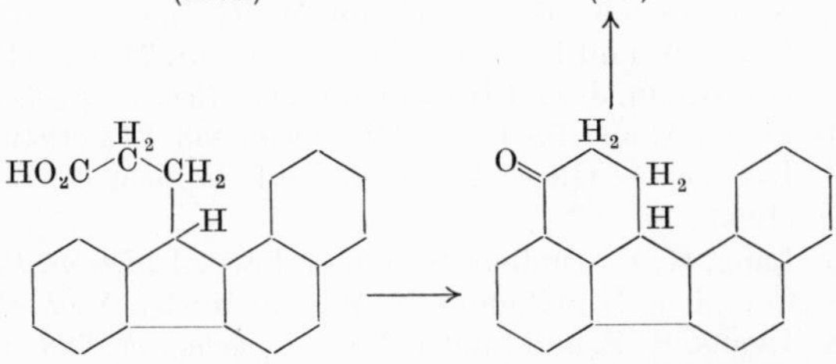

(XVII)   (XVIII)

dioxide.[1, 2, 3] Zinc-dust distillation of the cyclic oxide (XIV) also gives benzofluoranthene.[4] It has also been prepared from coal-tar[5] and by the pyrolysis of naphthalene.[6]

3.4-Benzofluorenone and methyl magnesium iodide give the carbinol (XV). This reacts with maleic anhydride to form the anhydride (XVI).

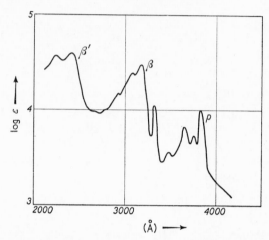

FIG. 189. Absorption spectrum of 10.11-benzofluoranthene in ethanol: p, 3830 (4·00), 3760 (3·73), 3650 (3·82), 3490 (3·56); β, 3180 (4·48), 3080 (4·38); β', 2420 (4·60), 2260 (4·58). (Orchin, M., Reggel, L., Friedel, R. A., and Woolfolk, E. O., U.S. Dept. of Interior, Bureau of Mines Techn. paper, 708, 19 (1948).)

Decarboxylation leads to benzofluoranthene.[7] The latter can be directly obtained from 1-tetralone and polyphosphoric acid. The octahydro compound (IX) is formed as a by-product.[8] The cyclization of the acid (XVII) leads to the cyclic ketone (XVIII) which, after reduction and dehydrogenation, gives benzofluoranthene (IV).[9]

10.11-Benzofluoranthene (IV) crystallizes from alcohol in yellow plates or needles (m.p. 165°). The picrate has a m.p. of 195°. The absorption spectrum is given in Fig. 189.

REFERENCES

1. Nenitzescu, C. D. and Avram, M., *J. Amer. chem. Soc.* **72**, 3486 (1950).
2. Dansi, A. and Ferri, C., *Gazz. chim. ital.* **71**, 648 (1941).
3. von Braun, J. and Kirschbaum, G., *Ber. dtsch. chem. Ges.* **54**, 597 (1921).
4. Zinke, A. and Pack, G., *Mh. Chem.* **158**, 213 (1949).
5. Kruber, O., Oberkobusch, R. and Rappen, L., *Ber. dtsch. chem. Ges.* **86**, 534 (1953).
6. Lang, K. F., Buffleb, H. and Kalowy, J., *Chem. Ber.* **90**, 2888 (1957).
7. Campbell, N., Khanna, N. M., and Marks, A., *J. chem. Soc.* 2511 (1951).
8. Evans, R. F. and Smith, J. C., *J. chem. Soc.* 798 (1954).
9. Orchin, M. and Reggel, L., *J. Amer. chem. Soc.* **73**, 436 (1951).

VI. 11.12-BENZOFLUORANTHENE

1,2'-Dinaphthyl (I) gives 11.12-benzofluoranthene (II) besides 10.11-benzofluoranthene by cyclodehydrogenation with a chromium oxide–aluminium oxide catalyst.[1]

(I)   (II)   (IV)   (III)

o-Phenylenediacetonitrile (III) condenses with acenaphthene quinone to form the compound (IV). Hydrolysis and decarboxylation leads to 11.12-benzofluoranthene (II).[2]

One of the isomers of the reaction of fluoranthene, succinic anhydride and aluminium chloride is the acid (V). The carbonyl can be reduced with hydrazine and potassium hydroxide in glycol and gives the corresponding butyric acid. Cyclization with aluminium chloride leads to the ketone (VI). Reduction of the carbonyl followed by dehydrogenation with selenium gives 11.12-benzofluoranthene.[3]

(V)   (VI)   (II)

Benzofluoranthene has also been isolated from coal-tar[4] and from a mixture obtained by the pyrolysis of naphthalene.[5]

11.12-Benzofluoranthene (II) crystallizes from benzene in colourless needles (m.p. 217°), which form a picrate (m.p. 170–171°) and an adduct with trinitrobenzene (m.p. 182°). The absorption spectrum is given in Fig. 190.

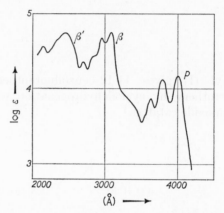

FIG. 190. Absorption spectrum of 11.12-benzofluoranthene in ethanol: p, 4000 (4·16), 3800 (4·12), 3610 (3·86); β, 3080 (4·75), 2960 (4·67), 2820 (4·42), 2690 (4·36); β', 2400 (4·75); 2150 (4·56). (Orchin, M., Reggel, L., Friedel, R. A. and Woolfolk, E. O., U.S. Dept. of Interior, Bureau of Mines, Techn. paper 708, 19 (1948).)

A diphenyl derivative (IX) (m.p. 267°) can be obtained by a condensation of acenaphthylene with diphenylisobenzofuran (VII).[6]

(VII)   (VIII)   (IX)

11.12-Benzofluoranthene-1′,4′-quinone (XI) can be prepared by the reaction of the diol (X) with benzoquinone.[7] It forms yellow prisms (m.p. 265°), which dissolve in concentrated sulphuric acid to give a blue solution. Alkaline sodium dithionite yields a red vat.[7] Direct oxidation of 11.12-benzofluoranthene gives another quinone (m.p. 226°).[2,4] It probably has the structure (XII).

(X)   (XI)   (XII)

1'-Methyl-11.12-benzofluoranthene (m.p. 207°) has been synthesized.[8]

REFERENCES

1. Orchin, M. and Reggel, L., *J. Amer. chem. Soc.* **69**, 505 (1947).
2. Mourev, H., Chovin, P. and Pivod, G., *C. R. Acad. Sci., Paris* **223**, 951 (1946).
3. Buu-Hoï, N. P., Lavit, D. and Lamy, J., *J. chem. Soc.* 1845 (1959).
4. Kruber, O., Oberkobusch, R. and Rappen, L., *Chem. Ber.* **86**, 534 (1953).
5. Lang, K. F., Buffleb, H. and Kalowy, J., *Chem. Ber.* **90**, 2888 (1957).
6. Bergmann, E. D., *J. Amer. chem. Soc.* **74**, 1075 (1952).
7. Campbell, N. and Gow, R. S., *J. chem. Soc.* 1555 (1949).
8. Buu-Hoï, N. P. and Lavit, D., *J. chem. Soc.* 536 (1960).

VII. 3.4,11.12-DIBENZOFLUORANTHENE

2.3-Benzofluorene (I) can be condensed with *o*-chlorobenzaldehyde to give the compound (II). Cyclization is effected in boiling quinoline with potassium hydroxide.[1] However, this synthesis is not unambiguous and structure (III) was proved by another synthesis.

Tetrahydrobenzofluoranthene reacts with succinic anhydride and aluminium chloride to yield the acid (IV). Reduction of the carbonyl and cyclization via the chloride with aluminium chloride gives the ketone (V). Dehydrogenation with selenium leads to dibenzofluoranthene (III).[2]

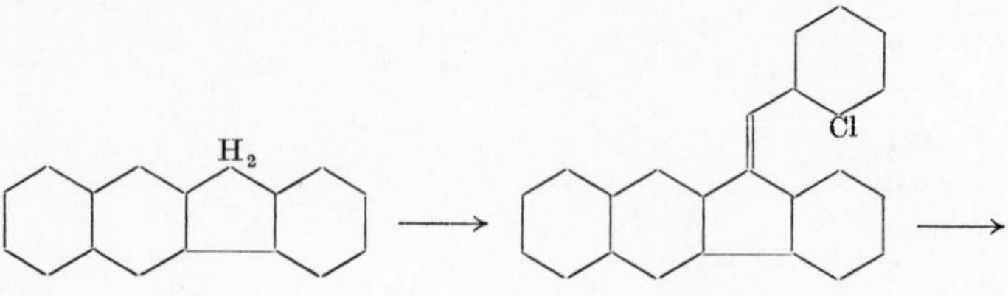

(I)   (II)

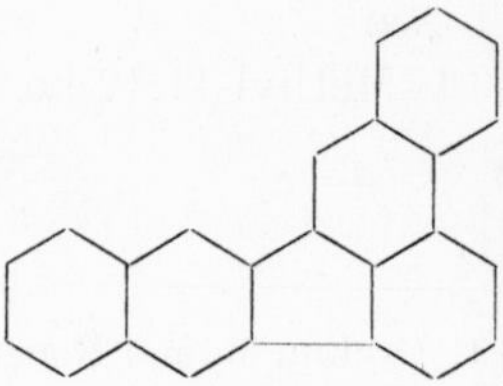

(III)

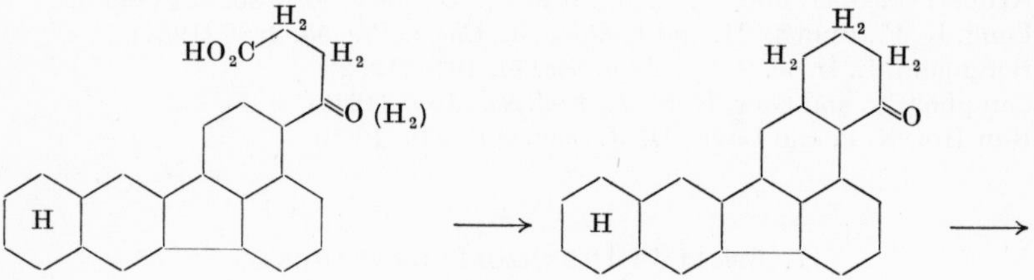

(IV)   (V)

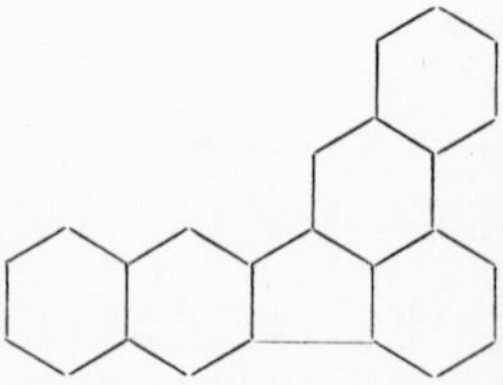

(III)

3.4,11.12-Dibenzofluoranthene (III) forms pale yellow needles (m.p. 236°).

REFERENCES

1. I. G. Farbenindustrie AG, Brit. Patent 459108 (1936); *Chem. Zbl.* **1937 II**, 2262; French Patent 807704 (1936); *Chem. Zbl.* **1937 I**, 5053.
2. Buu-Hoï, N. P. and Lavit, D., *J. chem. Soc.* 536 (1960).

VIII. 9.10,11.12-Dibenzofluoranthene

The cyclization of the acid (I) with anhydrous hydrogen fluoride yields the ketone (II). A reaction with phenyl lithium yields the hydrocarbon (III). Dehydrogenation with palladium–charcoal at 340–345° gives dibenzofluoranthene (IV). This is also obtained by dehydrogenation of diphenylacenaphthylene (V) with palladium–charcoal.

9.10,11.12-Dibenzofluoranthene (IV) crystallizes in golden yellow needles (m.p. 253–254°).[1]

REFERENCE

1. Buchta, E. and Maar, H., *Chem. Ber.* **95**, 1826 (1962).

IX. 2.3,6.7,10.11-Tribenzofluoranthene

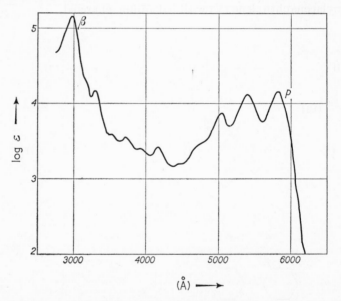

Tetracenone (I) reacts with 1-naphthyl lithium to give naphthyl-tetracene (II). Cyclization in a sodium chloride–aluminium chloride melt yields two hydrocarbons: 2.3,6.7,10.11-tribenzofluoranthene (III) and 1.2,5.6-dibenzoperylene (see p. 51). They are separated by chromatography.[1]

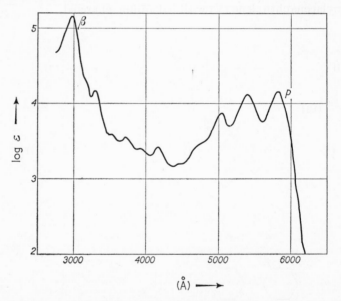

FIG. 191. Absorption spectrum of 2.3,6.7,10.11-tribenzofluoranthene in benzene: p, 5800 (4·22), 5390 (4·16), 5030 (3·90); 4160 (3·44), 3920 (3·41), 3710 (3·57); 3320 (4·14); β, 2980 (5·22).

The condensation of the hexachloro compound (IV) with naphthalene and aluminium chloride gives tribenzofluoranthene.[2]

2.3,6.7,10.11-Tribenzofluoranthene (III) crystallizes from benzene in long blue needles (m.p. 298°), which dissolve in concentrated sulphuric acid to give a yellow solution which changes to green on standing. The red solution in benzene shows an orange fluorescence and is photo-oxidizable. The hydrocarbon forms a colourless adduct with maleic anhydride. The absorption spectrum is given in Fig. 191.[1]

(I)   (II)

(III)   (IV)

REFERENCES

1. Clar, E. and Willicks, W., *Liebigs Ann.* **601**, 193 (1956).
2. Lang, K. F. and Theiling, E. A., *Chem. Ber.* **89**, 2734 (1956).

X. NAPHTHO-(1'.2':2.3)-FLUORANTHENE AND NAPHTHO-(2'.1':2.3)-FLUORANTHENE

The reaction between fluorene carboxylic chloride, naphthalene and aluminium chloride results in the formation of the two ketones (I) and (III). Their relative yields depend on the choice of the solvent, i.e. whether carbon disulphide, tetrachloroethane or nitrobenzene is used. The pyrolysis of the ketone (I) gives naphtho-(2'.1':2.3)-fluoranthene (II) and the ketone (III) yields naphtho-(1'.2':2.3)-fluoranthene (IV).[1]

II—11

Naphtho-(2′.1′:2.3)-fluoranthene (II) crystallizes from benzene in yellow needles (m.p. 181–181·3° (corr.)), which form a brick red picrate (m.p. 174·5–175·5°). It is related to cholanthrene and shows weak carcinogenic activity.[2]

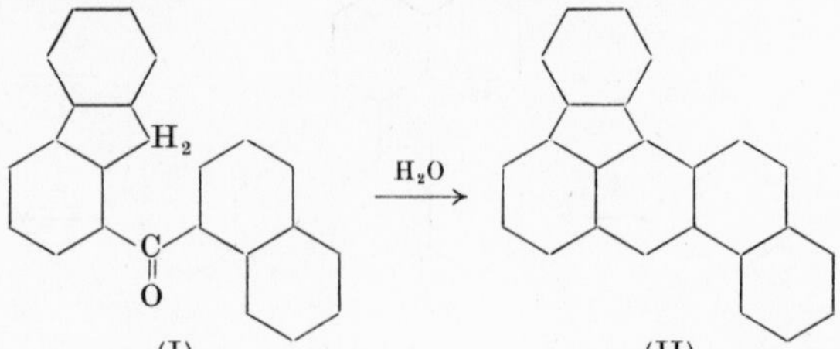

(I)   (II)

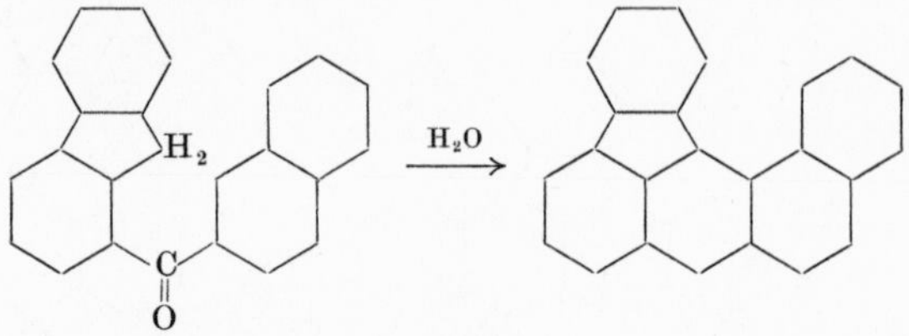

(III)   (IV)

Naphtho-(1′.2′:2.3)-fluoranthene (IV) crystallizes from a mixture of benzene and ether in golden yellow needles (m.p. 178–179° (corr.)). It forms a picrate (m.p. 181–182°).[1]

REFERENCES

1. Fieser, L. F. and Seligman, A. M., *J. Amer. chem. Soc.* **57**, 2174 (1935).
2. Fieser, L. F., Fieser, M., Hershberg, E. B., Newman, M. S., Seligman, A. M. and Shear, M., *Amer. J. Cancer*, **29**, 260 (1937).

XI. NAPHTHO-(2′.3′:3.4)-FLUORANTHENE

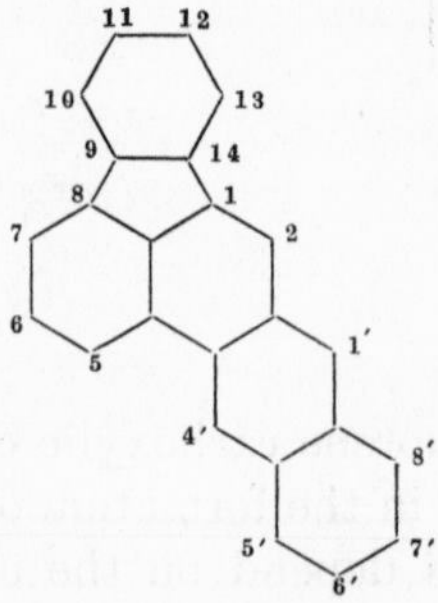

One of the isomers resulting from the reaction of fluoranthene, *o*-toluyl chloride and aluminium chloride is the ketone (I). Its pyrolysis yields two hydrocarbons: naphtho-(2'.3',3.4)-fluoranthene (II) and the colour-less hydrocarbon (III) (m.p. 208–210°).

Naphtho-(2'.3':3.4)-fluoranthene (II) forms yellow sublimable needles (m.p. 229–230°). Its solution shows a blue fluorescence.[1]

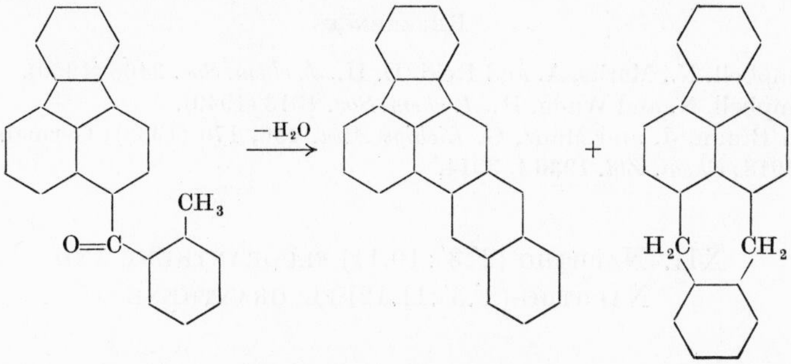

(I)   (II)   (III)

The carbinol (IV) condenses with naphthoquinone in acetic anhydride to form the quinone (V).[2] The same compound can be obtained if the acid (VI) is cyclized. An isomer, phthaloylfluoranthene (m.p. 296–297°), is formed as a by-product.[2, 3] The latter probably has the structure (VII).

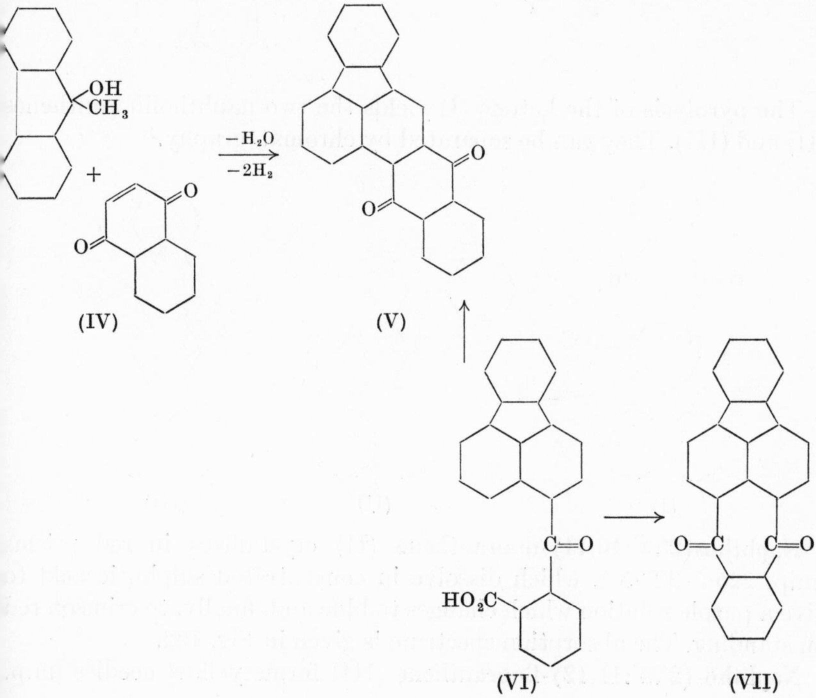

(IV)   (V)

(VI)   (VII)

Naphtho-(2'.3':3.4)-fluoranthene-1',4'-quinone (V) crystallizes from nitrobenzene in orange-red needles (m.p. 252–253°), which dissolve in concentrated sulphuric acid to give a blue-green solution. Alkaline sodium dithionite solution produces a bluish-violet vat.[2]

REFERENCES

1. Campbell, N., Marks, A. and Reid, D. H., *J. chem. Soc.* 3466 (1950).
2. Campbell, N. and Wang, H., *J. chem. Soc.* 1513 (1949).
3. von Braun, J. and Manz, G. *Liebigs Ann.* **496**, 170 (1932); German Patent 624918; *Chem. Zbl.* **1936 I**, 3914.

XII. NAPHTHO-(2'.3':10.11)-FLUORANTHENE AND NAPHTHO-(2'.3':11.12)-FLUORANTHENE

The pyrolysis of the ketone (I) yields the two naphthofluoranthenes (II) and (III). They can be separated by chromatography.[1]

Naphtho-(2'.3':10.11)-fluoranthene (II) crystallizes in red prisms (m.p. 225·5–227·5°), which dissolve in concentrated sulphuric acid to give a purple solution which changes to blue and, finally, to crimson red on standing. The absorption spectrum is given in Fig. 192.

Naphtho-(2'.3':11.12)-fluoranthene (III) forms yellow needles (m.p.

301–303°). They dissolve in concentrated sulphuric acid to give a pink solution which turns to brown and greenish-brown on storage. The absorption spectrum is given in Fig. 193.

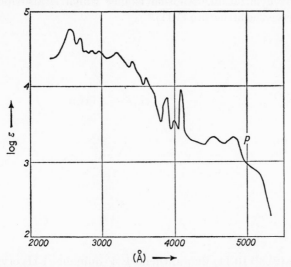

FIG. 192. Absorption spectrum of naphtho-(2′.3′:10.11)-fluoranthene in ethanol: p, 4820 (3·33), 4520 (3·34); 4075 (3·96), 3980 (3·55), 3870 (3·86); 3590 (4·14), 3420 (4·33), 3190 (4·45), 2960 (4·46), 2870 (4·47), 2770 (4·48), 2690 (4·65): β', 2550 (4·78).

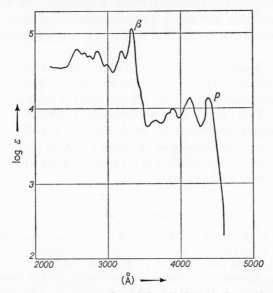

FIG. 193. Absorption spectrum of naphtho-(2′.3′:11.12)-fluoranthene in ethanol: p, 4380 (4·14), 4130 (4·14), 3900 (4·00), 3640 (3·86); β, 3340 (5·07), 3195 (4·77), 2980 (4·60), 2870 (4·77). 2770 (4·70), 2680 (4·74), 2560 (4·80).

The reaction of acenaphthenequinone with methyl magnesium iodide yields the diol (IV). This reacts with naphthoquinone to form the 11,12-phthaloylfluoranthene (V).[2] The same compound is obtained from the acid (VI) by cyclization.[3] Another isomer which is also formed must therefore have the structure (VII).[2]

(IV)   (V)   (VI)   (VII)

Naphtho-(2′.3′:10.11)-fluoranthene-1′,4′-quinone (VII) crystallizes in yellow plates (m.p. 319–320°), which dissolve in concentrated sulphuric acid with a red colour. Alkaline sodium dithionite forms no vat.

Naphtho-(2′.3′:11.12)-fluoranthene-1′,4′-quinone (V) forms golden yellow crystals (m.p. 338–340°). They dissolve in concentrated sulphuric acid with a deep blue colour and give a blue vat with alkaline sodium dithionite.

Higher condensed quinones of the phthaloylfluoranthene type have been described. Naphthalenedicarboxylic anhydride can be condensed with fluoranthene and aluminium chloride and the resulting acid cyclized to a quinone. This forms yellow needles (m.p. > 300°).[4]

A diphthaloylfluoranthene (or more likely a mixture of isomers) is obtained from a direct condensation of an excess of phthalic anhydride with fluoranthene. This product is a brown powder which dyes cotton from a blue vat reddish-yellow.[5]

REFERENCES

1. Campbell, N., Marks, A. and Reid, D. H., *J. chem. Soc.* 3466 (1950).
2. Campbell, N. and Gow, R. S., *J. chem. Soc.* 1555 (1949).
3. von Braun, J. and Manz, G., *Liebigs Ann.* **496**, 170 (1932).
4. I. G. Farbenindustrie AG, German Patent 624918 (1932); *Chem. Zbl.* **1936 I**, 3914.
5. Gesellschaft für Chemische Industrie in Basel, Brit. Patent 468648 (1936); French Patent 816853 (1937); *Chem. Zbl.* **1938 I**, 738.

XIII. 10.11-BENZONAPHTHO-(2″.3″:3.4)-FLUORANTHENE

The carbinol (I) can be prepared from 3.4-benzofluorene and methyl magnesium bromide. It condenses with naphthoquinone in boiling acetic anhydride to the quinone (II). This forms red prisms (m.p. > 360°), which dissolve in concentrated sulphuric acid to give a greenish-brown solution. Alkaline sodium dithionite forms a blue vat.[1]

REFERENCE

1. Campbell, N. and Wang, H., *J. chem. Soc.* 1513 (1949).

XIV. 2.3-BENZONAPHTHOFLUORANTHENES

The pyrolysis of anthracene yields 2,2'-dianthryl, bisanthene and three benzonaphthofluoranthenes, the highest melting of which has the structure (I). It adds first one molecule of maleic anhydride to form the monoadduct (II) and then forms a diadduct (III). The structures of the

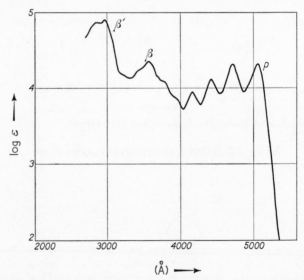

(I)   (II)   (III)

other two possible 2.3-benzonaphthofluoranthenes are due to two hydrocarbons having m.p. 227–229° and 241–242° respectively. Both hydrocarbons are red and form diadducts with maleic anhydride.

Fig. 194. Absorption spectrum of 2.3-benzonaphtho-(2″.3″:11.12)-fluoranthene in benzene: p, 5050 (4·32), 4720 (4·32), 4410 (4·12), 4160 (3·95), 3800 (4·10); β, 3570 (4·36); β', 2980 (4·90), 2840 (4·86).[1]

2.3-Benzonaphtho-(2″.3″:11.12)-fluoranthene (I) crystallizes from xylene in orange-red needles (m.p. 319–320°), which dissolve in concentrated sulphuric acid to give a green solution which changes to greenish-blue on standing. The absorption spectrum is given in Fig. 194.[1]

REFERENCE

1. Lang, K. F., Buffleb, H. and Kalowy, J., *Chem. Ber.* **94**, 1075 (1961).

XV. 2.3-*o*-PHENYLENEPYRENE
(*Indeno-(1,2,3-cd)-pyrene*)

Indenoperinaphthene (I) adds readily maleic anhydride in boiling acetic acid or xylene to form the adduct (II). This is dehydrogenated by

boiling nitrobenzene to (III). Decarboxylation with soda-lime yields phenylenepyrene (IV).

3-Iodopyrene (V) can be condensed with *o*-bromonitrobenzene and copper powder to the nitro compound (VI). Reduction of the nitro group, diazotization of the amine followed by decomposition of the diazo compound with copper powder gives phenylenepyrene.[1]

II—11*

Phenylenepyrene (IV) can be also prepared by the pyrolysis of pyrene (VII) and benzene. It is also a main constituent of the high boiling fraction of coal-tar.[2]

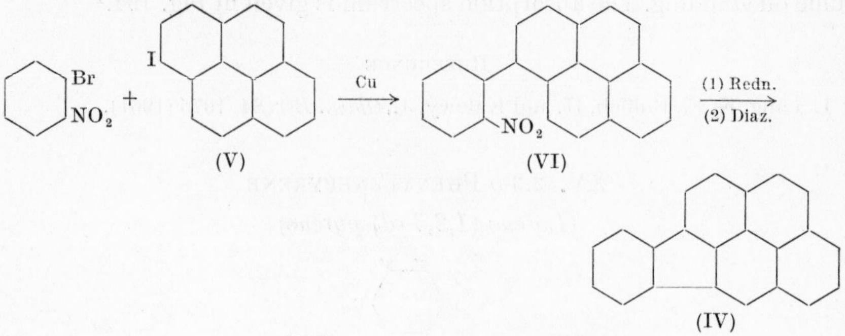

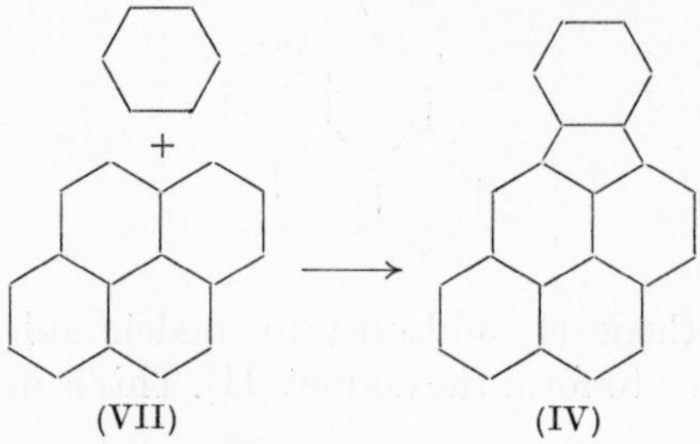

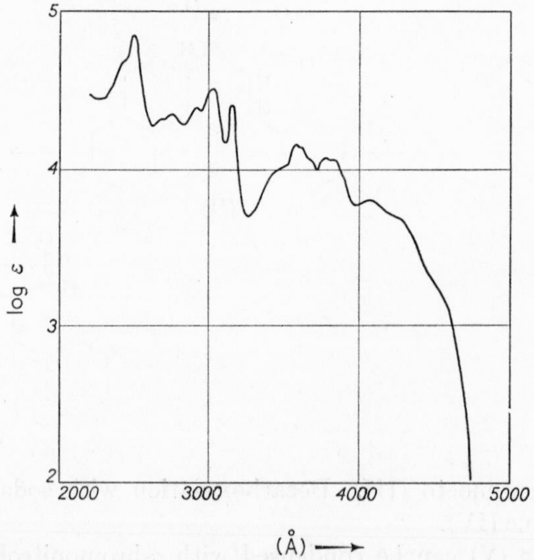

Fig. 195. Absorption spectrum of 2.3-o-phenylenepyrene in cyclohexane: 4620 (3·14), 4540 (3·25), 4340 (3·65), 4080 (3·79), 3860 (4·06), 3780 (4·14), 3610 (4·21), 3160 (4·51), 3040 (4·56), 2920 (4·43), 2760 (4·39), 2700 (4·36), 2500 (2·84). (Lang, K. F. and Buffleb, H., *Chem. Ber.* **90**, 2894 (1957).)

2.3-*o*-Phenylenepyrene (IV) crystallizes from light petroleum in yellow plates (m.p. 162·5–163·5°). The solution shows a greenish-yellow fluorescence. It forms a picrate (m.p. 150–180° (dec.)). The absorption spectrum is given in Fig. 195.

REFERENCES

1. Aitken, I. M. and Reid, D. H., *J. chem. Soc.* 3487 (1956).
2. Lang, K. F. and Buffleb, H., *Chem. Ber.* **90**, 2894 (1957); Lang, K. F., Buffleb, H. and Schweym, E., *Brennstoff-Chemie* **40**, 369 (1959).

XVI. 2.3-*o*-PHENYLENE-4.5-BENZOPYRENE

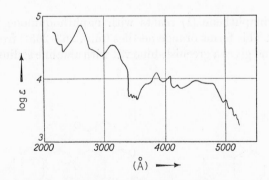

Indenoperinaphthene (I) condenses with benzyne to form phenylene-benzopyrene (II) directly. Two hydrogen atoms are probably taken up by the excess of benzyne.[1]

FIG. 196. Absorption spectrum of 2.3-*o*-phenylene-4.5-benzopyrene in cyclohexane: 5200 (3·44), 5110 (3·59), 5030 (3·64), 4760 (3·94), 4530 (3·98), 4200 (3·91), 4090 (4·02), 3870 (4·09), 3530 (3·71), 3500 (3·73), 3460 (3·78), 3100 (4·54), 2590 (4·85), 2290 (4·55). (Aitken, I. M. and Reid, D. H., *J. chem. Soc.* 663 (1960).)

(I)   (II)

2.3-*o*-Phenylene-4.5-benzopyrene (II) forms orange-red needles (m.p. 262–264°), which dissolve in concentrated sulphuric acid to give a violet solution. The absorption spectrum is given in Fig. 196.

REFERENCE

1. Aitken, I. M. and Reid, D. H., *J. chem. Soc.* 663 (1960).

XVII. 2.3-*o*-Phenylenenaphtho-(2″.3″:4.5)-pyrene

Indenoperinaphthene (I) reacts with naphthoquinone to yield the quinone (II). This forms orange needles (m.p. 263–265°) from dimethyl-formamide and gives a greenish-blue vat with alkaline sodium dithionite.

(I)   (II)

Indenoperinaphthene (I) condenses in an analogous way with benzoquinone. Formula (III) represents one of the two possible isomers.

(III)

This quinone crystallizes from nitrobenzene in orange needles (m.p. >
400°), which do not form a vat.[1]

REFERENCE

1. Aitken, I. N. and Reid, D. H., *J. chem. Soc.* 3487 (1960).

XVIII. 4″.5-o-PHENYLENENAPHTHO-(2″.3″ : 3.4)-PYRENE

The condensation of diphenylnaphthopyrene (I) in a sodium chloride–
aluminium chloride melt results partly in splitting off one phenyl group
and pericyclization of the other one to yield the hydrocarbon (II).
2.3,4.5-Dibenzanthanthrene is also formed (see p. 211).

4″.5-o-**Phenylenenaphtho-(2″.3″,3.4)-pyrene** (II) crystallizes from
xylene in red-brown needles (m.p. 292–294°), which dissolve in concentrated sulphuric acid to give a reddish-brown solution. The light red-
brown solution in benzene shows an orange-yellow fluorescence.[1] The
absorption spectrum is given in Fig. 197.[1]

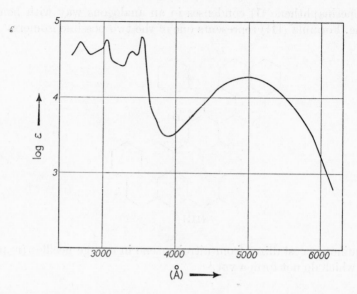

Fig. 197. Absorption spectrum of 4″,5-o-phenylenenaphtho-(2″.3″:3.4)-pyrene in benzene: p, 5000 (4·28); β, 3540 (4·81), 3380 (4·60); β′, 3040 (4·74); β″, 2680 (4·72).

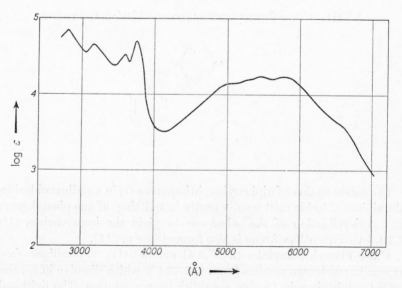

Fig. 198. Absorption spectrum of 2.3,4.5-dibenzo-1.12-o-phenyleneanthanthrene in benzene: p, 5810 (4·24), 5440 (4·23), 5020 (4·16); β, 3760 (4·71), 3590 (4·53); β″, 3160 (4·65); in dioxane: 2810 (4·84).

Condensation of (I) without fission results in the formation of the hydrocarbon (III).

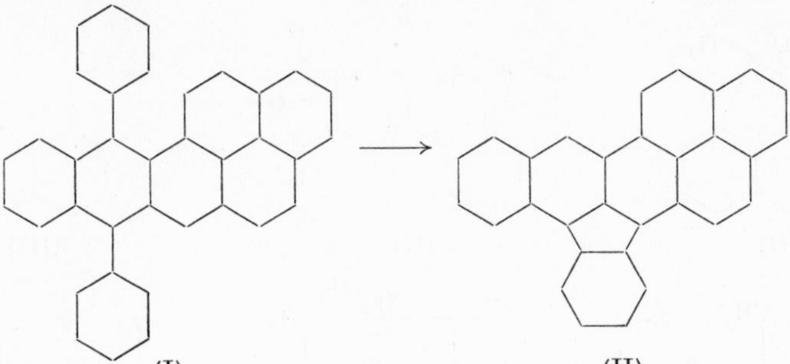

(I)   →   (II)

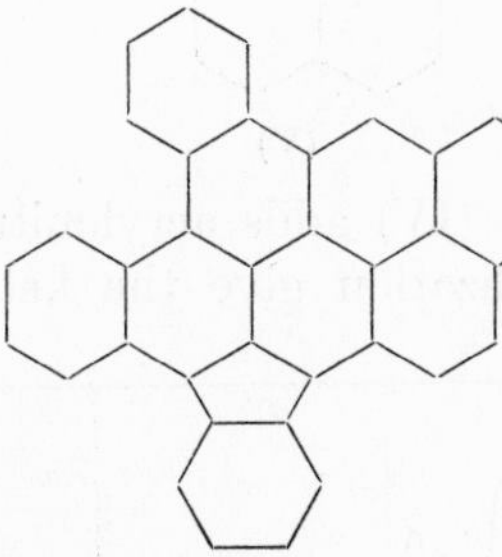

(III)

2.3,4.5-Dibenzo-1.12-o-phenyleneanthanthrene (III) forms deep blue needles (m.p. 334°), which give a blue solution with concentrated sulphuric acid. The purple-violet solutions in organic solvents show an orange-red fluorescence. The absorption spectrum is given in Fig. 198.[1]

REFERENCE

1. Clar, E. and Willicks, W., *Chem. Ber.* **89**, 743 (1956).

XIX. 2.13-BENZOFLUORANTHENE

(*Benzo(mno)fluoranthene*)

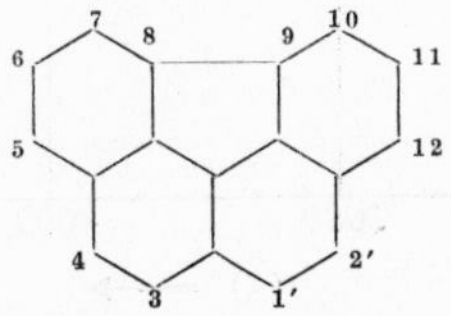

4.5-Benzofluorenone reacts with methyl magnesium iodide to give the carbinol (I). Treatment with maleic anhydride and acetic anhydride splits out one molecule of water and brings about a diene synthesis with the formation of the anhydride (II). Decarboxylation yields benzo-fluoranthene (III).

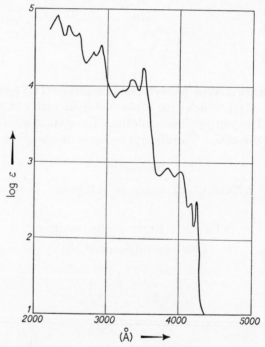

(I)   (II)   (III)

(IV)   (V)   (VI)

Methylenephenanthrene (IV) adds acrylonitrile to form the nitrile (V). Hydrolysis and cyclization give the ketone (VI) which, after

Fig. 199. Absorption spectrum of 2.13-benzofluoranthene in ethanol: α, 4240 (2·50), 4160 (2·47), 4010 (2·89), 3820 (2·95); p, 3500 (4·24), 3350 (4·09); β, 2910 (4·55), 2800 (4·45); 2610 (4·70), 2450 (4·80), 2320 (4·94).

reduction and dehydrogenation, yields benzofluoranthene.[1] Benzofluoranthene (III) has also been isolated from the coal-tar fraction boiling at 425–428°.[2]

2.13-Benzofluoranthene (III) crystallizes from alcohol in thin yellow needles (m.p. 149°), which dissolve in warm concentrated sulphuric acid to give a green solution. The picrate has a m.p. of 228–229°. The absorption spectrum is given in Fig. 199.

REFERENCES

1. Campbell, N. and Reid, D. H., *J. chem. Soc.* 3281 (1952).
2. Kruber, O. and Grigoleit, G., *Chem. Ber.* **87**, 1895.

XX. 2.13-*o*-PHENYLENEFLUORANTHENE

Cyclodehydrogenation of the hydrocarbon (I) with a palladium–platinum–charcoal catalyst at 490° gives a yellow hydrocarbon which is believed to be phenylenefluoranthene (II).

(I)   (II)

2.13-*o*-Phenylenefluoranthene (II) crystallizes in pale yellow needles (m.p. 179·5°), which dissolve in concentrated sulphuric acid to a green solution. The picrate has a m.p. of 231°.[1]

REFERENCE

1. Copeland, P. G., Dean, R. E. and McNeil, D., *J. chem. Soc.* 1687 (1960).

XXI. 2.13,11.12-Dibenzofluoranthene

4,5-Methylenephenanthrene (I) condenses with o-chlorobenzaldehyde to give the compound (II). Cyclization is effected in boiling quinoline with potassium hydroxide.[1]

(I)   (II)   (III)

2.13,11.12-Dibenzofluoranthene (III) crystallizes in pale green needles (m.p. 147–149°). They dissolve in warm concentrated sulphuric acid to give a green solution which changes to brown on standing.

Reference

1. Campbell, N. and Reid, D. H., *J. chem. Soc.* 3281 (1952).

CHAPTER 42

Hydrocarbons Containing Two Five-membered Rings

I. 4.5-*o*-PHENYLENEFLUORANTHENE

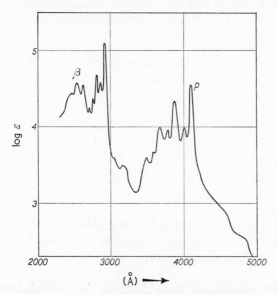

Condensation of 4-iodofluoranthene (I) with *o*-bromonitrobenzene and copper powder gives nitrophenyl-fluoranthene (II). Reduction of the nitro group, diazotization of the amino group and decomposition in

Fig. 200. Absorption spectrum of 4.5-*o*-phenylenefluoranthene in ethanol: *p*, 4100 (4·56), 4020 (3·98), 3870 (4·34), 3795 (3·96), 3670 (4·00), 3490 (3·58); 3170 (3·50), 3040 (3·60), 2925 (5·10), 2865 (4·60), 2810 (4·70), 2760 (4·38), 2705 (4·26); β, 2625 (4·56), 2530 (4·58).

the presence of copper powder leads to 4.5-o-phenylenefluoranthene
(III).

(I)   (II)   (III)

4.5-o-Phenylenefluoranthene (III) forms orange needles (m.p. 261–
262°). They do not dissolve in concentrated sulphuric acid with any
characteristic colour. The absorption spectrum is given in Fig. 200.[1]

2-Methyl-4.5-o-phenylenefluoranthene (m.p. 205–206°) has been
synthesized.[2]

REFERENCES

1. Stubbs, H. W. D. and Tucker, S. H., *J. chem. Soc.* 2936 (1951).
2. Beaton, J. M. and Tucker, S. H., *J. chem. Soc.* 3870 (1952).

II. ISORUBICENE

The reaction of phenyl magnesium bromide with 1,4-dichloroanthra-
quinone yields the diol (I). Cyclization to (II) is carried out in a melt
with oxalic acid, sodium acetate, copper powder and aluminium
powder.[1, 2]

Isorubicene crystallizes from benzene in reddish-brown needles
(m.p. 279°). They dissolve in nitrobenzene containing aluminium
chloride with a greenish-brown colour. The absorption spectrum is given
in Fig. 201.[2]

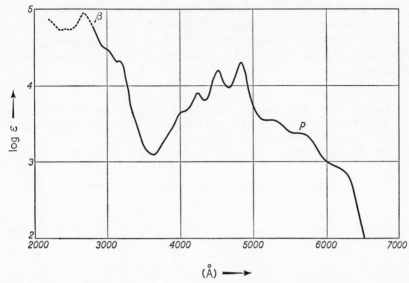

FIG. 201. Absorption spectrum of isorubicene in benzene: p, 6250 (2·87), 5630 (3·37), 5300 (3·54), 4850 (4·31), 4530 (4·20), 4250 (3·90), 4020 (3·66), 3170 (4·34); in ethanol: β, 2680 (4·97).

In contrast to the analogous formation of rubicene, isorubicene cannot be obtained from dichlorodiphenylanthracene (III) with boiling quinoline and potassium permanganate. A short reaction gives phenylchlorofluoranthene (IV) and a longer treatment yields only alkali-soluble products.[2]

REFERENCES

1. Federov, B. P., *Bull. Acad. Sci. U.R.S.S.*, *Classe sci. Chim.* 397 (1947); *Amer. Abstr.* 1585 (1948); Setkina, O. N. and Federov, B. P., *Izv. Akad. Nauk S.S.S.R., Otdel Khim. Nauk* 545 (1949); *Amer. Abstr.* 1333 (1950).
2. Clar, E. and Willicks, W., *J. chem. Soc.* 942 (1958).

III. 5.6,11.12-Di-*o*-phenylenetetracene

5,11-Diphenyl-6,12-dichlorotetracene (I) splits out hydrochloric acid at 200° and condenses to 5-chloro-4-phenyl-2.3,6.7-dibenzofluoranthene (II). This is a violet photo-oxidizable compound which splits out another molecule of hydrochloric acid when treated with potassium hydroxide in boiling naphthalene and yields diphenylenetetracene (III).[1]

Treatment of dehydrorubrene (IV) with sodium in ether yields diphenylenetetracene (III) and its dihydro derivative (V). The two phenyl groups are split off as phenyl sodium.[2] 5,11-Diphenyltetracene also forms diphenylenetetracene by a short reaction with concentrated sulphuric acid.[3]

Tetrachlorotetracene dichloride (VI) reacts with benzene and aluminium chloride to give diphenylenetetracene. In an analogous reaction

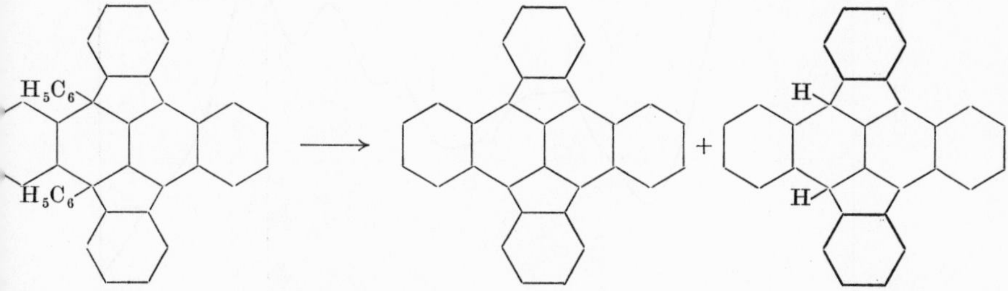

(IV)   (III)   (V)

(VI)   (III)

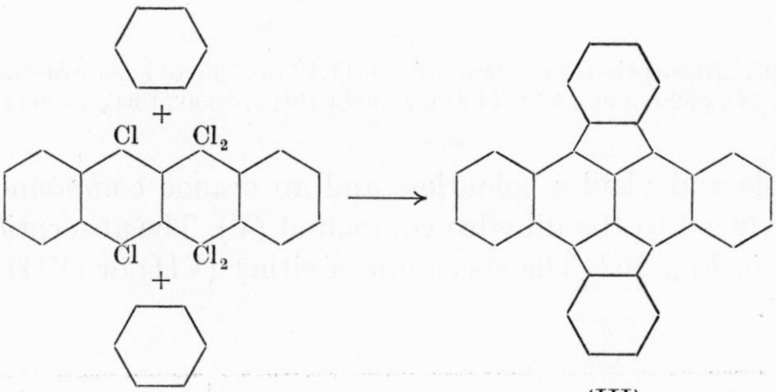

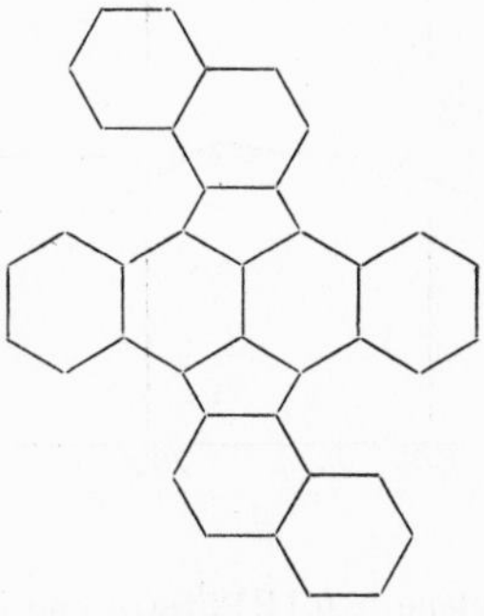

(VII) 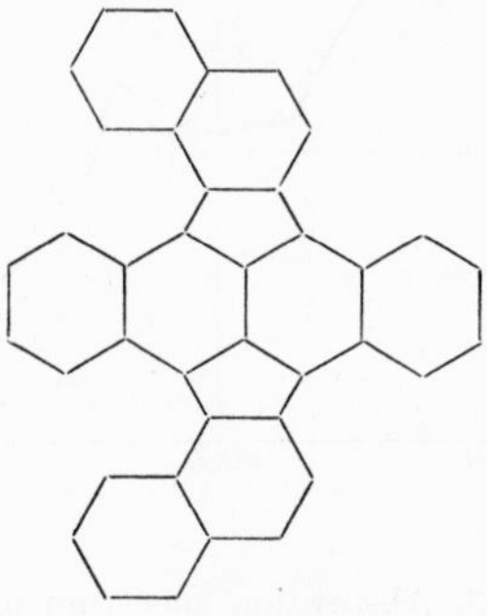   (VIII)

replacing benzene by naphthalene a green hydrocarbon (m.p. 402°), was obtained which could have the structure (VII) or (VIII).[4]

5.6,11.12-Di-o-phenylenetetracene (III) crystallizes from xylene in blue needles (m.p. 465°). The blue solutions of the hydrocarbon are photo-

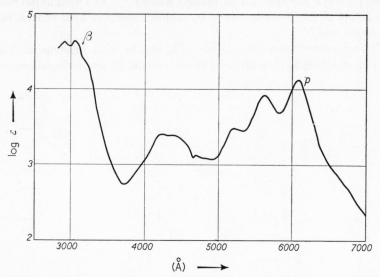

FIG. 202. Absorption spectrum of 5.6,11.12-di-o-phenylenetetracene in benzene: p, 6090 (4·14), 5620 (3·92), 5220 (3·48), 4200 (3·40); β, 3050 (4·64), 2900 (4·63).

oxidizable and yield a colourless and an orange compound. It can be easily reduced to the dihydro compound (V). The absorption spectrum is given in Fig. 202. The spectrum of either (VII) or (VIII) is given in Fig. 203.

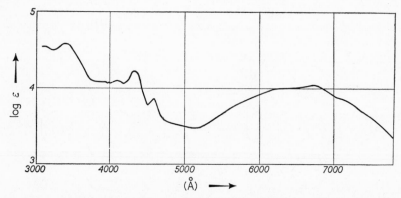

FIG. 203. Absorption spectrum of di-(1,2-naphthylene)-5.6,11.12-tetracene in 1,2,4-trichlorobenzene: 6700 (4·04), 4600 (3·87), 4325 (4·21), 4100 (4·10), 3400 (4·60).[4]

Some of the above compounds have been previously formulated in a different way. The changes have been considered in a review.[5]

REFERENCES

1. Dufraisse, Ch., Buret, R. and Girard, R., *Bull. Soc. chim. Fr.* (4) **53**, 782 (1932); (5) **1**, 1359 (1934).
2. Badoche, M., *Ann. Chim. Fr.* (10) **20**, 200 (1933).
3. Loury, M., *Ann. Chim. Fr.* **10**, 807 (1955).
4. Lang, K. F. and Theiling, E. A., *Chem. Ber.* **89**, 2734 (1956).
5. Dufraisse, Ch., *Bull. Soc. chim. Fr.* (5) **3**, 1857 (1936).

IV. RUBICENE

The distillation of diphenic acid yields a red hydrocarbon which was believed to have the structure (I).[1] This formula was seemingly supported by the formation of rubicene by pyrolysis.[2, 3] However, the true constitution was established by the synthesis of rubicene (III) by a condensation of fluorenone (II) with calcium hydride,[4] or magnesium.[5]

The diol (V) gives rubicene in a melt of oxalic acid, sodium acetate, copper powder and aluminium powder at 365°.[6] The dilactone (IV) also yields rubicene when distilled with zinc dust.[7] Rubicene is obtained in good yield from (VI) with boiling quinoline and potassium hydroxide.[8]

Fluorenone (VII) reacts with hydrogen sulphide to give the disulphide (VIII) which, when heated to 275°, goes over into rubicene.[9]

Rubicene crystallizes in red needles (m.p. 306°). Solutions in organic solvents have a yellow fluorescence. It dissolves in warm concentrated sulphuric acid with a reddish-brown colour. Zinc dust in acetic acid reduces rubicene to the green-blue fluorescing dihydro-rubicene.[9] Nitrobenzene containing aluminium chloride dissolves rubicene with a green colour which soon changes to violet-black. The absorption spectrum is given in Fig. 204.

The hydrogenation of rubicene with sodium in amyl alcohol yields a perhydro compound. This loses twelve atoms of hydrogen on distillation or when boiled with oxygen-containing solvents, and gives a hydro-carbon $C_{26}H_{28}$. Hydrogenation with nickel and hydrogen under pressure yields perhydrorubicene and the hydrocarbons $C_{26}H_{34}$ and $C_{26}H_{28}$.[10]

Rubicene forms a red sulphonic acid with sulphuric acid, which is a dyestuff. Nitration gives a dinitro compound from which a diamino compound is obtained by reduction. Sulphonation of the latter gives a greyish-blue dyestuff. Rubicene can be condensed with two molecules of

(I)   (III)   (II)

$-2CO_2$ $-2HCl$
                          $-H_2O$
$-H_2$ $-O$

(IV)   (V)   (VI)

$\xrightarrow{\text{H}_2\text{S}}$
HCl

(VII)   (VIII)   (III)

phthalic anhydride using aluminium chloride. The dicarboxylic acid thus obtained is a red dyestuff. Other condensations have been carried out with o-chlorophthalanhydride, succinic anhydride and maleic anhydride.[11]

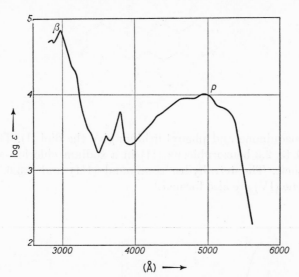

FIG. 204. Absorption spectrum of rubicene in benzene: p, 5300 (3·92), 4940 (4·00), 4650 (3·95); 3790 (3·77), 3600 (3·45); β, 2970 (4·85); in ethanol: 2510 (5·00), 2300 (5·10).

REFERENCES

1. Fittig, R. and Ostermayer, E., *Liebigs Ann.* **166**, 373 (1873); Fittig, R. and Schmitz, A., *Liebigs Ann.* **193**, 117 (1878); Pummerer, R., *Ber. dtsch. chem. Ges.* **45**, 294 (1912); **58**, 1806 (1925).

2. Dziewoński, K. and Suszko, J., *Bull. Acad. polon. Sci. Lettres* (Sept. 1921); C. **1923 I**, 528; *Ber. dtsch. chem. Ges.* **58**, 2544 (1925).

3. Eckert, A., *J. prakt. Chem.* (2) **121**, 278 (1929); Lang, K. F., Buffleb, H. and Kalowy, J., *Chem. Ber.* **94**, 523 (1961).

4. Schlenk, W. and Karplus, M., *Ber. dtsch. chem. Ges.* **61**, 1675 (1928).

5. Chmelewski, W. I. and Postowski, I. J., *J. gen. Chem., U.S.S.R.* **9** (71) 620 (1939); *Chem. Zbl.* **1941 I**, 891.

6. Federov, B. P., *Bull. Acad. Sci. U.R.S.S., Classe Sci. Chim.* 397 (1947); *Amer. Abstr.* 1585 (1948).

7. Scholl, R. and Meyer, K., *Ber. dtsch. chem. Ges.* **65**, 926 (1932).

8. Clar, E. and Willicks, W., *J. chem. Soc.* 942, (1958).

9. Schönberg, A. and Brosowski, K. H., *Chem. Ber.* **93**, 2149 (1960), **95**, 1910 (1962).

10. von Braun, J., *Ber. dtsch. chem. Ges.* **67**, 214 (1934); Dziewoński, K. and Suszko, J., *Roczniki Chem.* 409 (1921).

11. I. G. Farbenindustrie AG, German Patent 655649 ,656554 (1936); *Chem. Zbl.* **1938 I**, 4538; Dziewoński, K. and Suszko, J., *Bull. int. Acad. polon. Sci. Lettres* (Jan.–Dec. 1921); *Chem. Zbl.* **1923 I**, 528.

V. 2.3-BENZORUBICENE

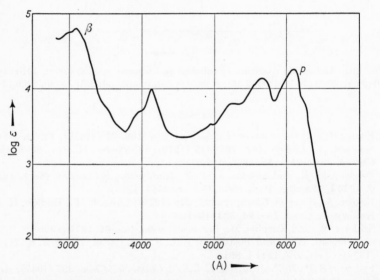

Tetracenequinone and phenyl lithium give the diol (I). This can be condensed to 2.3-benzorubicene (II) in a sodium chloride–aluminium chloride melt. The tetrahydro compound (III) and 2.3,6.7-dibenzo-fluoranthene (IV) are also formed.[1]

FIG. 205. Absorption spectrum of 2.3-benzorubicene in benzene: p, 6100 (4·26), 5650 (4·14), 5300 (3·80), 4960 (3·52), 4140 (3·99); β, 3100 (4·80).

2.3-Benzorubicene (II) crystallizes from benzene in deep blue needles (m.p. 250°), which dissolve in concentrated sulphuric acid to give a green solution. The blue solution in benzene shows a red fluorescence. The absorption spectrum is given in Fig. 205. The tetrahydro compound (III) forms red-brown needles (m.p. 182°), and shows the absorption spectrum of a rubicene derivative. 2.3-Benzorubicene adds maleic anhydride to form the adduct (V), which has a spectrum related to 4-phenylfluoranthene.[1]

REFERENCE

1. Clar, E. and Willicks, W., *J. chem. Soc.* 942 (1958).

VI. DIBENZORUBICENES

If, in the rubicene synthesis from fluorenone and calcium hydride, fluorenone is replaced by 2.3-benzofluorenone (I), a dibenzorubicene is obtained which can have the structure (II) or (IIa). Its m.p. is 310° and its sulphonic acid is a dyestuff.[1]

Anthraquinone-1,5-dicarboxylic dichloride gives a dilactone with naphthalene and aluminium chloride. This dilactone was believed to have the structure (III). Its distillation with zinc dust yields a dibenzo-rubicene which would have the structure (IV) accordingly.[2] However, there are indications that the dilactone has in fact the structure (V).[3] The dibenzorubicene resulting from the zinc-dust distillation would then have the formula (VI).

(I)   (II)   or   (IIa)

(III)   (IV)

(V)   (VI)

The dibenzorubicene thus obtained crystallizes in brownish-black needles. The red solutions in organic solvents show a yellow fluorescence. It is insoluble in cold concentrated sulphuric acid.

REFERENCES

1. I. G. Farbenindustrie AG, German Patent 655649 (1936); *Chem. Zbl.* **1938 I**, 4538.
2. Scholl, R. and Meyer, K., *Ber. dtsch. chem. Ges.* **67**, 1229 (1934).
3. Clar, E. and Kelly W., *J. chem. Soc.* 3875 (1956).

VII. 2.3,7.8-DI-(o-PHENYLENE)-PYRENE

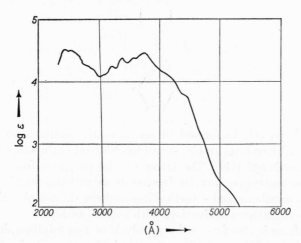

The pyrolysis of pyrene and benzene at 750° yields diphenylenene-pyrene and other hydrocarbons.

FIG. 206. Absorption spectrum of 2.3,7.8-di-(o-phenylene)-pyrene in dioxane: 3750 (4·46), 3380 (4·39), 3220 (4·24), 2440 (4·52).

2.3,7.8-Di-(o-phenylene)-pyrene crystallizes from xylene in dark yellow needles (m.p. 371–375°). It does not dissolve in cold concentrated sulphuric acid. The absorption spectrum is given in Fig. 206.[1]

REFERENCE

1. Lang, K. F. and Buffleb, H., *Chem. Ber.* **90**, 2894 (1957).

VIII. PERIFLANTHENE

Periflanthene (II) is formed in an unusual condensation of fluoranthene (I) with sodium amide. It can be obtained in the same way from 4,4'-difluoranthenyl (III). The latter can be prepared from 4-bromofluoranthene and copper powder. In accordance with this reaction scheme, 4-phenylfluoranthene and 4-methylfluoranthene do not give the corresponding periflanthene derivatives with sodium amide.[1]

Periflanthene is also formed by pyrolysis of 1-(o-tolyl)-naphthalene.[2]

Periflanthene (II) crystallizes from trichlorobenzene in deep red leaflets (m.p. > 360°). The absorption spectrum is given in Fig. 207.

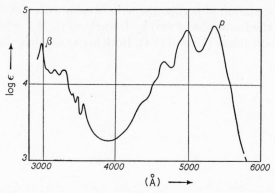

FIG. 207. Absorption spectrum of periflanthene in 1,2,4-trichlorobenzene: p, 5400 (4·80), 5030 (4·63), 4710 (4·25), 4400 (3·76); in dioxane, 3250 (4·13), 3150 (4·12): β, 2940 (4·60), 2820 (4·50).

(I)   (II)   (III)   (IV)

(V)   (VI)   (VII)   (VIII)

II—12

The hydrogenation of periflanthene in decalin with nickel and hydrogen leads to the formation of two hydrocarbons $C_{32}H_{28}$, which probably have the constitutions (V) and (VI). Both are easily dehydrogenated by

(IX)   (X)   (XI)   (XII)

(XIII)   (XIV)   (XV)   (XVI)

the presence of air when recrystallized from benzene, and give a hydrocarbon $C_{32}H_{32}$ which probably has the formula (VII). The same hydrocarbon can be obtained by a mild hydrogenation from periflanthene.[1] A mild dehydrogenation of the hydrocarbon (VII) yields the hydrocarbon $C_{32}H_{28}$ which probably has the structure (VIII).

Periflanthene gives a red dyestuff with concentrated sulphuric acid at 100°. Phthalic anhydride and aluminium chloride form a dark violet vat dye.

The oxidation of periflanthene in nitrobenzene with sodium bichromate in acetic acid yields the three quinones (IX), (X) and (XI). Further oxidation of (XI) leads to the acid (XII), which forms the anhydride (XIII). This loses CO_2 when sublimed and gives the triketone (XIV). Sublimation of the dicarboxylic acid leads to decarboxylation and the formation of the diketone (XV). This gives quaterphenyl (XVI) when distilled with zinc dust or with soda-lime.[3]

REFERENCES

1. von Braun, J. and Manz, G., *Ber. dtsch. chem. Ges.* **70**, 1603 (1937).
2. Orchin, M., Reggel, L., Friedel, R. A. and Woolfolk, E. O., *Bur. Mines, Techn. Paper* **708**, 26 (1948).
3. Zinke, A. and Ammerer, L., *Mh. Chem.* **84**, 422 (1953); Zinke, A., Ammerer, L. and Zeschko, E., *Mh. Chem.* **95**, 1117 (1962).

IX. 1.16-BENZOPERIFLANTHENE

Periflanthene (I) reacts with boiling maleic anhydride and chloranil to form the anhydride (II). Sublimation with soda-lime *in vacuo* yields 1.16-benzoperiflanthene (III).

1.16-Benzoperiflanthene (III) crystallizes from trichlorobenzene or sublimes in long red needles (m.p. 441–442°), which do not dissolve in concentrated sulphuric acid. The absorption spectrum is given in Fig. 208.[1]

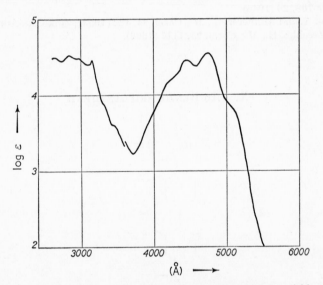

(I)   (II)   (III)

FIG. 208. Absorption spectrum of 1.16-benzoperiflanthene in 1,2,4-trichlorobenzene: p, 4750 (4·56), 4450 (4·45), in dioxane: β, 3150 (4·47), 2960 (4·50), 2840 (4·54).[1]

REFERENCE

1. Lang, K. F. and Zander, M., *Chem. Ber.* **95**, 673 (1962).

X. 10.11-*peri*-NAPHTHYLENEFLUORANTHENE

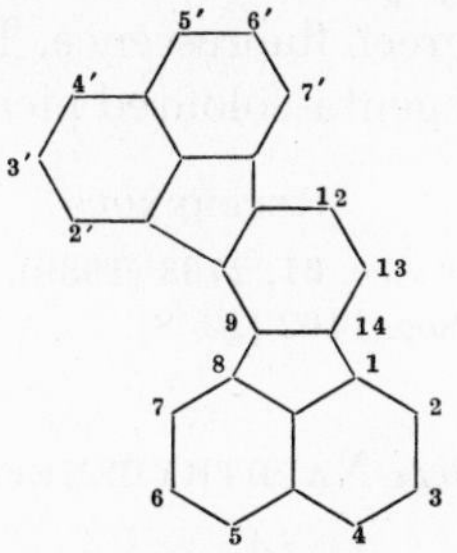

Dinaphthylenethiophene (I) reacts readily with maleic anhydride to give the anhydride (II).[1] Decarboxylation of the corresponding barium salt with copper powder yields naphthylenefluoranthene (III).[2]

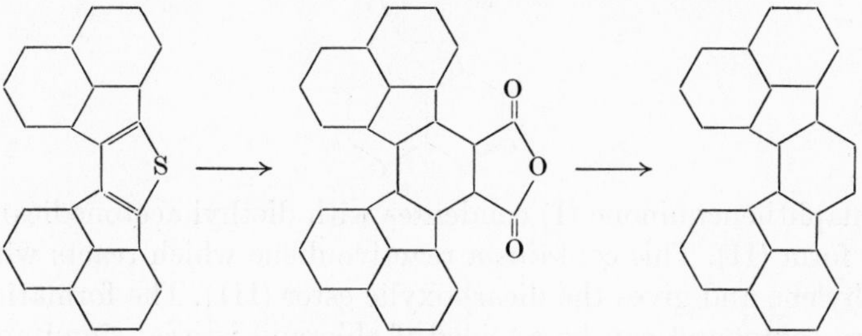

(I)   (II)   (III)

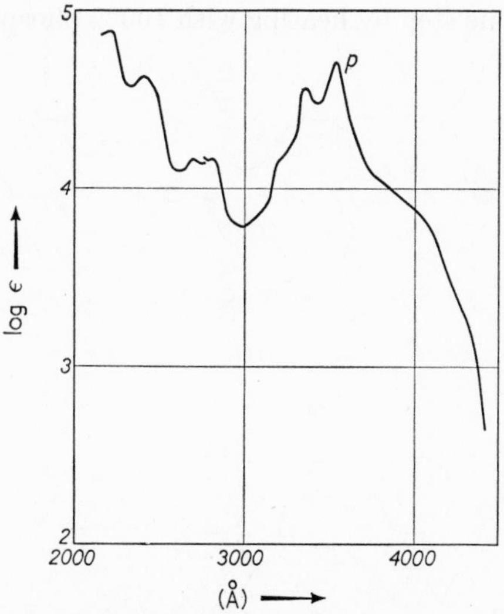

FIG. 209. Absorption spectrum of 10.11-*peri*-naphthylenefluoranthene in benzene: *p*, 4000 (3·92), 3540 (4·74), 3370 (4·56), 2820 (4·14); in ethanol: 2720 (4·16), 2440 (4·62). (Lang, K. F. and Zander, *Chem. Ber.* **94**, 1871 (1961).)

10.11-*peri*-Naphthylenefluoranthene (III) crystallizes from benzene or ethyl acetate in canary-yellow needles (m.p. 232–233°). Solutions in organic solvents show a green fluorescence. The absorptions spectrum is given in Fig. 209. The magenta-coloured picrate has a m.p. of 239–240°.

REFERENCES

1. Clapp, J., *J. Amer. chem. Soc.* **61**, 2733 (1939).
2. Tucker, S. H., *J. chem. Soc.* 1462 (1958).

XI. 11.12-*peri*-NAPHTHYLENEFLUORANTHENE

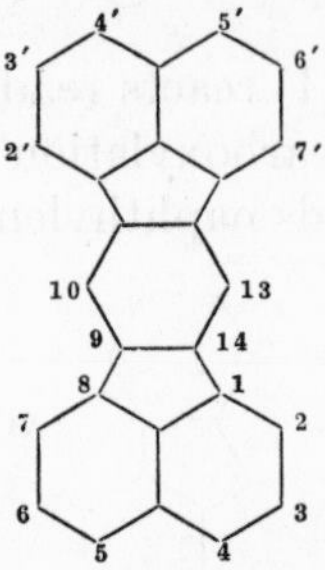

Acenaphthenequinone (I) condenses with diethyl acetonedicarboxylate to form (II). This contains a reactive diene which reacts with acenaphthylene and gives the dicarboxylic ester (III). The formation of a dihydro compound can be avoided if chloranil is used simultaneously as a dehydrogenating agent. The diester (III) is hydrolysed and decarboxylated in one step by heating with 100% phosphoric acid.

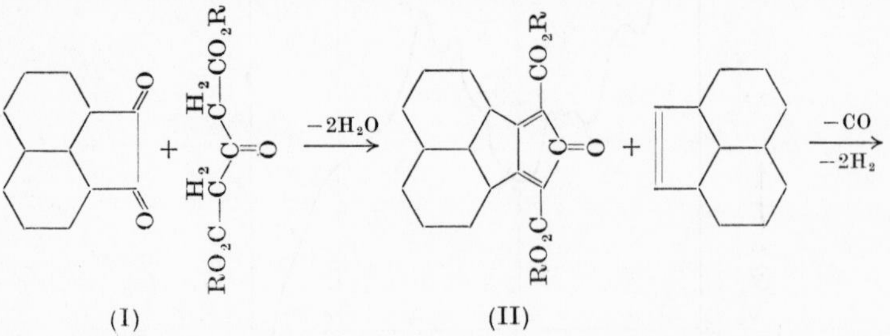

(I)   (II)

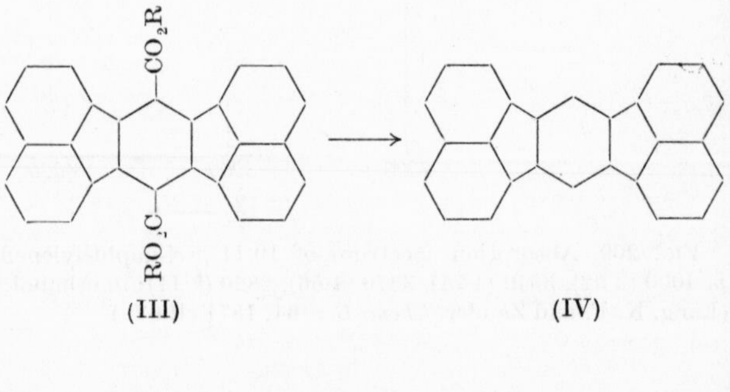

(III)   (IV)

11.12-*peri*-Naphthylenefluoranthene (IV) crystallizes from benzene in golden yellow needles (m.p. 315°). The absorption spectrum is given in Fig. 210.[1]

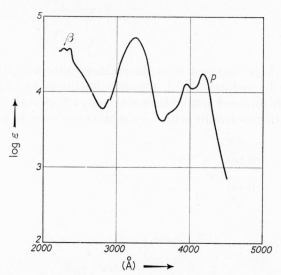

FIG. 210. Absorption spectrum of 11.12-*peri*-naphthylenefluoranthene in benzene: p, 4170 (4·24), 3940 (4·10); β, 3250 (4·72), in cyclohexane: β', 2360 (4·58).

A diphenyl derivative of (IV) can be prepared from acecyclone (V) and acenaphthylene. This derivative (VI) forms yellow needles (m.p. 403°), which dissolve in organic solvents with a yellow colour and a green fluorescence.[2]

(V)   (VI)

REFERENCES

1. Tucker, S. H., *J. chem. Soc.* 1462 (1958).
2. Dilthey, W., Henkels, S. and Schaefer, A., *Ber. dtsch. chem. Ges.* **71**, 974 (1938).

XII. 2.3,6.7-DI-(*peri*-NAPHTHYLENE)-NAPHTHALENE

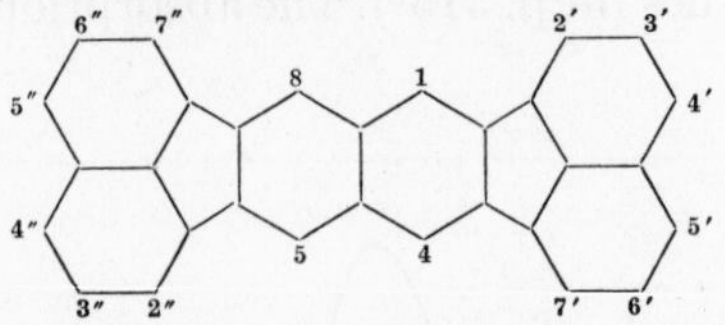

The diol (I) is obtained from fluoranthene dicarboxylic anhydride (see p. 297) by reduction with lithium aluminium hydride. The two hydroxyls are replaced first by Br and then by CN groups. The resulting dinitrile condenses readily with acenaphthenequinone in pyridine and

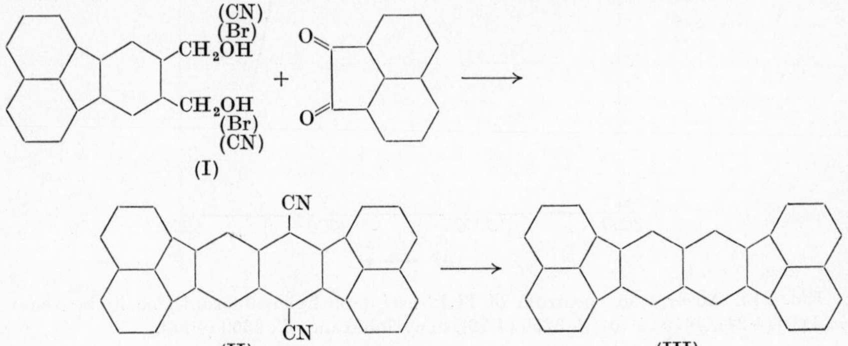

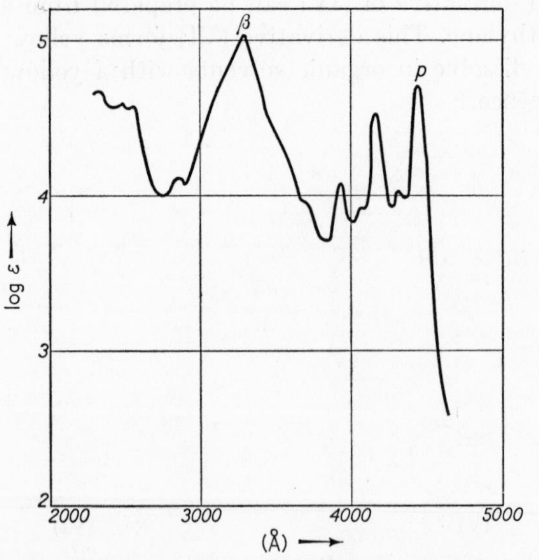

FIG. 211. Absorption spectrum of 2.3,6.7-di-(*peri*-naphthylene)-naphthalene in benzene: p, 4450 (4·74), 4180 (4·54), 3940 (4·09); β, 3290 (5·04), 2850 (4·10), in cyclohexane: 2320 (4·66).

piperidine to the compound (II). A sublimation with soda-lime and potassium hydroxide yields directly the hydrocarbon (III).

2.3,6.7-Di-(*peri*-naphthylene)-naphthalene (III) crystallizes from xylene in needles or leaflets (m.p. 368–370°) which dissolve very slowly in concentrated sulphuric acid to give a green solution. The solution in organic solvents shows a strong blue fluorescence. The absorption spectrum is given in Fig. 211.[1]

REFERENCE

1. Clar, E. and Stephen, J. F., *Tetrahedron*, in press.

XIII. 1.2,3.4-DI-(*peri*-NAPHTHYLENE)-ANTHRACENE

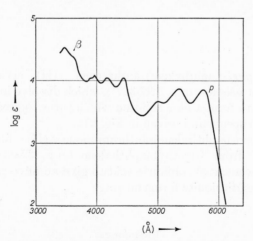

Diacenaphthylidene (I) can be dehydrogenated and subjected to a diene synthesis in one step by heating it with naphthoquinone in boiling

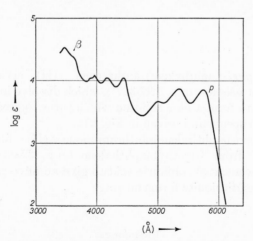

FIG. 212. Absorption spectrum of 1.2,3.4-di-(*peri*-naphthylene)-anthracene in 1,2,4-trichlorobenzene: p, 5750 (3·85), 5350 (3·86), 5020 (3·67), 4440 (4·04), 4180 (4·05), 3980 (4·08); β, 3490 (4·52). (Lang, K. F. and Zander, M., *Chem. Ber.* **94**, 1871 (1961).)

II—12*

xylene. The quinone (II) is reduced to the hydrocarbon (III) by a reduction with pyridine, zinc dust and acetic acid. This gives first the dihydro
compound of (III) (m.p. 324–325°), which is easily dehydrogenated with
chloranil in xylene or by sublimation with copper powder.

(I)   (II)

(III)

1.2,3.4-Di-(peri-naphthylene)-anthracene (III) crystallizes from
xylene in violet needles (m.p. 326–327°), which dissolve in concentrated
sulphuric acid to form a blue solution which turns to green on storage.
The absorption spectrum is given in Fig. 212.

1.2,3.4-Di-(peri-naphthylene)-anthraquinone (II) forms orange-
yellow needles from 1-methylnaphthalene (m.p. 328·5–330°), which
dissolve in concentrated sulphuric acid to give an olive-green solution.
Alkaline sodium dithionite forms no vat.[1]

REFERENCE

1. Zander, M., *Chem. Ber.* **92**, 2740 (1959); Lang, K. F. and Zander, M., *Chem.
   Ber.* **94**, 1871 (1961).

XIV. 2.3,6.7-Di-(*peri*-NAPHTHYLENE)-ANTHRACENE

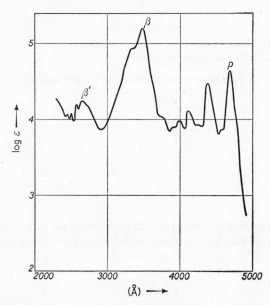

The diol (I) undergoes a double diene synthesis with benzoquinone and forms the quinone (II).

FIG. 213. Absorption spectrum of 2.3,6.7-di-(*peri*-naphthylene)-anthracene in benzene: p, 4730 (4·66), 4420 (4·46), 4160 (4·12), 4030 (4·00); β, 3540 (5·22), 3380 (4·96), in cyclohexane: β', 2700 (4·28).

This crystallizes as brown prisms (m.p. > 360°), which dissolve in concentrated sulphuric acid to give a blue solution. A blue unstable vat is obtained with alkaline sodium dithionite.[1]

The hydrocarbon (III) is obtained from the quinone (II) by reduction with pyridine, acetic acid and zinc dust.[2]

2.3,6.7-Di-(*peri*-naphthylene)-anthracene (III) crystallizes from nitrobenzene in golden yellow leaflets (m.p. 460°) which dissolve very slowly in concentrated sulphuric acid to give a red brown solution. The solution in benzene shows a strong green fluorescence. The absorption spectrum is given in Fig. 213.[2]

(III)

REFERENCES

1. Campbell, N. and Gow, R. S., *J. chem. Soc.* 1555 (1949).
2. Stephen, J. F., Thesis, Glasgow (1964).

XV. DI-(*o*-PHENYLENE)-PHENANTHRENE

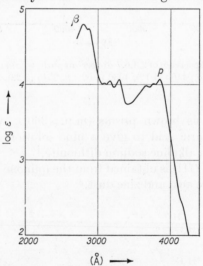

The pyrolysis of fluorene gives dibenzochrysene (see Vol. 1, p. 283), rubicene and a yellow hydrocarbon which was given the above structure.

FIG. 214. Absorption spectrum of di-(*o*-phenylene)-phenanthrene in benzene: *p*, 3850 (4·06), 3770 (4·00), 3650 (3·98); 3280 (4·06), 3160 (4·04); *β*, 2880 (4·72), 2800 (4·80).

It crystallizes from xylene in yellow needles (m.p. 288–289°), which are insoluble in cold concentrated sulphuric acid, but dissolve on heating with a faint yellow colour. The absorption spectrum is given in Fig. 214.[1]

REFERENCE

1. Lang, K. F., Buffleb, H. and Kalowy, J., *Chem. Ber.* **94**, 523 (1961).

XVI. 2.3-*o*-PHENYLENE-4.5-*peri*-NAPHTHYLENEPYRENE

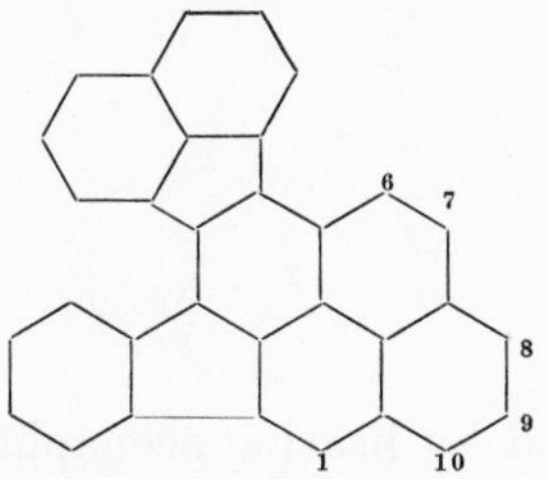

Indenoperinaphthene (I) (see p. 467) condenses with bromoace-naphthylene to give the hydrocarbon (II).[1]

2.3-*o*-Phenylene-4.5-*peri*-naphthylenepyrene (II) crystallizes in orange needles (m.p. 350°).[1]

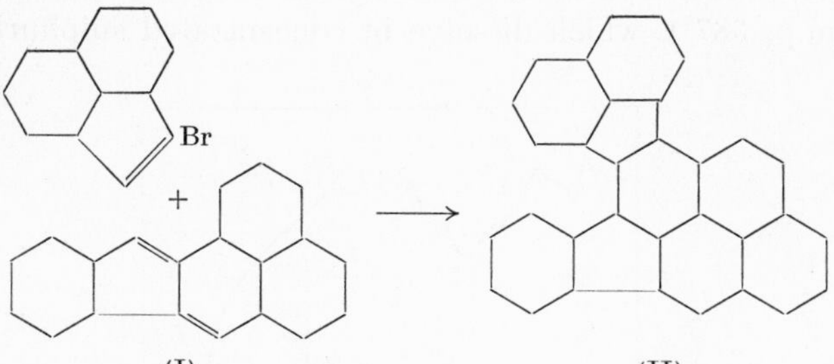

(I)   (II)

REFERENCE

1. Aitken, I. M. and Reid, D. H., *J. chem. Soc.* 663 (1960).

CHAPTER 43

Hydrocarbons Containing Three Five-membered Rings

DECACYCLENE

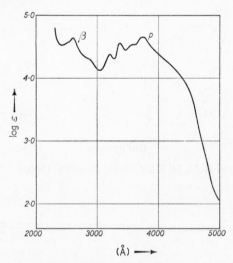

Decacyclene is obtained by heating acenaphthene (I) with sulphur[1] or with lead dioxide.[2] In the latter case fluorocyclene (III) is formed as a by-product which also gives decacyclene by thermal decomposition.[3] Heating of acenaphthylene or polyacenaphthylene also yields decacyclene.[4] Dinapthylenethiophene (V) when fused with alkali and acenaphthene or acenaphthylene gives decacyclene.[5]

Decacyclene (II) crystallizes from xylene or nitrobenzene in yellow needles (m.p. 387°), which dissolve in concentrated sulphuric acid to

FIG. 215. Absorption spectrum of decacyclene in dioxane: p, 3760 (4·65), 3375 (4·55), 3220 (4·36); 2900 (4·32); β, 2600 (4·64).

give a dark brownish-green solution. It is sparingly soluble in organic solvents and shows a green fluorescence. The absorption spectrum is given in Fig. 215.

The hydrogenation of decacyclene with hydrogen and nickel in decalin yields trisdecahydrodecacyclene $C_{36}H_{48}$. The additional thirty hydrogen atoms are located in the naphthalene complexes, because oxidation with nitric acid under pressure gives mellitic acid. Partial dehydrogenation with sulphur results in the dehydrogenation of one of the decalin complexes and the formation of the hydrocarbon $C_{36}H_{38}$. Hydrogenation of decacyclene containing a trace of sulphur gives the hydrocarbon $C_{36}H_{30}$ in which the three naphthalene complexes of decacyclene are replaced by tetralin complexes.[6]

The oxidation of decacyclene with chromic acid gives a tribenzoylene-benzene-tricarboxylic acid, probably (IV).[7] The chlorination of decacyclene in carbon disulphide yields an enneachlorodecacyclene.[8] Bromine gives under the same conditions tribromodecacyclene.[8] Dilute nitric acid produces trinitrodecacyclene.[8] Picric acid produces a picrate.[8] Strong nitric acid yields hexanitrodecacyclene.[9] Decacyclene-trisulphonic acid is obtained by the direct action of sulphuric acid. A trihydroxydecacyclene can be prepared from it by a melt with potassium hydroxide. This gives the tricarboxylic acid (IV) on oxidation.[10]

A number of sulphur dyes have been prepared from decacyclene and its derivatives.[9,11] A tribenzyldecacyclene is formed from 4-benzylacenaphthene and sulphur at 210–245°.[12]

REFERENCES

1. Dziewoński, K., *Ber. dtsch. chem. Ges.* **36**, 962 (1903); Rehländer, P., *Ber. dtsch. chem. Ges.* **36**, 1586 (1903).
2. Dziewoński, K. and Suknarowski, S., *Ber. dtsch. chem. Ges.* **51**, 460 (1918).
3. Dziewoński, K. and Gizler, L., *Bull. Int. Acad. polon. Sci. Lettres* Ser. A. 441 (1937).
4. Dziewoński, K. and Leyko, Z., *Ber. dtsch. chem. Ges.* **47**, 1686 (1914).
5. I. G. Farbenindustrie AG, German Patent 738446 (1940); *Chem. Zbl.* **1943 II**, 2210.
6. von Braun, J., *Ber. dtsch. chem. Ges.* **67**, 214 (1934).
7. Dziewoński, K., *Ber. dtsch. chem. Ges.* **46**, 2158 (1913).
8. Dziewoński, K., *Ber. dtsch. chem. Ges.* **36**, 3772 (1903).
9. I. G. Farbenindustrie AG, Swiss Patent 198892 (1937); *Chem. Zbl.* **1939 I**, 1074.
10. Dziewoński, K. and Pochwalski, P., *Bull. Int. Acad. polon. Sci. Lettres* 165 (1925).
11. I. G. Farbenindustrie AG, French Patent 799342 (1935); *Chem. Zbl.* **1936 II**, 3602; French Patent 799356 (1935); *Chem. Zbl.* **1937 I**, 1800; German Patent 693862 (1936); *Chem. Zbl.* **1940 II**, 2384.
12. Dziewoński, K. and Dotta, E., *Bull. Soc. chim. Fr.* (3) **31**, 930 (1904).

Chapter 44

Hydrocarbons Containing Four Five-membered Rings

1.2,3.4,5.6,7.8-Tetra-(*peri*-naphthylene)-anthracene

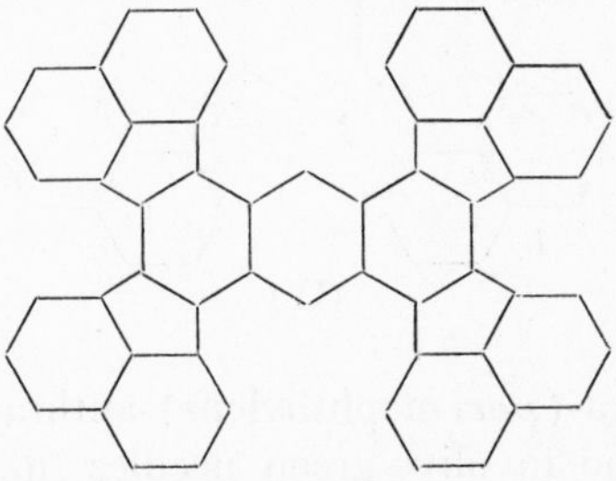

Diacenaphthylidene (I) is dehydrogenated by benzoquinone to (II) and two molecules of this resulting diene (II) condense with one molecule of benzoquinone to form the quinone (III).

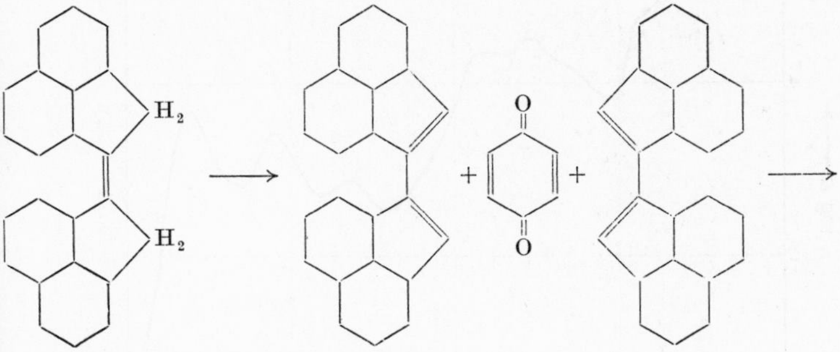

(I) (II)

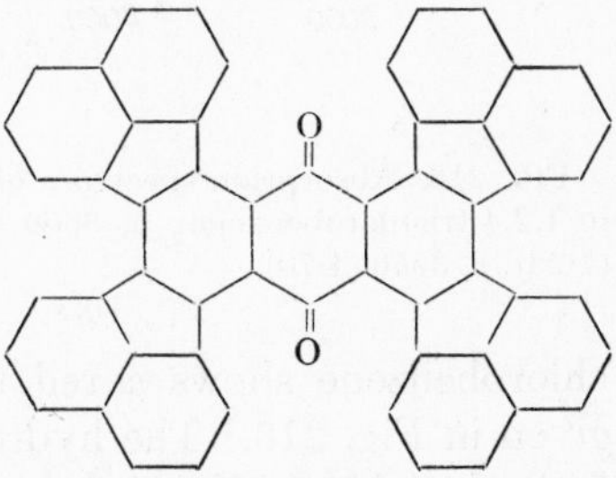

(III)

The reduction of the quinone (III) to the hydrocarbon (IV) is effected with zinc dust and sodium hydroxide solution under pressure at 200°. A colourless product is obtained which yields tetranaphthyleneanthracene (IV) on sublimation *in vacuo*.

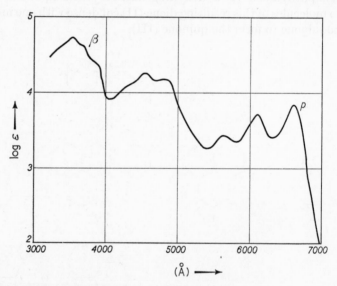

(IV)

1.2,3.4,5.6,7.8-Tetra-(*peri*-naphthylene)-anthracene (IV) crystallizes from trichlorobenzene in olive-green needles (m.p. > 500°), which do not dissolve in concentrated sulphuric acid. The green solution in tri-

FIG. 216. Absorption spectrum of 1.2,3.4,5.6,7.8-tetra-(*peri*-naphthylene)-anthracene in 1,2,4-trichlorobenzene: *p*, 6600 (3·83), 6100 (3·71), 5620 (3·43), 4800 (4·18), 4550 (4·26); *β*, 3550 (4·70).

chlorobenzene shows a red fluorescence. The absorption spectrum is given in Fig. 216.[1] The hydrocarbon readily adds maleic anhydride to form the adduct (V).

The quinone (III) crystallizes from 1-methylnaphthalene as yellow needles (m.p. 481–483°) which do not dissolve in concentrated sulphuric acid and do not produce a vat with alkaline sodium dithionite solution.[1]

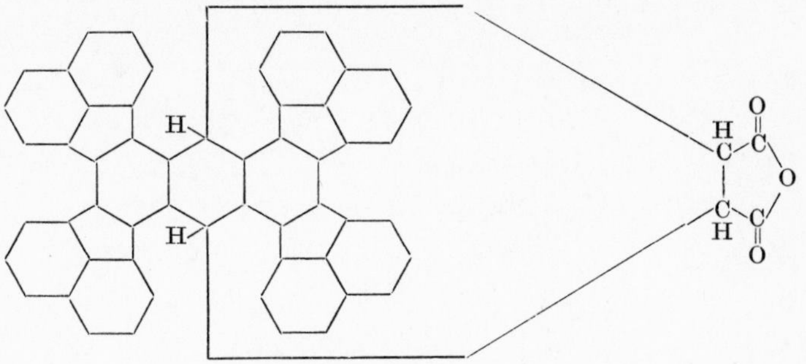

(V)

REFERENCE

1. Zander, M., *Chem. Ber.* **92**, 2740 (1959).

PART VIII

peri-Condensed Hydrocarbons consisting of Six-membered Rings in which One Carbon Atom is linked with Two Hydrogen Atoms

Hydrocarbons of this kind have outstanding properties. Their methylene group is more reactive than the methylene group in fluorene and its benzologues. Their ketone derivatives (perinaphthone, benzanthrones) resemble quinones more than fluorenones. The hydrocarbons cannot be treated as alkyl derivatives but must be dealt with as a separate class of condensed hydrocarbons.

Hydrocarbons Consisting of Six-membered Rings in which One Carbon Atom Is Linked with Two Hydrogen Atoms

I. PERINAPHTHENE

Perinaphthenone was first obtained by oxidation from pyrene. This gives a mixture of pyrenequinones and perinaphthenone-dicarboxylic acid (I). Decarboxylation of the latter yields perinaphthenone (II).[1] It is more easily accessible by a condensation of α- or β-naphthol with glycerol and sulphuric acid.[2] The yields can be considerably improved by the addition of sodium nitrobenzenesulphonate.[3]

Cyclization of naphthylpropionic chloride (VI) with aluminium chloride gives first dihydroperinaphthenone (VII), which can be dehydrogenated to perinaphthenone (II).[4]

(XI)   (XII)   (XIII)

(XIV)   (XV)

(XVI)   (XVII)   (XVIII)

If the cyclization is carried out in anhydrous hydrofluoric acid 4.5-benzindanone is obtained as a by-product.[5]

Anhydrous hydrofluoric acid can also be used for the condensation of naphthol with acrolein.[6] Acetylnaphthalene reacts with formaldehyde to form the compound (VIII). This can be cyclized to perinaphthenone (II) with sulphuric acid. The method can be applied for the preparation of derivatives of (II).[7] Unsaturated ketones of the type (IX) cyclize to perinaphthenone (X) with aluminium chloride. The preparation of the ketone and the cyclization can be united in one operation.[8]

α-Tetralone reacts with bromoacetic ester and zinc to form the compound (XI). Splitting out one molecule of water gives (XII) and reduction (XIII). The ester of the latter is reduced to (XIV) with sodium and alcohol. The hydroxyl in (XIV) is replaced first by bromine and then by a CN group. Hydrolysis yields the acid (XV) and cyclization with aluminium chloride the ketone (XVI). Clemmensen reduction gives (XVII). The dehydrogenation to (XVIII) has not been described in detail.[9] A zinc-dust melt of perinaphthenone (II) gives trimethylenenaphthalene (IV) besides peropyrene.[10] The same hydrocarbon is obtained by catalytic hydrogenation of perinaphthenone with copper chromite which also yields the alcohol (V).[11] Trimethylenenaphthalene (IV) has also been prepared from the dicarboxylic acid (III) by decarboxylation.[12]

1,8-Trimethylenenaphthalene (IV) crystallizes from methanol or acetic acid in colourless leaflets (m.p. 65·1–65·4°), which darken in contact with air. The picrate forms orange-red needles (m.p. 150–151°). Trinitrobenzene gives with trimethylenenaphthalene long yellow needles (m.p. 160–161°). Alkyl derivatives of trimethylenenaphthalene have been synthesized: 4-methyl-1,8-trimethylenenaphthalene, which boils at 160–170°, 2,6-dimethyl-1,8-trimethylenenaphthalene (m.p. 43–44°), and 2,7-dimethyl-1,8-trimethylenenaphthalene (m.p. 75°).[13] An ace derivative of trimethylenenaphthalene the 3,4-aceperinaphthane was prepared.[14]

Perinaphthenone (II) crystallizes from benzene in large plates (m.p. 156°), which dissolve in concentrated sulphuric acid to give a yellow solution with an intense green fluorescence. It is also soluble in concentrated hydrochloric acid, from which it is precipitated on dilution. Perinaphthenone is in many ways related to benzanthrone and gives molecular compounds with stannic chloride, antimony pentachloride, ferric chloride and perchloric acid.[15] Deeply coloured adducts are also obtained with bromine and iodine.[16] Polarographic reduction of perinaphthenone proceeds reversibly by a one-electron process.[17] Fusion with alcoholic potassium hydroxide gives peropyrenequinone (see p. 243).

A number of derivatives of perinaphthenone have been prepared by synthesis.[18] Bromination of perinaphthenone in acetic acid gives first 8-bromoperinaphthenone-(9) and then 4,8-dibromoperinaphthenone-(9). Higher halogenated derivatives are obtained from perinaphthenone in nitrobenzene with bromine, iron powder and iodine, by boiling with bromine and iodine or with phosphorus halides, sulphuryl chloride, or with phosgene.[19]

Perinaphthenone gives an oxime with hydroxylamine[20] and with hydrogen peroxide an oxide is formed by addition across the double bond adjoining the carbonyl. This is re-arranged to 8-hydroxyperinaphthenone by treatment with concentrated sulphuric acid.[20] 8-Benzoylperinaphthenone is obtained with benzoyl chloride and aluminium chloride.[20] Phenyl magnesium bromide reacts with perinaphthenone to form 1-phenylperinaphthenone-(9).[21]

Perinaphthanedione (XX) can be prepared from naphthalene, malonyl chloride and aluminium chloride (XIX)→(XX).[22] It is also obtained from naphthalyl chloride (XXII) and sodium acetoacetic ester. The intermediately formed carboxylic acid (XXI) is decarboxylated by heating with aqueous alkali.[23] Naphthoylacetic ester (XXIII) is cyclized to (XX) with concentrated sulphuric acid.[24] Naphthalic anhydride (XXV), malonic ester and zinc chloride yield perinaphthanedione (XX).[25] A similar condensation can be achieved with naphthalic anhydride, phenylacetic acid and potassium acetate (XXV)→(XXVI).[26]

(XIX)   (XX)   (XXI)   (XXII)

(XXIII)   (XXIV)   (XXV)   (XXVI)

Perinaphthanedione (XX) crystallizes in yellow prisms (m.p. 265° (dec.)). The oxidation in boiling nitrobenzene with selenium dioxide leads to acenaphthenequinone.[27] The enol form of (XX) gives an ether which reacts with Grignard compounds like benzanthrone under 1,4-addition.[28] Alkyl derivatives of perinaphthanedione have been prepared.[29]

(XXVII)   (XXVIII)

The interesting triketone (XXVIII) can be obtained by splitting out one molecule of water from the hydrate (XXVII). It has a m.p. of 265°

and crystallizes in orange-red needles, which dissolve in concentrated sulphuric acid with a violet colour changing to orange on standing. The solution in sodium hydroxide is blue.[30]

Perinaphthene was synthesized only recently. The hydrazone of perinaphthenone when decomposed with solid sodium hydroxide *in vacuo* at 130–140° gives perinaphthene.[31] Reduction of perinaphthenone with lithium aluminium hydride yields the alcohol (V, see p. 375). Hydrochloric acid splits out one molecule of water and gives perinaphthene.[32]

Perinaphthene forms colourless needles (m.p. 85–86°), which rapidly become yellow in contact with air. Chromic acid oxidizes it to perinaphthenone. The picrate of perinaphthene has a m.p. of 205–207° (dec.).

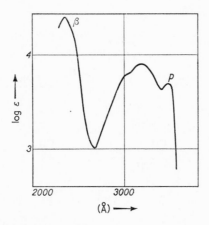

Fig. 217. Absorption spectrum of perinaphthene in ethanol: p, 3480 (3·70), 3200 (3·90); β, 2340 (4·40).[32]

Phenyl lithium readily forms a lithium compound. Catalytic hydrogenation of perinaphthene gives 1,8-trimethylenenaphthalene. A red compound is formed by condensation with benzaldehyde. The absorption spectrum of perinaphthene is given in Fig. 217.

The alkyl derivatives of perinaphthene are of particular interest. Five isomeric methylperinaphthenes should be possible, namely, 1-, 3-, 4-, 6- and 7-methylperinaphthene. However, only one methylperinaphthene (m.p. 63–65°) has been obtained, independently of the method applied.

Thus splitting out one molecule of water from the carbinol (XXIX) yields the same methylperinaphthene[33] as the one which can be obtained by the same treatment of the carbinols (XXX), (XXXI)[34] and (XXXII). The same methylperinaphthene results from the reaction of the lithium compound of perinaphthene (**XXXIII**) with methyl magnesium iodide,[34] or by a reaction of methyl magnesium iodide with perinaphthane (**XXXIV**).[33, 35]

(XXIX)   (XXX)   (XXXI)   (XXXII)

(XXXIII)   (XXXIV)

(XXXV)   (XXXVI)   (XXXVII)   (XXXVIII)

8-Methylperinaphthene (**XXXVI**) (m.p. 57–58°) can be obtained from the carbinol (**XXXV**).[34] 8-Methylperinaphthene gives a lithium compound which on treatment with methyl iodide yields dimethylperinaphthene (**XXXVII**). A repetition of these reactions leads finally to trimethylperinaphthene (**XXXVIII**).[36] The high reactivity of the H atoms in the methylene group was also observed in other derivatives of perinaphthene.[37]

Perinaphthyl

Perinaphthenone (**XXXIX**) shows a considerable tendency to form aromatic systems with a frame of alternating double bonds. Thus perinaphthenone disolves in concentrated hydrochloric acid to yield a yellow compound, which can be formulated as hydroxyperinaphthylium chloride (**XL**). Similar compounds are obtained with acid chlorides

(XLI). If these compounds are treated with zinc dust or activated magnesium in ether, deep blue solutions are obtained which can even be chromatographed and freed from starting material and impurities. The blue solution prepared from perinaphthenone (XXXIX), acetyl chloride and magnesium shows absorption bands at 6130, 3330, 3170, 3050, 2400 Å. The blue colour fades on cooling and returns on warming. It disappears permanently on boiling, and peropyrene (see p. 242) is

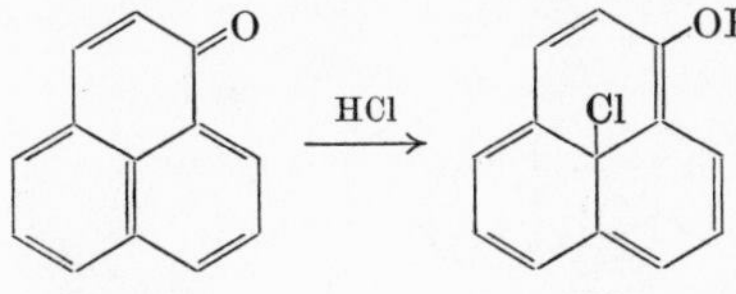

(XXXIX)   (XL)

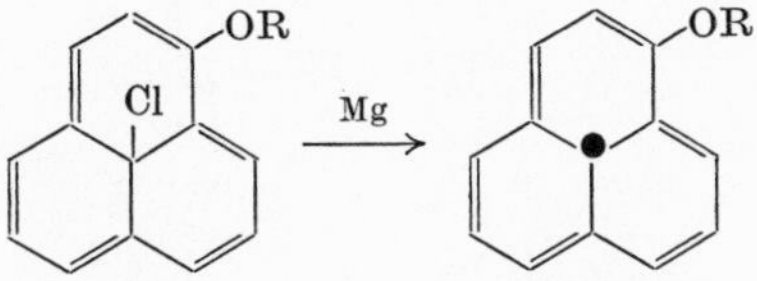

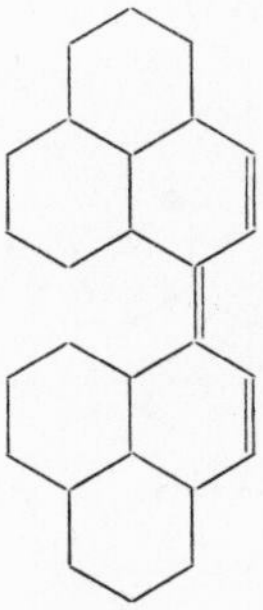

(XLI)   (XLII)   (XLIII)

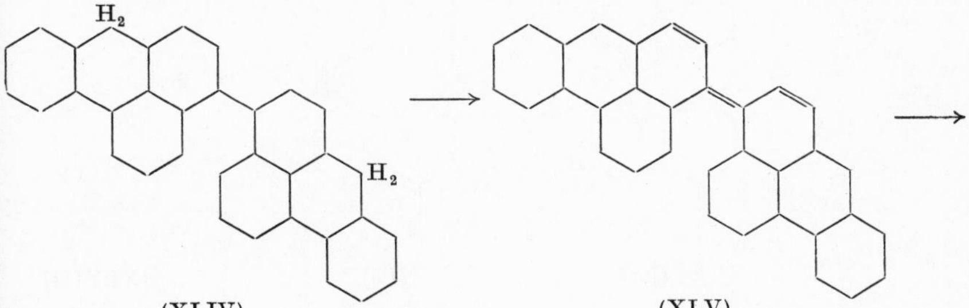

(XLIV)   (XLV)

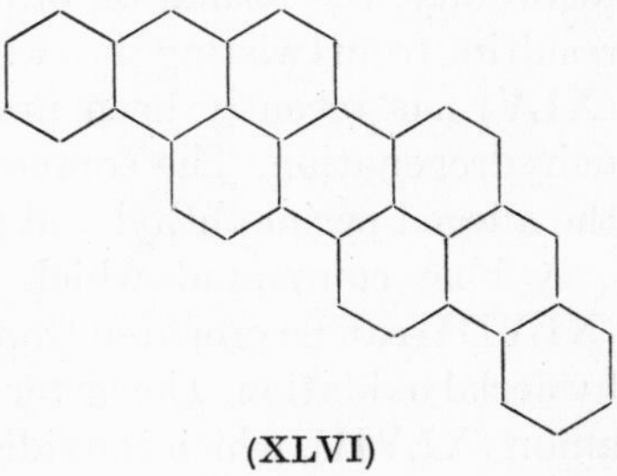

(XLVI)

formed. The blue solution was believed to contain the 1-acetoxyperi-
naphthyl radical (XLII, R = OCCH$_3$).[38] However, as long as an analysis
is not possible another interpretation of the properties of the blue solution must be considered. It seems possible that an acid chloride like
acetyl chloride or benzoyl chloride does nothing more than activate the
magnesium, which removes the oxygen. In this case the blue product
would have the structure (XLIII). This structure would also explain the

(XLVII)

(XLVIII)

(XLIX)

(La)

(Lb)

(XLVIII)

instability, the formation of peropyrene and a possible paramagnetism
resulting from twisting the two moieties out of plane. The blue compound
(XLV) has recently been prepared from dibenzanthrenyl (XLIV) by
dehydrogenation. The compound (XLV) shows the same properties as
the alleged perinaphthyl and gives violanthrene (XLVI) on heating.[39]

A blue compound which is given the structure of perinaphthyl
(XLVIII) can be prepared from perinaphthene and potassium methoxide
by aerial oxidation. The latter two compounds form the perinaphthenide
anion (XLVII), which is oxidized to perinaphthyl by molecular oxygen.

The reduction of perinaphthanone with aluminium amalgam in anhydrous ethanol–benzene solution yields the diol (XLIX). Hydrochloric acid removes two molecules of water and gives (La or b). It is assumed that these hydrocarbons undergo spontaneous fission with the formation of two molecules of perinaphthyl (XLVIII). Perinaphthyl obtained in these two ways has the same properties as the one described above. It also forms peropyrene on warming.[40]

A quite different radical is obtained if perinaphthene in carbon tetrachloride solution is exposed to a limited amount of air. A yellow product is formed which is paramagnetic as measured by electron spin resonance absorption. It retains its paramagnetism for months.[41] It is obvious that the discrepancies in the description of perinaphthyl will be cleared up in the future. It can also be obtained by cracking of petroleum and is enriched by distillation.[42]

Perinaphthylium perchlorate was prepared from acenaphthylene (LI). The addition of diazoacetic ester gives the adduct (LII). Hydrolysis, transformation into the acid chloride and reaction with sodium azide leads to (LIII). Treatment with hydrochloric acid gives the amine (LIV) and reaction with HONO leads to (LV). The Cl atom reacts with silver perchlorate to form perinaphthylium perchlorate (LVI).[43]

The perchlorate is a stable compound and gives peropyrene when reduced with zinc dust. The perinaphthylium perchlorate is yellow in the solid state and dissolves in nitromethane or alcohol with a green colour.[43]

REFERENCES

1. Bamberger, E. and Philip, M., *Liebigs Ann.* **240**, 154 (1887); Vollmann, H., Becker, H., Corell, M., and Streeck, H., *Liebigs Ann.* **531**, 7 (1937).
2. Bad. Anilin- und Soda-Fabrik, German Patent 283066 (1913).

3. I. G. Farbenindustrie AG, German Patent 614940 (1932); C. **1935 II**, 3832; Silbermann, G. B. and Barkow, S. M., *Chem. J.* Ser, A., *J. gen. Chem.*, *U.S.S.R.* 7 (69), 1733 (1937); *Chem. Zbl.* **1938 I**, 588; Fieser, L. F., and Hershberg, E. B., *J. Amer. chem. Soc.* **60**, 1658 (1938).

4. Meyer, Fr. and Sieglitz, A. *Ber. dtsch. chem. Ges.* **55**, 1835 (1922); von Braun, J., Manz, G. and Reinsch, E., *Liebigs Ann.* **468**, 277 (1929); Cook, J. W. and Hewett, C. L., *J. chem. Soc.* 365 (1934); Darzens, G. and Levy, A., *C. R. Acad. Sci.*, *Paris* **201**, 902 (1935); Koelsch, C. F., *J. Amer. chem. Soc.* **58**, 1326 (1936).

5. Fieser, L. F. and Gates, M. D., *J. Amer. chem. Soc.* **62**, 2335 (1940); Ansell, M. F., *J. chem. Soc.* 575 (1954); Shein, S. M., *Zh. Priklad. Khim.* **32**, 2824 (1959); *Amer. Abstr.* 9869 (1960).

6. E. I. du Pont de Nemours & Co. (Weinmayr, V.); Amer. Patent 2145905 (1937); *Chem. Zbl.* **1939 II**, 230; Calcott, W. S., Tinker, J. M. and Weinmayr, V., *J. Amer. chem. Soc.* **61**, 949 (1939).

7. I. G. Farbenindustrie AG, German Patent 489571, 490358 (1926); *Chem. Zbl.* **1930 II**, 468.

8. I. G. Farbenindustrie AG, 491089 (1926); *Chem. Zbl.* **1930 II**, 469.

9. von Braun, J. and Reutter, J., *Ber. dtsch. chem. Ges.* **59**, 1922 (1926); von Braun, J., Gruber, H. and Kirschbaum, G., *Ber. dtsch. chem. Ges.* **55**, 3664 (1922).

10. Clar, E., *Ber. dtsch. chem. Ges.* **76**, 458 (1943).

11. Fieser, L. F. and Hershberg, E. B., *J. Amer. chem. Soc.* **60**, 1658 (1938).

12. Langstein, E., *Mh. Chem.* **31**, 867 (1910).

13. Buu-Hoï, N. P. and Cagniant, P., *Rev. Sci.*, *Paris* **79**, 644 (1941); **80**, 130 (1942).

14. Dannenberg, H. and Dannenberg, D., von Dresler, *Liebigs Ann.* **585**, 23 (1954); *Liebigs Ann.* **593**, 219 (1955).

15. Silbermann, G. B. and Barkow, S. M., *J. gen. Chem.*, *U.S.S.R.* 7 (69) 1733 (1937); *Chem. Zbl.* **1938 I**, 588.

16. Brass, K. and Clar, E., *Ber. dtsch. chem. Ges.* **72**, 1882 (1939); Lukin, A. M., *Bull. Acad. Sci. U.R.S.S.*, *Classe sci. Chim.* 695 (1941); 55 (1942); *Chem. Zbl.* 1873 (1943).

17. Beckmann, P. and Silberman, H., *Chem. & Ind. (Rev.)* 1635 (1955).

18. I. G. Farbenindustrie AG, French Patent 823261 (1937); *Chem. Zbl.* **1938 I**, 3539; Klyne, W. and Robinson, R., *J. chem. Soc.* 1991 (1938).

19. General Aniline Works, Inc. Amer. Patent 2145051 (1937); *Chem. Zbl.* **1939 I**, 4685.

20. Fieser, L. F. and Newton, L. W., *J. Amer. chem. Soc.* **64**, 917 (1942).

21. Koelsch, C. F. and Anthes, J. A., *J. org. Chem.* **6**, 558 (1941).

22. I. G. Farbenindustrie AG, French Patent 729191 (1932); *Chem. Zbl.* **1933 II**, 783; Black, R., Shaw, H., and Walker, T. K., *J. chem. Soc.* 272 (1931).

23. Suszko, J. and Szych, B., *Roczniki Chem.* **17**, 111 (1937); *Chem. Zbl.* **1937 II**, 221.

24. Wojak, G., *Ber. dtsch. chem. Ges.* **71**, 1102 (1938).

25. Errera, G. *Gazz. chim. ital.* **41**, I, 191 (1911); Gesellschaft für Chemische Industrie in Basel, Swiss Patent 199450 (1937); *Chem. Zbl.* **1939 I**, 2873; French Patent 843424 (1938); Amer. Patent 2163110 (1938); *Chem. Zbl.* **1939 II**, 3346.

26. Koelsch, C. F. and Rosenwald, R. H., *J. Amer. chem. Soc.* **59**, 2166 (1937).

27. I. G. Farbenindustrie AG, French Patent 729191 (1932); *Chem. Zbl.* **1933 II**, 783.

28. Koelsch, C. F. and Rosenwald, R. H., *J. Amer. chem. Soc.* **59**, 2166 (1937); *J. org. Chem.* **3**, 462 (1938).

29. Wojak, G., *Ber. dtsch. chem. Ges.* **71**, 1102 (1938); Freund, M. and Fleischer, K., *Liebigs Ann.* **373**, 317 (1910).
30. Errera, G., *Gazz. Chim. ital.* **43** I, 585; **44** II, 18 (1913); Moubasher, R. and Awad, W. I., *J. Chem. Soc.* 1137 (1949).
31. Lock, G. and Gergely, G., *Ber. dtsch. chem. Ges.* **77**, 461 (1944).
32. Boekelheide, V. and Larrabbee, C. F., *J. Amer. chem. Soc.* **72**, 1245 (1950).
33. Fieser, L. F. and Newton, W., *J. Amer. chem. Soc.* **64**, 917 (1942); Klyne, W. and Robinson, R., *J. chem. Soc.* 199 (1938).
34. Boekelheide, V. and Larrabbee, C. E., *J. Amer. chem. Soc.* **72**, 1240, 1245 (1950).
35. Craig, L. C., Jacobs, W. A. and Lavin, G. I., *J. biol. Chem.* **139**, 277 (1941).
36. Boekelheide, V. and Goldman, M., *J. org. Chem.* **19**, 575 (1954).
37. Badger, G. M., Carruthers, W. and Cook, J. W., *J. chem. Soc.* 1768 (1949).
38. Clar, E. and Stewart, D. G., unpublished result.
39. Clar, E., Fell, G. S., Ironside, C. T. and Balsillie, A., *Tetrahedron* **10**, 26 (1960).
40. Reid, D. H., *Chem. & Ind. (Rev.)* 1504 (1956); *Tetrahedron* **3**, 339 (1958).
41. Sogo, P. B., Nokazaki, M. and Calvin, M., *J. chem. Phys.* **26**, 1343 (1957).
42. Stehling, F. C. and Bartz, K. B., *J. chem. Phys.* **34**, 1076 (1961); Bennet, J. E., *J. chem. Soc.* 144 (1961).
43. Pettit, R., *Chem. & Ind. (Rev.)* 1306 (1956); *J. Amer. chem. Soc.* **82**, 1972 (1960).

II. BENZANTHRENES

Benzanthrone can be prepared by a condensation of anthraquinone with glycerol and sulphuric acid.[1] The anthraquinone can be replaced by anthracene but the reaction is best carried out with anthrone.[2] However, the use of anthraquinone gives good results if aniline is added as a reducing agent. It is also possible to reduce anthraquinone in sulphuric acid partially with copper powder, zinc or aluminium powder at room temperature and then heat the mixture with glycerol.[3] There are two interpretations of the reaction mechanism. The first assumes a condensation of anthrone with acrolein to form the compound (I), which is believed to cyclize to benzanthrone (II).[4] However, it was shown later that anthrone reacts with compounds with reactive double bonds, like benzylidene-malonic ester, by addition to this double bond. In fact, the adduct (III) thus formed can be isolated.[5] A similar adduct (V) is obtained from anthrone and vinylphenylketone. The adduct (V) can be cyclized to phenylbenzanthrone (VI).[6] It appears likely that an analogous reaction takes place with anthrone and acrolein with the formation of (IV).

II—13

The reaction between anthrone and cinnamaldehyde follows a different route. The first stage is a condensation to (VII) involving the carbonyl of the aldehyde and the two H atoms of the methylene group of the anthrone. The second stage with the cyclization to (VI) involves the

double bond.[6, 7] However, crotonaldehyde reacts first with the double bond, and gives 1-methylbenzanthrone the constitution of which is confirmed by another synthesis.[8] There is a wide application of the condensation of anthrone with unsaturated aldehydes, ketones or acids in order to obtain benzanthrone derivatives.[9]

Benzanthrone is also prepared by condensation of phenanthrene-quinone (X) with glycerol and sulphuric acid, ferrous sulphate being used as a reducing agent.[10] Heating of 1-benzoylnaphthalene (XII) with aluminium chloride yields benzanthrone.[11] However, this method involves sometimes the migration of substituents. Thus o-toluylnaphthalene (XVI) and m-toluylnaphthalene (XVIII) give the same methylbenzanthrone (XVII).[12] 1-Methyl-4-benzoylnaphthalene and 2-methyl-1-benzoylnaphthalene yield the same 4-methylbenzanthrone.[12]

o-Chlorobenzoylnaphthalene (XIII) can be cyclized with alkali at higher temperatures.[13] Benzanthrone has also been obtained by cyclization of the acid (XI) with sulphuric acid.[14] Benzanthrone-11-carboxylic acid (XV) can be prepared similarly from the dicarboxylic acid (XIV).[15]

Another benzanthrone synthesis starts from methyleneanthrone (XIX), which reacts readily with compounds with reactive double bonds.[16] Methyleneanthrone (XIX) and maleic anhydride give a diadduct (XX) when boiled in acetic acid. This decomposes to benzanthrone-dicarboxylic anhydride (XXI) when heated in nitrobenzene or concentrated sulphuric acid.

The condensation yields directly the anhydride (XXI) when carried out in boiling nitrobenzene or boiling maleic anhydride.[16] Methylene-anthrone reacts in an analogous way with acetylene derivatives.[17]

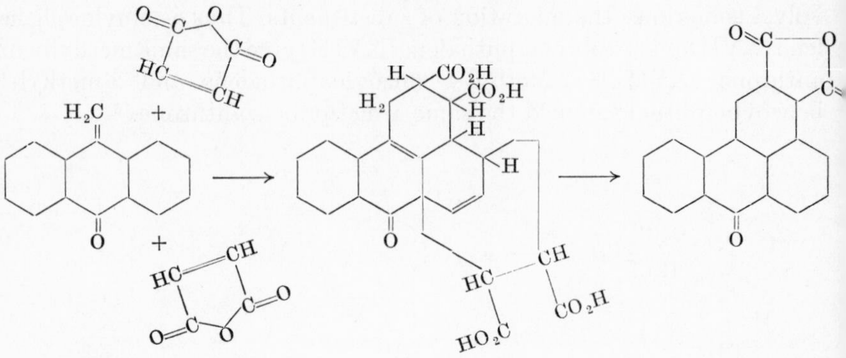

(XIX)   (XX)   (XXI)

In some cases the formation of fluorene derivatives replaces the expected benzanthrene derivatives in the course of the cyclization with aluminium chloride. Thus 1-hydroxy-4-benzoylnaphthalene (XXII)

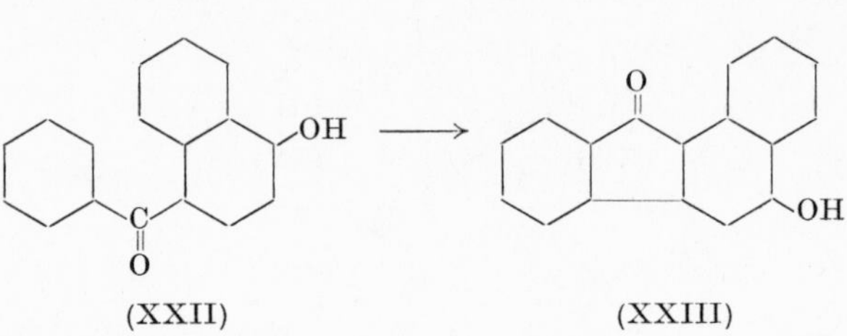

(XXII)   (XXIII)

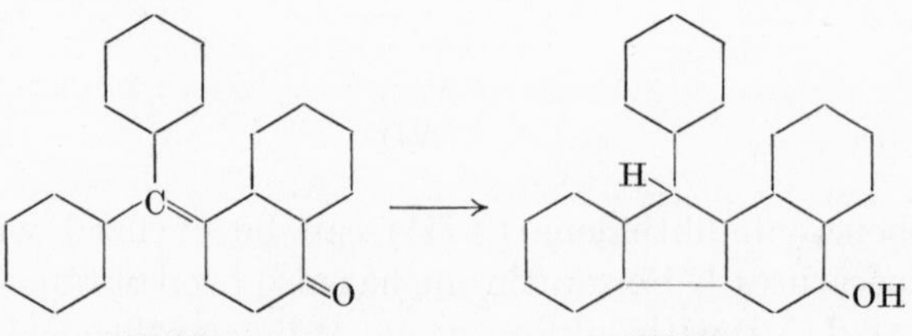

(XXIV)   (XXV)

does not yield 4-hydroxybenzanthrone as was assumed earlier[18] but 3-hydroxy-1.2-benzofluorene (XXIII).[19] Naphthofuchsone (XXIV) does not give a benzanthrone derivative but quantitatively the fluorene derivative (XXV).[20]

Benzanthrone can be built up from perinaphthenone system. Thus perinaphthenone-carboxylic acid (XXVI) adds dimethylbutadiene to form the compounds (XXVII) and (XXVIII), which are easily dehydrogenated to dimethylbenzanthrone.[21]

Benzanthrone crystallizes from acetic acid in long yellow needles (m.p. 170–171°), which dissolve in concentrated sulphuric acid to form a red solution with a red fluorescence. It gives molecular compounds with ferric chloride, stannic chloride and other metal chlorides[22] as well as a compound with trichloroacetic acid.[23]

(XXVI)   (XXVII)   (XXVIII)

Chlorination of benzanthrone under mild conditions gives 3-chlorobenzanthrone.[24] Further chlorination gives two chlorobenzanthrones,[25] which are the 3,9- and the 3,10-compound.[26]

Benzanthrone forms deeply coloured compounds with bromine or iodine in benzene solution. Their composition is one molecule of benzanthrone, one atom of halogen. The halogen can be completely removed with sodium thiosulphate.[27] These compounds are not paramagnetic[28] and do not catalyse the ortho–para hydrogen transformation.[29]

Bromination in acetic acid yields 3-bromobenzanthrone.[30] Higher chlorinated or brominated benzanthrones are obtained by halogenation in concentrated sulphuric acid or chlorosulphonic acid and with catalysts.[31] Halogenated benzanthrones can be prepared by synthesis.[32]

Nitration of benzanthrone in acetic acid gives 3-nitrobenzanthrone.[33, 34] Reduction yields 3-aminobenzanthrone.[33, 34] Further nitration with nitric and sulphuric acids leads to trinitro- and tetranitrobenzanthrone.[33]

The sulphonation of benzanthrone yields benzanthrone-9-sulphonic acid and probably a little benzanthrone-3,9-disulphonic acid.[35] Sulphonation with oleum gives the 3,9-disulphonic acid.[36] Sulphur derivatives of benzanthrone are obtained with sulphur chloride and iodine or by the exchange of halogen atoms with sodium sulphide.[37]

Benzanthrone needs rather drastic conditions to enter into Friedel–Crafts reactions. 3-Benzoylbenzanthrone and 9-benzoylbenzanthrone[38] are obtained as by-products when benzanthrone, benzoyl chloride and aluminium chloride are heated together to form 3.4,8.9-dibenzopyrene-5,10-quinone (see p. 154). Phthalic anhydride, benzanthrone and aluminium chloride give 2,3-phthalylbenzanthrone (see p. 425). Benzanthrone, carbon tetrachloride and aluminium chloride yield at 100° dibenzanthronyl-dichloromethane.[39]

Sodium amide and benzanthrone yield 6-aminobenzanthrone, and sodium hydroxide solution and oxygen give 4-hydroxybenzanthrone.[40] Mercurous acetate and benzanthrone form 3-benzanthronyl-mercuric acetate.[41] Benzanthrone and sodium acetylide give an acetylene-glycol.[42] A dibenzanthronylmethane is obtained by condensation of benzanthrone with formaldehyde and sulphuric acid.[43]

(XXIX) (XXX)

(XXXI)

(XXXII) (XXXIII)

The halogen atoms in halogenated benzanthrones can be exchanged with CuCN to form nitriles.[44] Halogen-benzanthrones and copper powder in boiling nitrobenzene yield dibenzanthronyl.[45] Benzanthronescarboxylic acids can be prepared from methylbenzanthrones with alkali in nitrobenzene[46] or with selenium dioxide.[47] Aldehydes can also be obtained by the latter method.

Benzanthrone is rather sensitive towards alkali. At low temperatures dibenzanthronyl is formed which condenses further at higher temperatures to violanthrone (see p. 251). Alkali is also useful for a number of other condensations. Benzanthrone condenses with aniline and sodium amide to form 4-phenylaminobenzanthrone (XXIX). In this reaction aniline can be replaced by other amines in order to obtain other derivatives of benzanthrone.[48]

Benzanthrone can be condensed with phenols and potassium hydroxide. Thus benzanthrone and β-naphthol give the compound (XXX).[49] Compounds with reactive methylene groups also react with benzanthrone under the influence of potassium hydroxide. Acetone yields in this way the ketone (XXXI).[50] Piperidine, benzanthrone and potassium hydroxide give 4-piperidinobenzanthrone.[51] Benzanthrone can be oxidized to 6-hydroxybenzanthrone with potassium hydroxide and potassium chlorate.[52] Benzyl cyanide and potassium hydroxide condense with benzanthrone to form the compound (XXXII).[53] Benzanthrone condenses also with potassium t-butyrate to a compound which is, however, given the structure (XXXIII).[54]

Cautious oxidation of benzanthrone in concentrated sulphuric acid with manganese dioxide or chromic acid gives hydroxybenzanthrones which are capable of forming violanthrones. Dibenzanthronyl is obtained as a by-product.[55]

(XXXIV)   (XXXV)

(XXXVI)   (XXXVII)

Benzanthrone reacts with Grignard compounds like unsaturated ketones, namely, with a 1,4-addition. Thus 6-alkyl- and 6-arylbenzanthrones are obtained which result from aerial oxidation of the primary dihydro compounds.[56] Even phenyl sodium reacts in this way.[57] Benzanthrone gives an oxime with hydroxylamine.[58]

The oxidation of benzanthrone with chromic acid in acetic acid or in suspension in dilute sulphuric acid yields anthraquinone-1-carboxylic acid (XXXV)→(XXXIV).[59] However, alkaline potassium permanganate gives 2′,3-dicarboxydiphenyl-2-glyoxylic acid (XXXVI) which can be further oxidized to diphenyltricarboxylic acid (XXXVII) in acid solution.[60]

Benzanthrone in acetic acid is oxidized by ozone to anthraquinone-1-carboxylic acid and anthraquinone-1-aldehyde.[61]

1. Reduction of Benzanthrone

A boiling solution of benzanthrone in acetic acid becomes red when zinc dust is added. The red stage, which is followed by a colourless stage, is due to a radical or a quinhydrol-like intermediate product. Dihydrobenzanthrone (XXXVIII) is very sensitive to air and light and is readily oxidized to benzanthrone, the red colour being again observed as an intermediate stage. Dihydrobenzanthrone absorbs two atoms of oxygen in xylene solution which indicates the formation of a peroxide. The acetate of dihydrobenzanthrone is completely stable. Dihydrobenzanthrone is soluble in alkali. This indicates that the hydrogen atom adjacent to the hydroxyl can migrate into other rings, thus giving the hydroxyl phenolic character.[62]

Dihydrobenzanthrone disproportionates with strong alkali or hydrochloric acid to benzanthrone and trimethylenehydroxyphenanthrene (XXXIX).[62] The same compound is obtained by prolonged reduction with alkaline sodium dithionite solution, or zinc dust and sodium hydroxide solution or with zinc and hydrochloric acid in acetic acid.[63] 1,10-Trimethylene-9-hydroxyphenanthrene which was formerly believed to be 1,9-trimethyleneanthranol[64] gives ethers and esters.[65]

The distillation of trimethylenehydroxyphenanthrene with zinc dust or zinc chloride yields benzanthrene (XL),[63] whilst the zinc-dust distillation of benzanthrone gives only a low yield of impure benzanthrene.[66] Another efficient reduction method uses aluminium isopropylate.[67] The reduction of benzanthrone with hydrogen iodide yields

1,10-trimethylene-phenanthrene (XLI). This hydrocarbon can be also prepared by pyrolysis of 1-benzylnaphthalene (XLII).[68] Its constitution as a phenanthrene derivative was revealed by the absorption spectrum.[63] Pyrolysis of 1-benzylnaphthalene in the presence of dehydrogenation catalysts yields benzanthrene (XL).[69] Benzanthrene was also obtained as a degradation product of perylene.[70]

2. Benzanthrene

Benzanthrene crystallizes from alcohol in colourless leaflets (m.p. 81–82°), which dissolve in concentrated sulphuric acid to give a red solution with a red fluorescence. Its colourless solutions in organic

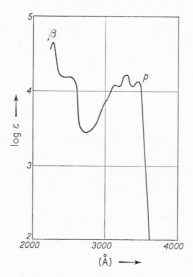

Fig. 218. Absorption spectrum of benzanthrene in ethanol: p, 3440 (4·13), 3290 (4·25), 3120 (4·08); 2500 (4·20); β, 2280 (4·66).

solvents show a blue fluorescence. The absorption spectrum is given in Fig. 218. Benzanthrene soon becomes brownish-yellow in the light. It forms a picrate (m.p. 110–111°), which crystallizes in dark red needles. Benzanthrene is oxidized to benzanthrone by air at higher temperatures in the presence of an oxidation catalyst.[71]

Benzanthrene and benzanthrone give yellow, green-fluorescing hydrocarbons when treated with condensing agents at 300°.[72] Similar products are obtained by heating benzanthrone with iron powder to 300–350°.[73] These are mixtures of dibenzoperopyrenes (see pp. 255, 257) just as are the products resulting from a treatment of benzanthrone with

II—13*

phosphorus oxychloride.[74] Benzanthrene adds maleic anhydride to form a substituted succinic anhydride (see p. 128).

4,6-Dimethylbenzanthrene is prepared by dehydrogenation of 1,2,3,4-tetrahydro-5,7,8-trimethyl-1-phenylnaphthalene with selenium.[75]

1,10-Trimethylenephenanthrene (XLI) crystallizes from alcohol in long needles (m.p. 81–82°), which dissolve in concentrated sulphuric acid to give a red solution. The blue solution in alcohol shows a violet fluorescence. A comparison with phenanthrene and 1,10-trimethylene-9-hydroxyphenanthrene (XXXIX) shows the phenanthrene complex in these two reduction products of benzanthrone.[76] The picrate of trimethylenephenanthrene has a m.p. of 125°.

Trimethylenephenanthrene was also prepared by cyclization and reduction of β-(1-phenanthryl)-propionic acid and β-(10-phenanthryl)-propionic acid.[77]

Catalytic hydrogenation of 1,10-trimethylene-9-hydroxyphenanthrene gives a tetrahydro derivative and tetrahydro-1,10-trimethylenephenanthrene.[78] An ace derivative of 1,10-trimethylenephenanthrene has been synthesized.[79]

3. *1H-Benzanthrene*

The cyclization of the anthrenyl-propionic acid (XLIII) with stannic chloride gives the cyclic ketone (XLIV). This can be reduced to the alcohol (XLV) with lithium aluminium hydride. The chromatography of (XLV) on neutral alumina gives 1*H*-benzanthrene (XLVI).

(XLIII)   (XLIV)   (XLV)

(XLVI)   (XLVII)

1H-Benzanthrene crystallizes from light petroleum in colourless crystals (m.p. 96–98°), which dissolve in concentrated sulphuric acid to form a red solution. Eighty per cent sulphuric acid as well as hydrochloric acid isomerize 1*H*-benzanthrene into the stable 7*H*-benzanthrene

(XLVII). The absorption spectrum of 1H-benzanthrene is given in Fig. 219. In contrast to the spectrum of 7H-benzanthrene (XLVII) it shows the first absorption bands of an anthracene derivative. The infra-red spectrum also shows bands characteristic for the anthracene complex.

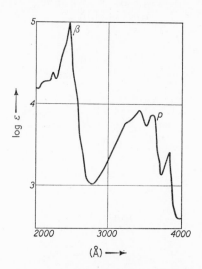

FIG. 219. Absorption spectrum of 1H-benzanthrene in ethanol: 3890 (2·64), 3740 (3·48); p, 3540 (3·90), 3370 (3·97), 3240 (3·81); β, 2510 (4·94), 2330 (4·37) (Dannenberg, H. and Kessler, H. J., *Liebigs Ann.* **606**, 184 (1957)).

3-Methyl-1H-benzanthrene (m.p. 113–114°) was synthesized from the ketone (XLIV) with methyl magnesium chloride followed by dehydration. It is easily isomerized to 3-methyl-7H-benzanthrene (m.p. 130–132°).[80]

4. 3H-Benzanthrene

Oxo-octahydroanthracene (XLVIII) is submitted to a Stobbe condensation which yields the ester (XLIX). Hydrolysis and decarboxylation give the acid (L). Dehydrogenation with palladium–charcoal at 290° leads to the propionic acid (LI). The cyclization is effected through the chloride with stannic chloride in benzene and gives the cyclic ketone (LII). This is reduced with lithium aluminium hydride to the carbinol (LIII). The dehydration to (LIV) takes place during chromatography on neutral or basic alumina.

3H-Benzanthrene (LIV) is yellow and has not been obtained in a crystalline state. It is extremely easily oxidized in air, rapidly becoming green and then black. It dissolves in concentrated sulphuric acid with a

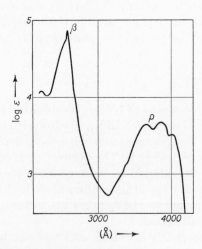

(XLVIII) → (XLIX) → (L) → (LI) → (LII) → (LIII) → (LIV) → (XLVII)

red colour. Hydrochloric acid in ethanol causes isomerization to the
stable 7H-benzanthrene (XLVII). The absorption spectrum is given in
Fig. 220.

Fig. 220. Absorption spectrum of 3H-benzanthrene in petroleum ether: p, 4020 (3·54),
3860 (3·71), 3670 (3·68); β, 2570 (4·89).[81]

Attempts to synthesize 4H-benzanthrene (LV) and 6H-benzanthrene (LVI) in an analogous way were unsuccessful because of immediate isomerization to the stable 7H-benzanthrene (XLVII). This applies also to methyl-benzanthrenes derived from (LV) and (LVI). Isomerization here produces 4-methyl-7H-benzanthrene (m.p. 115°), and 6-methyl-7H-benzanthrene (m.p. 117–118°).[81]

(LV)   (LVI)   (XLVII)

7-Chlorobenzanthr-3-one can be prepared by cyclization of the acid chloride (LVII) with aluminium chloride in chlorobenzene. The corresponding acid to (LVII) is obtained by a Perkin synthesis from anthracenealdehyde. Treatment of the benzanthrone (LVIII) with concentrated sulphuric acid produces the hydroxybenzanthrone (LIX).[82]

(LVII)   (LVIII)   (LIX)

REFERENCES

1. Bally, O., *Ber. dtsch. chem. Ges.* **38**, 194 (1905); Bad. Anilin- und Soda-Fabrik, German Patent 176018, 176019 (1904).
2. Bally, O. and Scholl, R., *Ber. dtsch. chem. Ges.* **44**, 1656 (1911).
3. E. I. du Pont de Nemours & Co., Amer. Patent 1601319 (1924); 1626392 (1920); *Chem. Zbl.* **1927 II**, 2572.
4. Bally, O. and Scholl, R., *Ber. dtsch. chem. Ges.* **44**, 1656 (1911).
5. Meerwein, H., *J. prakt. Chem.* **97**, 284 (1918).
6. Allen, C. F. H. and Overbaugh, S. C., *J. Amer. chem. Soc.* **57**, 1322 (1935).
7. I. G. Farbenindustrie AG, Brit. Patent 297129 (1927); *Chem. Zbl.* **1929 I**, 447; Grasselli Dyestuff Corp., Amer. Patent 1713571 (1926); *Chem. Zbl.* **1939 II**, 1073.
8. Baddar, F. G. and Warren, F. L., *J. chem. Soc.* 944 (1939).
9. I. G. Farbenindustrie AG, French Patent 631995 (1927); *Chem. Zbl.* **1928 I**, 2210; German Patent 488608 (1926); *Chem. Zbl.* **1930 II**, 3860; German Patent 552269 (1927); *Chem. Zbl.* **1932 II**, 2736.
10. Turksi, J. S. and Pragierowa, R., *Przem. chem.* **13**, 33; *Chem. Zbl.* **1929 I**, 1692.
11. Scholl, R. and Seer, C., *Liebigs Ann.* **394**, 111 (1912); *Mh. Chem.* **33**, 1 (1912); Scholl, German Patent 239671 (1910).
12. Meyer, Fr., Fleckenstein, E. and Günther, H., *Ber. dtsch. chem. Ges.* **63**, 1464 (1930); Fieser, L. F. and Martin, E. L., *J. Amer. chem. Soc.* **58**, 1443 (1936).

13. I. G. Farbenindustrie AG, French Patent 629806 (1926); *Chem. Zbl.* **1928 I**, 2459.
14. Schaarschmidt, A., *Ber. dtsch. chem. Ges.* **50**, 294 (1917); Schaarschmidt, A. and Geogeacopol, E., *Ber. dtsch. chem. Ges.* **50**, 1082 (1917).
15. Rule, H. G., Pursell, W. and Barnett, A. J. G., *J. chem. Soc.* 571 (1935).
16. I. G. Farbenindustrie AG, German Patent 591496, 597325; French Patent 754842 (1933); *Chem. Zbl.* **1934 II**, 2044; Clar, E., *Ber. dtsch. chem. Ges.* **69**, 1686 (1936); German Patent 619246 (1934); *Chem. Zbl.* **1936 I**, 1123.
17. Irving, F. and Johnson, A. W., *J. chem. Soc.* 2037 (1948).
18. Scholl, R. and Seer, C. *Liebigs Ann.* **394**, 111 (1912); *Mh. Chem.* **33**, 1 (1912).
19. Fierz-David, H. E. and Jaccard, G., *Helv. chim. Acta* **11**, 1042 (1928).
20. Clar, E., *Ber. dtsch. chem. Ges.* **63**, 512 (1930).
21. Fieser, L. F. and Newton, L. W., *J. Amer. chem. Soc.* **64**, 917 (1942).
22. Perkin, A. G., *J. chem. Soc.* **117**, 696 (1920); Perkin, A. G. and Spencer, D., *J. chem. Soc.* **121**, 474 (1922); Bradshaw, G. G. and Perkin, A. G., *J. chem. Soc.* **121**, 911 (1922).
23. Campbell, N. and Woodham, *J. chem. Soc.* 843 (1952).
24. Lüttringhaus, A. and Neresheimer, H., *Liebigs Ann.* **473**, 259 (1929).
25. Bad. Anilin- und Soda-Fabrik, German Patent 193959 (1906).
26. Cahn, R. S., Jones, W. O. and Simonsen, J. L., *J. chem. Soc.* 444 (1933).
27. Brass, K. and Clar, E., *Ber. dtsch. chem. Ges.* **69**, 690 (1936).
28. Müller, Eugen and Wiesemann, W., *Ber. dtsch. chem. Ges.* **69**, 2173 (1936).
29. Schwab, G. M. and Schwab-Agallidis, E., *Z. phys. chem.* **B49**, 196 (1941).
30. Bad. Anilin- und Soda-Fabrik, German Patent 193959 (1906).
31. General Aniline Works Inc., Amer Patent 1955135 (1932); *Chem. Zbl.* **1935 I**, 1618.
32. I. G. Farbenindustrie AG, German Patent 471021 (1925); Brass, K. and Lauer, K., *Chim. et Ind.* **29**, Nr. 6, 876 (1933); *Chem. Zbl.* **1933 II**, 3695.
33. Pieroni, A., *Annali chim. appl.* **21**, 155 (1931); *Chem. Zbl.* **1931 II**, 235.
34. Lauer, K. and Atarashi, K., *Ber. dtsch. chem. Ges.* **68**, 1373 (1935).
35. Lauer, K. and Irie, K., *J. prakt. Chem.* (2) **145**, 281 (1936); Pritchard, R. R. and Simonsen, J. L., *J. chem. Soc.* 2047 (1938).
36. Ioffe, I. S. and Pavlova, I., *J. gen. Chem.*, *U.S.S.R.* **14**, 144 (1944); *Amer. Abstr.* 2288 (1945).
37. Höchster Farbwerke, German Patent 410011 (1923); I. G. Farbenindustrie AG, German Patent 441748, 443022 (1924).
38. Moschtschinskaja, *J. gen. Chem.*, *U.S.S.R.* **11**, (73), 45 (1941); Russian Patent 59980 (1940); *Chem. Zbl.* **1941 II**, 1016; **1942 II**, 2645.
39. E. I. du Pont de Nemours & Co., Amer. Patent 1990506 (1932); *Chem. Zbl.* **1936 I**, 1123.
40. Bradley, W., *J. chem. Soc.* 1175 (1948).
41. Bernardi, A., *Gazz. chim. ital.* **67**, 380 (1937).
42. I. G. Farbenindustrie AG, German Patent 636456 (1934); *Chem. Zbl.* **1937 I**, 2685.
43. I. G. Farbenindustrie AG, German Patent 488604 (1925); *Chem. Zbl.* **1930 II**, 820.
44. Kalle & Co., Brit. Patent 243026 (1925); *Chem. Zbl.* **1927 I**, 1377; Swiss Patent 122904 (1925); *Chem. Zbl.* **1928 I**, 1100.
45. Lüttringhaus, A. and Neresheimer, H., *Liebigs Ann.* **473**, 259 (1929); Bradley, W. and Jadhav, G. V., *J. chem. Soc.* 1622 (1948).
46. I. G. Farbenindustrie AG, Brit. Patent, 321916 (1928); *Chem. Zbl.* **1930 I**, 3240.
47. I. G. Farbenindustrie AG, German Patent 557249 (1930); *Chem. Zbl.* **1932 II**, 2376.
48. I. G. Farbenindustrie AG, German Patent 501610 (1927); *Chem. Zbl.* **1930 II**, 1779; German Patent 644537 (1935); *Chem. Zbl.* **1937 II**, 865; Bradley, W. and Sutcliffe, F. K., *J. chem. Soc.* 1708 (1954).

49. I. G. Farbenindustrie AG, Brit. Patent 300331; French Patent 640410 (1927); Swiss Patent 128993; 130609 (1927); *Chem. Zbl.* **1929 II**, 3072.

50. I. G. Farbenindustrie AG, German Patent 499320, 502042 (1927); 501082, 501083 (1928); Brit. Patent 322745 (1928); *Chem. Zbl.* **1930 II**, 2696–2698.

51. Bradley, W., *J. chem. Soc.* 1091 (1937).

52. Bradley, W. and Jadhav, G. V., *J. chem. Soc.* 1791 (1937).

53. I. G. Farbenindustrie AG, German Patent, 568783 (1931); *Chem. Zbl.* **1933 II**, 784.

54. Clemo, G. R., Munday, L. and Swan, G. A., *J. chem. Soc.* 1513 (1950).

55. Scottish Dyes Ltd., Brit. Patent 251313; *Chem. Zbl.* **1927 I**, 1230; I. G. Farbenindustrie AG, German Patent 431774 (1922); *Chem. Zbl.* **1926 II**, 2232; Imperial Chemical Industries Ltd., Brit. Patent 359937 (1930); *Chem. Zbl.* **1932 I**, 1446; I. G. Farbenindustrie AG, German Patent 515327 (1926); *Chem. Zbl.* **1931 I**, 1367.

56. Charrier, G. and Ghigi, E., *Gazz. chim. ital.* **62**, 928 (1932); Allen, C. F. H. and Overbaugh, S. C., *J. Amer. chem. Soc.* **57**, 740 (1935); Charrier, G. and Ghigi, E., *Ber. dtsch. chem. Ges.* **69**, 2211 (1936).

57. Bradley, W. and Sutcliffe, F. K., *J. chem. Soc.* 708 (1954).

58. Campbell, N. and Woodham, A. A., *J. chem. Soc.* 843 (1952).

59. Perkin, A. G., *J. chem. Soc.* 117 706, (1920); Barnett, E. de Barry, Cook, J. W. and Grainger, H. H., *Ber. dtsch. chem. Ges.* **57**, 1775 (1924).

60. Charrier, G. and Ghigi, E., *Gazz. chim. ital.* **63**, 685 (1933).

61. I. G. Farbenindustrie AG, French Patent 817584 (1937); Brit. Patent 472167 (1936); *Chem. Zbl.* **1938 I**, 728.

62. Clar, E., *Ber. dtsch. chem. Ges.* **68**, 2066 (1935).

63. Clar, E. and Furnari, Fr., *Ber. dtsch. chem. Ges.* **65**, 1420 (1932).

64. von Braun, J. and Bayer, O., *Ber. dtsch. chem. Ges.* **58**, 2667 (1925); Casella & Co., German Patent 453578 (1925); *Chem. Zbl.* **1928 I**, 2665.

65. Charrier, G. and Jorio, M., *Gazz. chim. ital.* **72**, 451 (1942).

66. Liebermann, C. and Roka, K., *Ber. dtsch. chem. Ges.* **41**, 1423 (1908); Bally, O. and Scholl, R., *Ber. dtsch. chem. Ges.* **44**, 1656 (1911).

67. Campbell, N. and Woodham, A. A., *J. chem. Soc.* 843 (1952).

68. Graebe, C., *Ber. dtsch. chem. Ges.* **27**, 953 (1894); Scholl, R. and Seer, C., *Ber. dtsch. chem. Ges.* **44**, 1671 (1911); I. G. Farbenindustrie AG, Brit. Patent 260000 (1926); *Chem. Zbl.* **1928 II**, 1489.

69. I. G. Farbenindustrie AG, German Patent 594564 (1932); *Chem. Zbl.* **1935 I**, 633.

70. Zinke, A. and Wenger, R., *Monatsh. Chem.* **56**, 143 (1930).

71. I. G. Farbenindustrie AG, German Patent 596592 (1932); *Chem. Zbl.* **1935 I**, 795.

72. I. G. Farbenindustrie AG, French Patent 767250 (1934); Brit. Patent 419062 (1933); *Chem. Zbl.* **1936 I**, 1312.

73. E. I. du Pont de Nemours & Co., Amer. Patent 2073663 (1934); *Chem. Zbl.* **1937 II**, 864.

74. Campbell, N. and Woodham, A. A., *J. chem. Soc.* 843 (1952).

75. Cocker, W. and Jenkinson, D. S., *J. chem. Soc.* 2420 (1954).

76. Clar, E. and Furnari, F., *Ber. dtsch. chem. Ges.* **65**, 1420 (1932).

77. Bachmann, W. E. and Kloetzel, M. C., *J. Amer. chem. Soc.* **59**, 2207 (1937).

78. von Braun, J. and Bayer, O., *Ber. dtsch. chem. Ges.* **58**, 2667 (1925).

79. Dannenberg, H. and Dannenberg, D. von Dresler, *Liebigs Ann.* **585**, 23 (1954); **593**, 219 (1955).

80. Dannenberg, H. and Kessler, H. J., *Leibigs Ann.* **606**, 184 (1957).

81. Dannenberg, H. and Kessler, H. J., *Leibigs Ann.* **620**, 32 (1959).

82. I. G. Farbenindustrie AG, German Patent 696637 (1936); *Chem. Zbl.* **1941 I**, 1610.

III. Naphtho-(2'.1':7.8)-perinaphthene

(1.2,5.10-Dibenzanthrene)

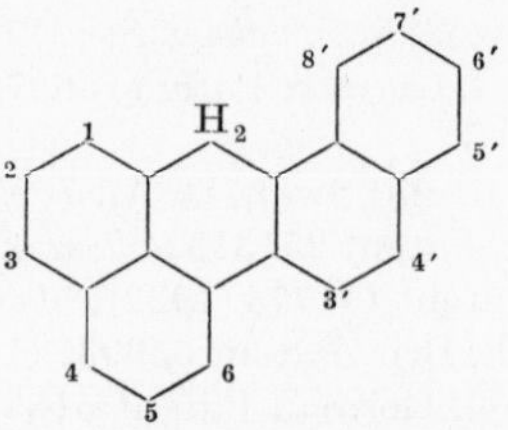

1,1'-Dinaphthylketone (I) can be cyclized to naphthoperinaphthone (II) with aluminium chloride.[1] Treatment of tetraphenequinone (III) with glycerol and sulphuric acid gives the same compound (II)[2] together with the isomer (IV).[3]

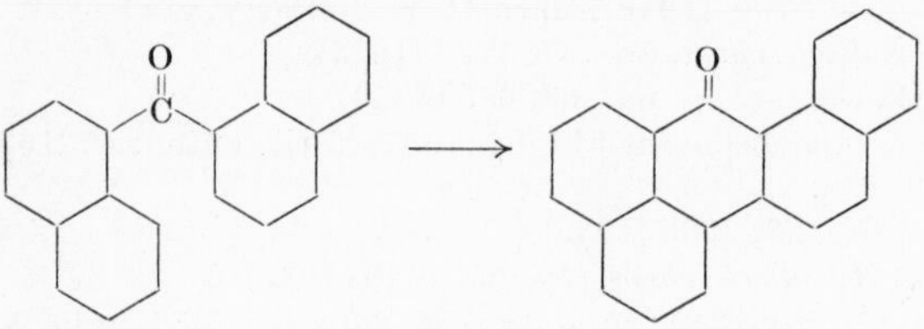

(I)   (II)

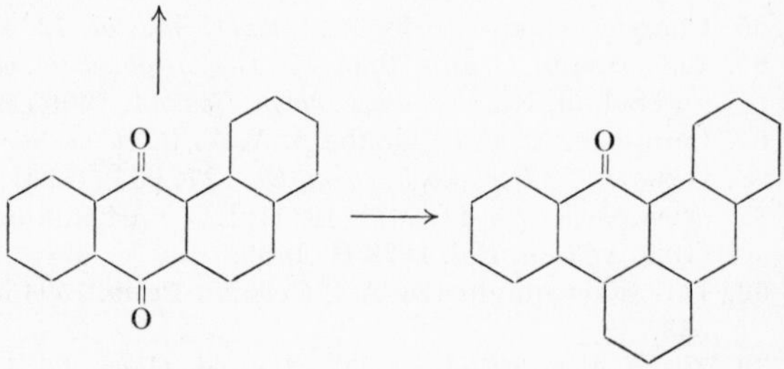

(III)   (IV)

Naphtho-(2'.1':7.8)-perinaphthone (II) crystallizes from acetic acid in orange needles (m.p. 184–185°). Oxidation with chromic acid in acetic acid leads to the acid (V) and further oxidation with potassium permanganate to the tricarboxylic acid (VI).[4]

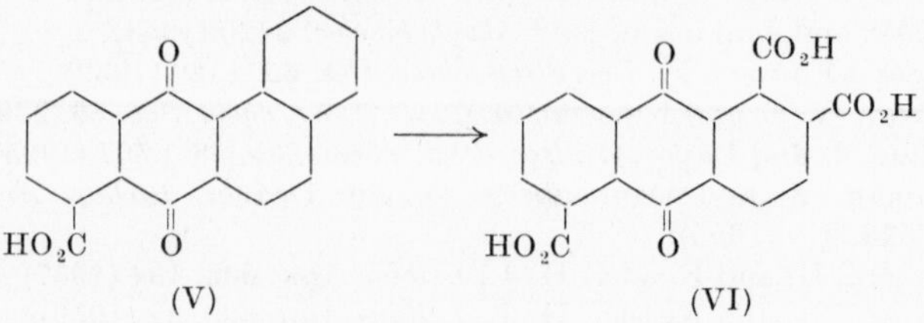

(V)   (VI)

3-Methylnaphtho-(2′.1′:7.8)-perinaphth-9-one (m.p. 221–222°) was synthesized by cyclization of 4-methyl-1,1′-dinaphthyl ketone.[5] A dicarboxylic acid of naphthoperinaphthene (II) is obtained by cyclization of 4-naphthoyl-naphthylic anhydride with aluminium chloride.[6]

Tetralyl magnesium bromide and α-naphthoyl chloride give the ketone (VIII). Pyrolysis at 400° yields 2,3-trimethylenechrysene (IX).

(VII)   (VIII)   (IX)

Its chrysene complex is shown by its absorption spectrum. The hydrocarbon (IX) forms colourless needles from alcohol (m.p. 116°–117°) and gives a picrate, red needles (m.p. 170–171°). Oxidation with sodium bichromate in acetic acid yields a quinone $C_{21}H_{12}O_3$. It probably has two carbonyls in the chrysene complex and forms orange needles (m.p. 268–270° (dec.)).[7]

REFERENCES

1. Scholl, R., German Patent 239671 (1910).
2. Cook, J. W. and de Worms, C. G. M., J. chem. Soc. 268 (1939); Bad. Anilin-und Soda-Fabrik, German Patent 181176 (1904).
3. Bradley, W. and Sutcliffe, F. K., J. chem. Soc. 1247 (1952).
4. Cook, J. W., J. chem. Soc. 1592 (1933).
5. Cook, J. W. and Robinson, A. M., J. chem. Soc. 505 (1938).
6. I. G. Farbenindustrie AG, Brit. Patent 308651 (1929); Chem. Zbl. 1929 II, 662; French Patent 39499; Chem. Zbl. 1932 I, 880.
7. Fieser, L. F. and Seligman, A. M., J. Amer. chem. Soc. 58, 478 (1936); 57, 228 (1935).

IV. NAPHTHO-(1′.2′:7.8)-PERINAPHTHENE

(1.9,7.8-Dibenzanthrene)

1,1′-Dinaphthyl-8,8′-dicarboxylic acid (I) can be partially cyclized with zinc chloride in acetic acid. The acid (II) is decarboxylated in

boiling quinoline with copper powder.[1] The reduction of the naphthoperinaphthenone (III) is carried out with aluminium isopropylate.[2]

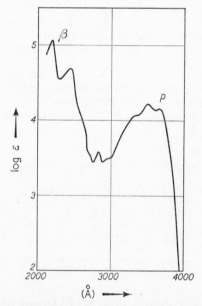

Naphtho-(1′.2′:7.8)-perinaphthene (IV) crystallizes from light
petroleum in colourless leaflets (m.p. 89·5–90·5°) which dissolve in
concentrated sulphuric acid to give an orange solution with a pink
fluorescence. The solutions in organic solvents show a blue fluorescence.
The absorption spectrum is given in Fig. 221.[3]

FIG. 221. Absorption spectrum of naphtho-(1′.2′:7.8)-perinaphthene in hexane:
p, 3650 (4·16), 3510 (4·22), 3350 (4·07); 2830 (3·58); β, 2450 (4·69), 2200 (5·06).

Naphtho-$(1'.2':7.8)$-perinaphthenone (III) forms long yellow needles (m.p. 186°), which dissolve in concentrated sulphuric acid with a brownish-red colour.[3] It can be also prepared from 2-naphthoyl amyl ester and N-nitrosoacetnaphthalide (V) via the naphthylnaphthoic ester (VI) followed by cyclization to (III).[4] It gives bromo derivatives with bromine in acetic acid or nitrobenzene.[5]

The reduction of (III) with hydrogen iodide and red phosphorus gives a dihydro compound which has the structure of a 8,9-trimethylene-3.4-benzophenanthrene (IX).[3] This has been synthesized by the reaction of tetralyl magnesium bromide (VII) with 2-naphthoyl chloride which yields the ketone (VIII). Its pyrolysis leads to trimethylenebenzophenanthrene (IX) and another hydrocarbon which was given the structure (X). Its oxidation yields a ketone which forms long yellow needles (m.p. 201°), which dissolve in concentrated sulphuric acid to form a green solution.[6] These properties are identical with the ones of naphtho-$(2'.3':7.8)$-perinaphthenone (see p. 406). Therefore it must be considered a possibility that the second product of the pyrolysis is naphtho-$(2'.3':7.8)$-perinaphthene (XI).

8,9-Trimethylene-3.4-benzophenanthrene (IX) crystallizes from light petroleum in colourless needles (m.p. 139°), which dissolve in concentrated sulphuric acid to form a yellow solution. The picrate has a m.p. of 125–126°. A hydrocarbon (m.p. 137°) which is isomeric with (IX) can be prepared by a zinc-dust melt from (III), or reduction with potassium hydroxide and zinc dust followed by sublimation *in vacuo*. Its absorption spectrum is different from that of the hydrocarbon (IX).

The hydrocarbon (X) or (XI) crystallizes from alcohol in leaflets (m.p. 149–149·5°) which dissolve in concentrated sulphuric acid with a green colour. The orange picrate has a m.p. of 146–147°.

REFERENCES

1. Bradley, W. and Sutcliffe, F. K., *J. chem. Soc.* 1247 (1952).
2. Clar, E. and Willicks, W., *Liebigs Ann.* **601**, 193 (1956).
3. Clar, E. and Willicks, W., *Liebigs Ann.* **601**, 193 (1956).
4. Swain, G. and Todd, A. R., *J. chem. Soc.* 674 (1941).
5. Stephenson, M. and Sutcliffe, F. K., *J. chem. Soc.* 3516 (1962).
6. Fieser, L. F. and Seligman, A. M., *J. Amer. chem. Soc.* **57**, 228 (1935); **58**, 478 (1936).

V. 2.3,7.8-DIBENZOPERINAPHTHENE

(*1.9,2.3-Dibenzanthrene*)

Octahydrophenanthrene reacts with benzoyl chloride and aluminium chloride to form the ketone (I). Its pyrolysis with copper powder at 400° yields 2.3,7.8-dibenzoperinaphthene (II).

(I)   (II)

(III)

2.3,7.8-Dibenzoperinaphthene crystallizes from xylene in thin long colourless needles (m.p. 171–171·5°), which dissolve in concentrated sulphuric acid to give a red solution with a red fluorescence. The absorption spectrum is given in Fig. 222. It is oxidized in air. It also reacts

FIG. 222. Absorption spectrum of 2.3,7.8-dibenzoperinaphthene in ethanol: α, 3720 (3·05); p, 3390 (4·02), 3270 (4·05), 3020 (3·86); β, 2850 (4·24), 2760 (4·26), 2690 (4·26).

quantitatively with maleic anhydride (see p. 149).[1] The ace derivative (VI) has been synthesized. It is also oxidizable in air.[2]

2.3,7.8-Dibenzoperinaphthenone (III), obtainable using selenium dioxide in acetic acid, crystallizes from xylene in long yellow needles

(IV)   (V)   (VI)

(m.p. 215–216°), which dissolve in concentrated sulphuric acid with a red colour and a red fluorescence. It can be also prepared from 9-benzoyl-phenanthrene (VII) by a cyclization with aluminium chloride. It reacts with Grignard compounds like benzanthrone and forms, with o-tolyl magnesium bromide and subsequent aerial oxidation of the initial dihydro derivative, the compound (VIII).[3] Further oxidation of (VII) gives the acid (IV) and decarboxylation gives tetracenequinone (V).

(VII)   (III)

(VIII)

REFERENCES

1. Clar, E., *Ber. dtsch. schem. Ges.* **76**, 611 (1943).
2. Dannenberg, H. and Dannenberg, D. von Dresler, *Chem. Ber.* **89**, 1316 (1956).
3. Arbuzov, B. A. and Grechkin, N. P., *Izv. Kazan. Filiala Akad. Nauk S.S.S.R.*, *Ser. Khim. Nauk* No. 2, 31–37 (1955); *Amer. Abstr.* 342 (1958).

VI. NAPHTHO-(2′.3′ : 7.8)-PERINAPHTHENE

(1.9,6.7-Dibenzanthrene)

An unusual Friedel–Crafts reaction takes place when 2-naphthoyl-chloride is condensed with 1-methylnaphthalene and aluminium chloride in carbon disulphide solution. The reaction yields the expected ketone if only one molecule of aluminium chloride is used. However, further cyclization to (I) takes place with 2·5 molecules of aluminium chloride at 0–10°.

The methyl group of the naphthoperinaphthone (I) can be oxidized to the acid (II) with barium oxide in boiling nitrobenzene. Decarboxylation with copper powder in boiling quinoline yields naphtho-(2′.3′ : 7.8)-perinaphthone (III). This forms yellow needles (m.p. 199–200°), which dissolve in concentrated sulphuric acid to give a bluish-green solution.

The oxidation of the methyl derivative (I) with chromic acid gives the acid (IV). Decarboxylation leads to the known methyltetracene quinone (V).

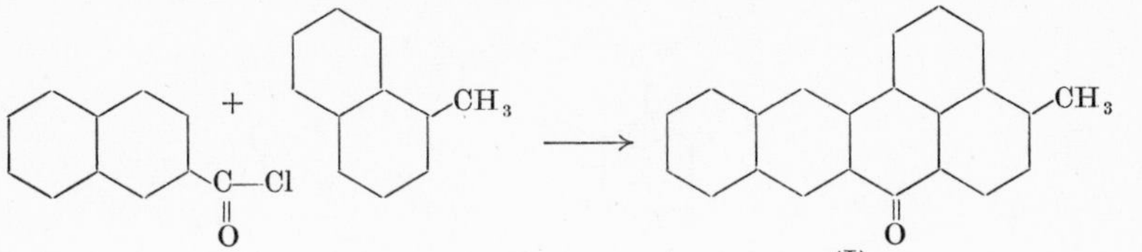

(I)

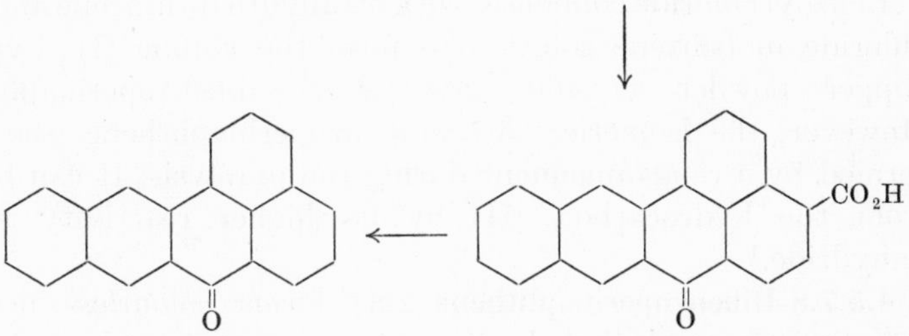

(III)   (II)

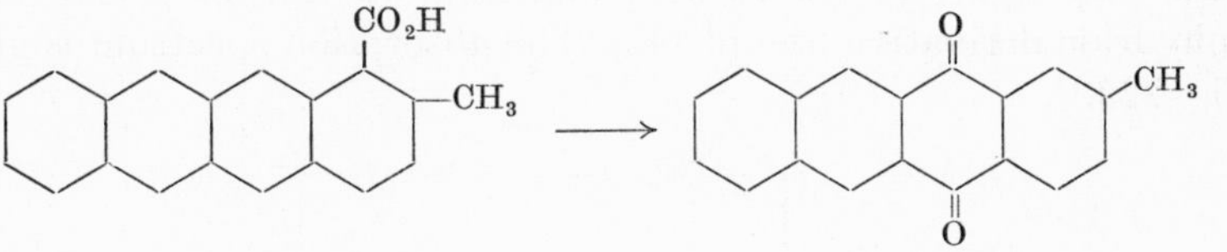

(IV)   (V)

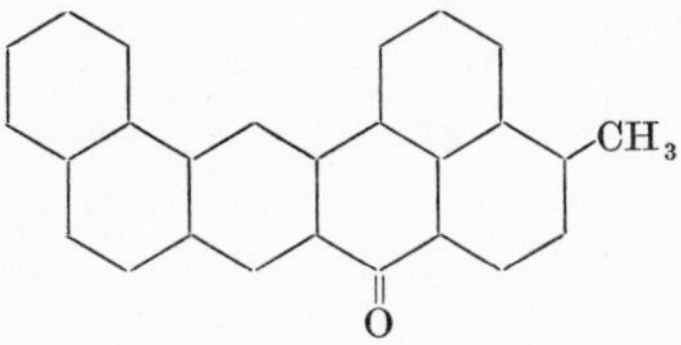

(VI) 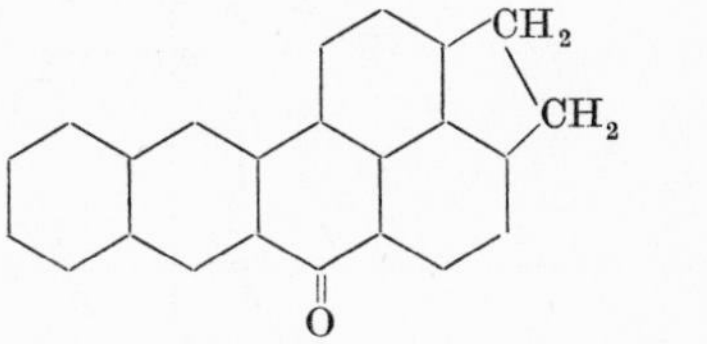   (VII)

The replacement of 2-naphthoyl chloride in the above synthesis by 2-phenanthroyl chloride gives the compound (VI) and 2-naphthoyl chloride and acenaphthene yields the compound (VII).[1]

REFERENCE

1. Buckley, G. D., J. chem. Soc. 561, 564 (1945). See also Vollmann, H., Liebigs Ann. 669, 34 (1963).

VII. 4.5,7.8-Dibenzoperinaphthene

Benzoyl chloride condenses with octahydroanthracene and aluminium chloride in benzene solution to form the ketone (I). Pyrolysis with copper powder at 400° gives 4.5,7.8-dibenzoperinaphthene (II). However, the isomeric 2.3,7.8-dibenzoperinaphthene (see p. 404), is formed by a re-arrangement during the pyrolysis. It can be separated from the hydrocarbon (II) by its higher reactivity with maleic anhydride.[1]

4.5,7.8-Dibenzoperinaphthene (II) forms colourless needles (m.p. 128–129°) from alcohol. It dissolves in concentrated sulphuric acid to give a red solution with a red fluorescence. This solution appears green in a thin layer. It reacts with maleic anhydride to give a succinic anhydride derivative (see p. 145). The absorption spectrum is given in Fig. 223.[1]

Fig. 223. Absorption spectrum of 4.5,7.8-dibenzoperinaphthene in ethanol: α, 3695 (3·20), 3590 (2·96), 3500 (3·58); p, 3410 (4·26), 3250 (4·24), 3110 (4·06), 3010 (3·92), 2870 (4·06), 2760 (4·30); β, 2660 (4·48), 2580 (4·44).

4.5,7.8-Dibenzoperinaphthen-9-one (III) is obtained from the hydro-carbon (II) with selenium dioxide in boiling acetic acid. It crystallizes from acetic acid in long yellow needles (m.p. 229°), which give a red solution with a red fluorescence in concentrated sulphuric acid.[1]

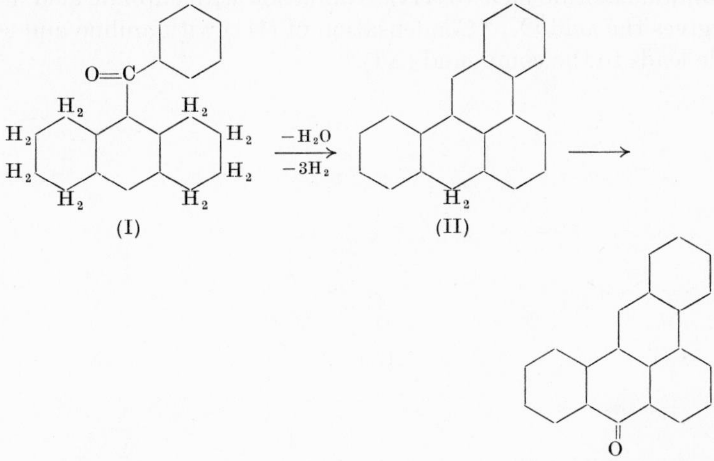

(I)   (II)

(III)

It can also be synthesized by a diene synthesis with o-tolylbutadiene and naphthoquinone (V). The tolylanthraquinone (VI) is brominated to (VII). Substitution of the bromine atom by CN and cyclization yield

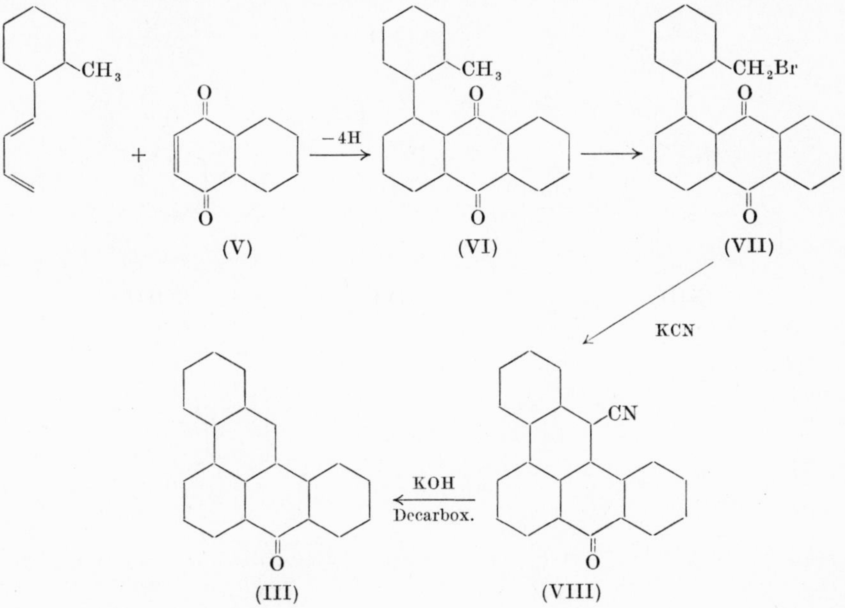

(V)   (VI)   (VII)

KCN

(III)   (VIII)

KOH
Decarbox.

the nitrile and hydrolysis and simultaneous decarboxylation give
dibenzoperinaphthenone (III).[2]

The condensation of anthrone with benzaldehyde in pyridine with
piperidine yields the compound (IX), which cyclizes in a sodium chloride-
aluminium chloride melt to (III).[3] Oxidation with chromic acid in acetic
acid gives the acid (X).[4] Condensation of (III) with aniline and sodium
amide leads to the compound (XI).[5]

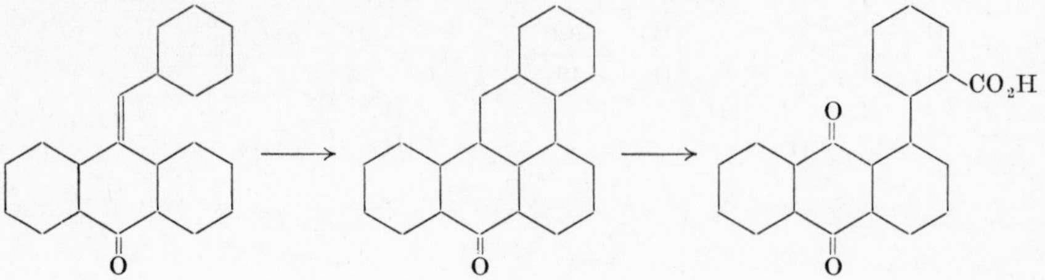

(IX)   (III)   (X)

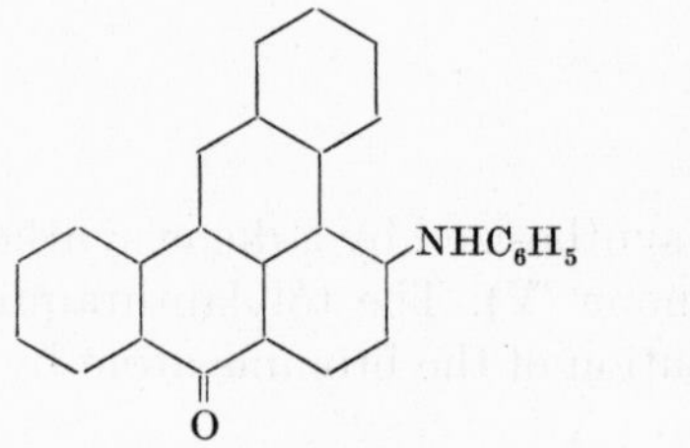

(XI)

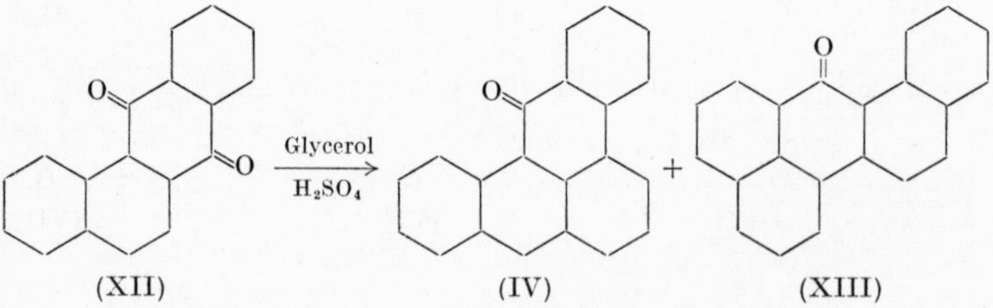

(XII)   Glycerol   (IV)   +   (XIII)
         H₂SO₄

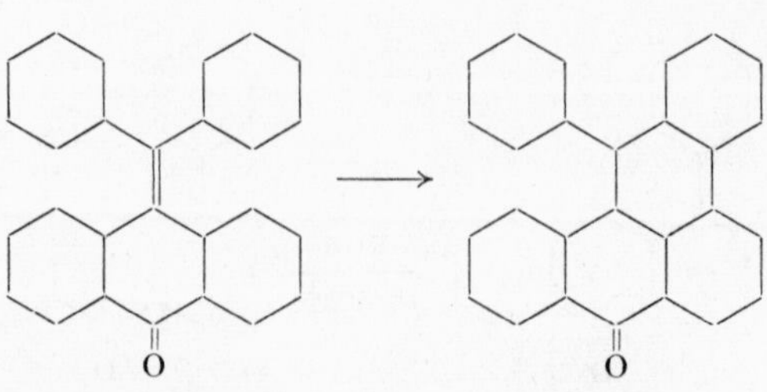

(XIV)   (XV)

The isomeric 4.5,7.8-dibenzoperinaphthen-6-one (IV) can be prepared from tetraphenequinone (XII) by a condensation with glycerol and sulphuric acid. The naphthoperinaphthenone (XIII, see p. 400) is also formed.[6]

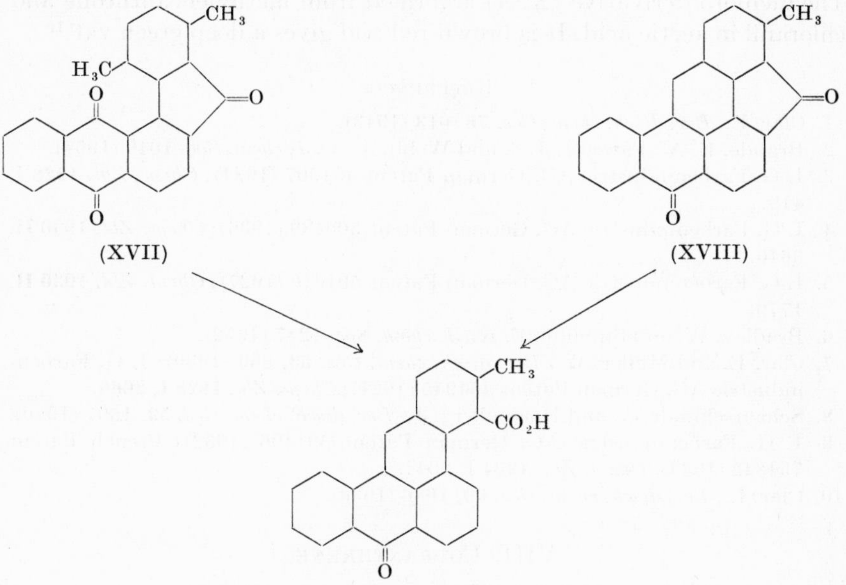

(XVII)

(XVIII)

(XVI)

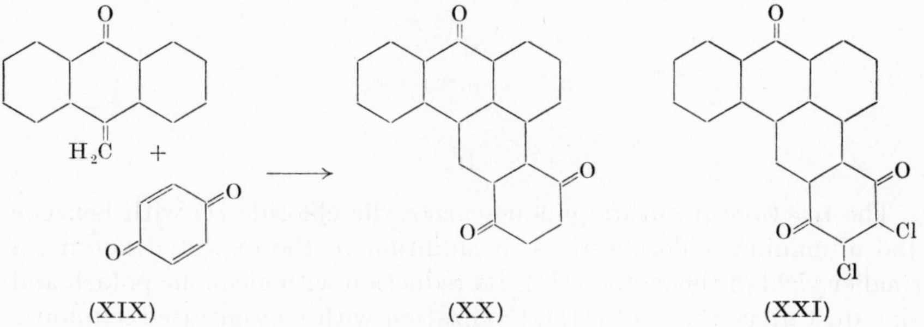

(XIX)   (XX)   (XXI)

4.5,7.8-Dibenzoperinaphthen-6-one (IV) crystallizes in red needles (m.p. 200°), which dissolve in concentrated sulphuric acid to give a red solution with a bluish tinge.

The condensation product of anthrone and benzophenone chloride, called anthrafuchsone (XIV), condenses with aluminium chloride in boiling benzene to give the phenyldibenzoperinaphthenone (XV).[7]

The acid (XVI) was prepared by a potassium hydroxide melt of the compounds (XVII) and (XVIII).[8]

4.5,7.8-Dibenzoperinaphthen-6-one-1′,4′-quinone (XX) is obtained from methyleneanthrone and benzoquinone (XIX) in boiling acetic acid. It is red and gives a bluish-green vat with alkaline sodium dithionite.[9] The dichloro derivative (XXI) is formed from methyleneanthrone and chloranil in acetic acid. It is brown-red and gives a deep green vat.[10]

REFERENCES

1. Clar, E., *Ber. dtsch. chem. Ges.* **76**, 613 (1943).
2. Braude, E. A., Fawcett, J. S. and Webb, A. A., *J. chem. Soc.* 1049 (1954).
3. I. G. Farbenindustrie AG, German Patent 451907 (1924); *Chem. Zbl.* **1928 I**, 419.
4. I. G. Farbenindustrie AG, German Patent 506439 (1936); *Chem. Zbl.* **1930 II**, 3640.
5. I. G. Farbenindustrie AG, German Patent 501610 (1927); *Chem. Zbl.* **1930 II**, 1779.
6. Bradley, W. and Sutcliffe, F. K., *J. chem. Soc.* 1247 (1952).
7. Clar, E. and Müller, W., *Ber. dtsch. chem. Ges.* **63**, 869 (1930); I. G. Farbenindustrie AG, German Patent 454945 (1924); *Chem. Zbl.* **1928 I**, 2666.
8. Schaarschmidt, A. and Herzenberg, J., *Ber. dtsch. chem. Ges.* **53**, 1807 (1920).
9. I. G. Farbenindustrie AG, German Patent 591496 (1932); French Patent 754842 (1933); *Chem. Zbl.* **1934 I**, 2044.
10. Clar, E., *Ber. dtsch. chem. Ges.* **69**, 1686 (1936).

VIII. COERANTHRENE

(5.6,7.8-Dibenzoperinaphthene)

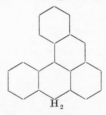

The reaction of anthraquinone-carboxylic chloride (I) with benzene and aluminium chloride gives, in addition to the expected ketone, a smaller yield of the lactone (II). Its reduction with alcoholic potash and zinc dust gives the acid (III). Cyclization with concentrated sulphuric acid at room temperature yields coeranthrone (IV).[1]

The Grignard compound of o-bromodiphenylmethane (VI) reacts with phthalic anhydride and forms the compound (VII). This can be condensed to coeranthrone (IV) with phosphoric acid, either directly or after cyclization to the compound (VIII).[2]

Another synthesis begins with the reaction of benzophenone-dicarboxylic dilactone (IX) with phenyl magnesium bromide to give (X).[3] This is cyclized to the lactone (XI)[4] which can be reduced to the acid (VIII) with potassium hydroxide and zinc dust.[3] Cyclization with phosphoric acid yields coeranthrone (IV).[2]

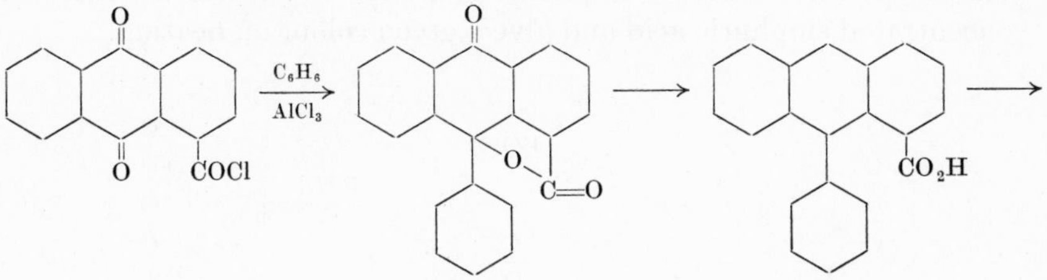

(I)   (II)   (III)

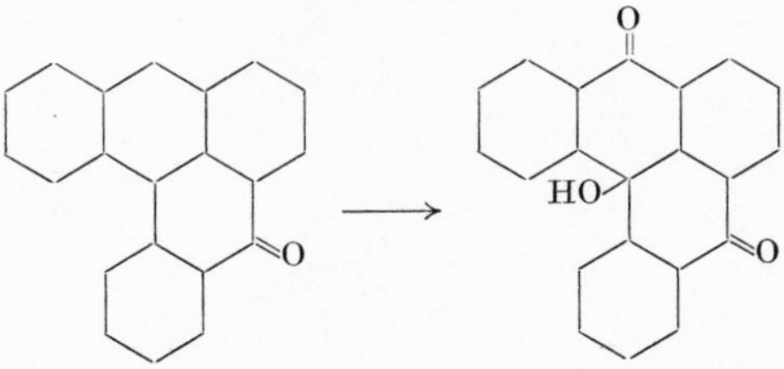

(IV)   (V)

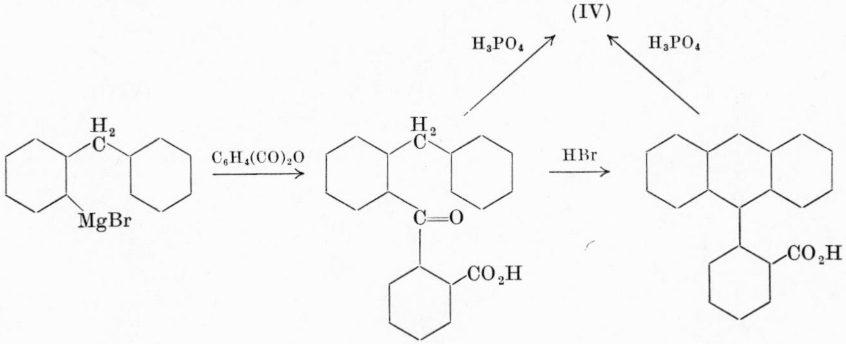

(IV)

H$_3$PO$_4$ H$_3$PO$_4$

(VI)   (VII)   (VIII)

The reduction of coeranthrone (IV) to coeranthrene (XIII) is carried out via the compound (XII), which is obtained with sodium hydroxide and zinc dust. Sublimation splits out water and gives coeranthrene (XIII).[5]

Coeranthrene (XIII) crystallizes from a mixture of benzene and petroleum ether in large orange-yellow plates (m.p. 138–139°), which dissolve in concentrated sulphuric acid to form a yellow solution which turns green on standing. The absorption spectrum is given in Fig. 224 and is related to 3.4-benzophenanthrene.[6]

The reduction of coeranthrone with hydriodic acid and red phosphorus yields 1,10-trimethylene-3.4-benzophenanthrene (XIV). This forms from benzene–petroleum ether flat prisms (m.p. 116–117°), which dissolve in concentrated sulphuric acid and give a green colour on heating.

Coeranthrone (IV) crystallizes from acetic acid in dark red needles (m.p. 178–179°), which dissolve in concentrated sulphuric acid with a green colour. The solution in organic solvents is yellow with a yellowish-green fluorescence. The colourless compound (V) is formed by oxidation with chromic acid in acetic acid.

If the lactone (II) is reduced to 9-phenylanthrone-1-carboxylic acid (XV) and then cyclized, the unstable blue coeranthranol (XVI) is obtained which yields the red chlorocoeranthrone (XVII) with phosphorus pentachloride.

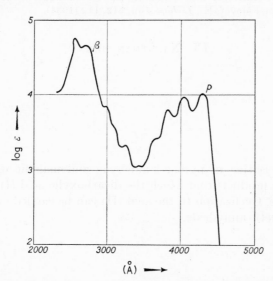

FIG. 224. Absorption spectrum of coeranthrene in ethanol: p, 4280 (4·02), 4040 (3·98), 3830 (3·80), 3650 (3·43); 3240 (3·34), 2990 (3·84); β, 2690 (4·66), 2570 (4·74).

A number of coeranthrone derivatives have been prepared. Starting from 2-methylanthraquinone-1-carboxylic chloride, methylcoeranthrone can be obtained.[7] Other derivatives are prepared with anthraquinone-1,4-dicarboxylic acid and by the replacement of benzene by benzene derivatives.[8]

(XVI)   (XV)   (XVII)

REFERENCES

1. Scholl, R. and Donat, J., *Liebigs Ann.* **512**, 1 (1934); Scholl, R., French Patent 601856 (1925).
2. Bradsher, C. K. and Vingiello, F. A., *J. org. Chem.* **13**, 786 (1948).

3. Scholl, R. and Donat, J., *Liebigs Ann.* **512**, 7, 22 (1934).
4. Cook, J. W., *J. chem. Soc.* **58**, 62 (1928).
5. Clar, E. and Stewart, D. G., *J. Amer. chem. Soc.* **74**, 6235 (1952).
6. Clar, E. and Stewart, D. G., *J. Amer. chem. Soc.* **74**, 6235 (1952).
7. Scholl, R., Dehnert, H. and Wanka L., *Liebigs Ann.* **493**, 56 (1932).
8. Scholl, R. and Meyer, K., *Liebigs Ann.* **512**, 112 (1934).

IX. NAPHTHANTHRENE

The condensation of pyrene-3-aldehyde and malonic ester gives a condensation product from which the dicarboxylic acid (I) is obtained by hydrolysis. Cyclization to the acid (II) can be carried out with zinc chloride in acetic anhydride.

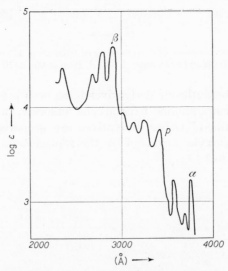

Fig. 225. Absorption spectrum of naphthanthrene in ethanol: α, 3750 (3·22), 3690 (2·85), 3565 (3·22); p, 3410 (3·76), 3260 (3·87), 3120 (3·83), 3020 (3·93): β, 2910 (4·64), 2800 (4·56), 2700 (4·34); β', 2360 (4·40).

Zinc-dust distillation of the acid (II) gives naphthanthrene (III). It can be also obtained in the same way from naphthanthrone (VI).[1]

Naphthanthrene (III) crystallizes from alcohol in pale yellow leaflets (m.p. 135°), which dissolve in concentrated sulphuric acid with a yellow colour and a green fluorescence. The colour of this solution changes to green on standing. Oxidation with chromic acid in acetic acid yields naphthanthrone-1,2-quinone (VII). The absorption spectrum is given in Fig. 225.

(I)   (II)   (III)   (IV)   (VI)   (VII)   (VIII)   (V)   (IX)   (X)

2,3-Trimethylenepyrene (IV) can be prepared from naphthanthrone with hydriodic acid and red phosphorus or by a zinc-dust melt. 2,3-Trimethylenepyrene, which is purified by chromatography, has a m.p. of 112–113° and forms colourless leaflets which dissolve in concentrated sulphuric acid to give a yellow solution.[2] It forms a red picrate

II—14

and can be dehydrogenated to naphthanthrene by sublimation over copper powder.[3]

Naphthanthr-6-one (VI) can be obtained by condensation of pyrene with glycerol and sulphuric acid.[3] It was formerly thought to have the structure (X). However, its formation from 1-hydroxypyrene, glycerol and sulphuric acid excludes this formula and confirms structure (VI).[4] It crystallizes after chromatography in greenish-yellow needles (m.p. 252–253°), which dissolve in concentrated sulphuric acid to form a yellowish-green solution with a red fluorescence.

Naphthanthrone (VI) gives a tetrabromide with bromine. All four bromine atoms can be easily eliminated. Further reaction with bromine gives 2-bromo- and then 2,10-dibromonaphthanthrone. Naphthanthrone forms 3-hydroxynaphthanthrone when treated with sodium hydroxide and manganese dioxide.[5] Boiling with concentrated nitric acid yields a dinitro compound which can be reduced to a diamino compound. Oxidation with chromic acid in acetic acid gives naphthanthrone-1,2-quinone (VII), which condenses with o-phenylenediamine to yield an azine.[4]

Naphthanthrone-1,2-quinone (VII) forms dark red needles from chlorobenzene (m.p. 378° (dec.)), which dissolve in concentrated sulphuric acid to a bluish-red solution with a brownish-red fluorescence. It forms a green vat with alkaline sodium dithionite. Naphthanthrone-quinone (VII) gives benzanthrone-dicarboxylic acid (VIII) when oxidized with hydrogen peroxide and alkali.[4]

REFERENCES

1. Vollmann, H., Becker, H., Corell, M. and Streeck, H., *Liebigs Ann.* **531**, 54 (1937).
2. Clar, E. and Stewart, D. G., *J. Amer. chem. Soc.* **75**, 2672 (1953).
3. Scholl, R. and Meyer, K., *Ber. dtsch. chem. Ges.* **69**, 152 (1937).
4. Vollmann, H., Becker, H., Corell, M. and Streeck, H., *Liebigs Ann.* **531**, 54 (1937).
5. Bradley, W. and Sutcliffe, F. K., *J. chem. Soc.* 2118 (1951).

X. 3H-4.5-BENZONAPHTHANTHRENE

(2.3-Benzylenepyrene)

3-Benzoylpyrene (I) is obtained from pyrene, benzoyl chloride and aluminium chloride in benzene solution. It cyclizes in a sodium chloride–aluminium chloride melt to benzonaphthanthrone (II).[1] The reduction to the hydrocarbon (IV) is carried out in a zinc-dust melt.[2]

3H-4.5-Benzonaphthanthrene (IV) forms colourless needles (m.p. 230–231°) from xylene. It dissolves in concentrated sulphuric acid to

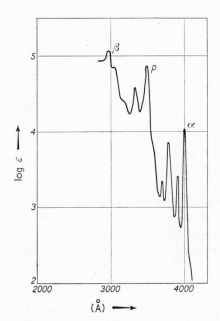

Fig. 226. Absorption spectrum of 3H-4.5-benzonaphthanthrene in benzene: α, 3990 (4·04), 3905 (3·43), 3780 (3·86), 3700 (3·34); p, 3490 (4·86); 3330 (4·60); 3170 (4·40); 3060 (4·85); β, 2960 (5·06).

give a green-blue solution. The solution in benzene shows a blue fluorescence. It forms a red picrate. The absorption spectrum given in Fig. 226 shows that it is a pyrene derivative.[2]

4.5-Benzonaphthanthr-3-one (II) crystallizes from chlorobenzene in golden yellow needles (m.p. 242°), which dissolve in concentrated sulphuric

(I)   (II)   (III)

acid with a blue colour. It forms the acid (III) if submitted to a potassium hydroxide melt.[1]

(IV)

(V)   (VI)

A phthaloyl derivative of benzonaphthanthrone (II) can be obtained by condensation of 3-benzoylpyrene with phthalic anhydride and aluminium chloride.[3] The phenyl derivative (VI) is obtained from pyrene, benzophenone chloride and aluminium chloride.[4]

REFERENCES

1. Vollmann, H., Becker, H., Corell, M. and Streeck, H., *Liebigs Ann.* **531**, 34 (1937).
2. Clar, E., *Chem. Ber.* **81**, 524 (1948).
3. Scholl, R., Meyer, K. and Donat, J., *Ber. dtsch. chem. Ges.* **70**, 2180 (1937).
4. Clar, E., *Chem. Ber.* **81**, 524 (1948); **69**, 1685 (1936).

XI. 3.4-BENZONAPHTHANTHRENE

Decahydropyrene (I) reacts with benzoyl chloride and aluminium chloride to yield the ketone (I), which gives 3.4-benzonaphthanthrene when pyrolysed in the presence of copper powder at 400–410°.

3.4-Benzonaphthanthrene (II) crystallizes from xylene in pale yellow needles (m.p. 181–182°), which dissolve in concentrated sulphuric acid to

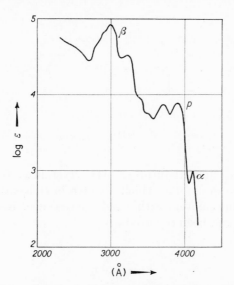

give an orange-brown solution with a strong green fluorescence. Solutions in benzene or xylene show a strong blue fluorescence. The absorption spectrum is given in Fig. 227. Picric acid gives a greyish-brown picrate (m.p. 182° (dec.)). The hydrocarbon reacts readily with maleic anhydride.

FIG. 227. Absorption spectrum of 3.4-benzonaphthanthrene in ethanol: α, 4110 (3·00); p, 3900 (3·90), 3690 (3·88), 3510 (3·76), 3400 (3·95), 3240 (4·53); β, 3005 (4·93).

Oxidation with selenium dioxide in acetic acid gives a mixture of the two compounds (III) and (IV).[1]

REFERENCE

1. Clar, E., *Chem. Ber.* **81**, 520 (1948).

XII. 1.2,10.11-DIBENZONAPHTHANTHRENE

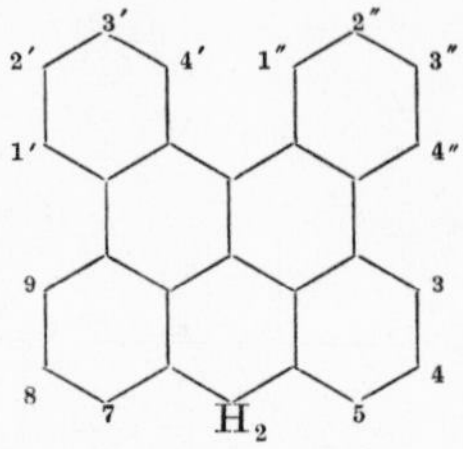

The condensation product of anthrone with benzophenone chloride (I), called anthrafuchsone, can be cyclized to (II) (see p. 410) then to dibenzonaphthanthrone (III)[1] in a sodium chloride–aluminium chloride melt at 140–160°.

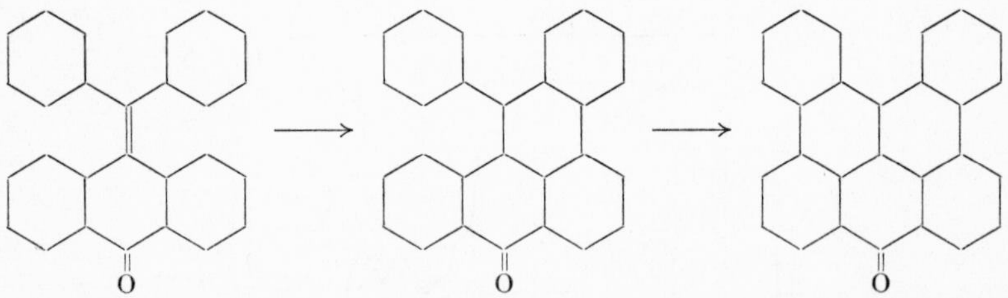

(I)   (II)   (III)

1.2,10.11-Dibenzonaphthanthrone (III) crystallizes from acetic acid in yellow needles (m.p. 305), which dissolve in concentrated sulphuric acid to form a blue solution with a red fluorescence. Reduction to the hydrocarbon has not been reported.

REFERENCE

1. Clar, E. and Müller, W., *Ber. dtsch. chem. Ges.* **63**, 869 (1930); I. G. Farbenindustrie AG, German Patent 454945 (1924); *Chem. Zbl.* **1928 I**, 2666.

XIII. 2.3-BENZONAPHTHO-(2″.3″ : 7.8)-PERINAPHTHENE

The ketone (I) can be cyclized with sodium hydroxide in boiling quinoline to form the hydroxybenzonaphthoperinaphthone (II) which, when submitted to a zinc-dust distillation, yields benzonaphtho-perinaphthene (III).[1]

The oxidation of 2.3,7.8-dibenzoperylene (IV) with chromic acid gives first a quinone (see p. 55) and then the acid (V), the zinc-dust distillation of which yields benzonaphthoperinaphthene (III). Another oxidation product of dibenzoperylene (IV), the compound (VI or VII), also gives the hydrocarbon (III) on zinc-dust distillation.

The structure of the compound (VI or VII) was proved by oxidation with chromic acid in acetic acid, which yielded the lactone (VIII), which on zinc-dust distillation gave a mixture of dihydro- and tetrahydro-pentacenes (IX) and (X) respectively, from which pentacene (see Vol. 1, p. 423) was obtained by dehydrogenation with chloranil.[2]

(VIII)

(IX)   +   (X)

2.3-Benzo-naphtho-(2″.3″:7.8)-perinaphthene (III) crystallizes from benzene–alcohol in pale yellow needles (m.p. 207–209°), which dissolve in concentrated sulphuric acid to give a red-brown solution with a red fluorescence. Picric acid forms a red-brown picrate.

The compound (VI or VII) forms red prisms (m.p. 303°) from xylene which dissolve in concentrated sulphuric acid with a brown-red colour. Alkaline sodium dithionite produces a violet vat.

REFERENCES

1. Holzer, K., Ziegler, E. and Zinke, A., *Mh. Chem.* **83**, 180 (1952).
2. Zinke, A., Holzer, K. and Ziegler, E., *Mh. Chem.* **82**, 645 (1951).

XIV. 7.8-BENZONAPHTHO-(2″.3″:4.5)-PERINAPHTHENE

Benzanthrone (I) condenses with phthalic anhydride in a melt with aluminium chloride to give phthalylbenzanthrone (II).[1] The same product is obtained from a condensation of methyleneanthrone (III) and naphthoquinone or dichloronaphthoquinone,[2] or 2-chloronaphthoquinone or naphthoquinone dichloride[3] in boiling nitrobenzene.

(I)   (II)   (III)

Derivatives of phthalylbenzanthrone (II) can be obtained by the use of substituted methylenanthrones or substituted naphthoquinones like naphthazarine.[4]

7.8-Benzo-naphtho-(2″.3″:4.5)-perinaphth-9-one-1″,4″-quinone (phthalylbenzanthrone, II) crystallizes from acetic acid–nitrobenzene in orange-yellow needles (m.p. 286°), which dissolve in concentrated sulphuric acid to give a brown-orange solution. A green vat is formed with alkaline sodium dithionite solution which dyes cotton golden yellow.

Phthalylbenzanthrone (II) condenses with 1-aminoanthraquinone, pyridine and potassium hydroxide to give a violet vat dye.[5]

REFERENCES

1. I. G. Farbenindustrie AG, German Patent 430558 (1924); *Chem. Zbl.* **1926 II**, 2230.
2. Clar, E., *Ber. dtsch. chem. Ges.* **69**, 1686 (1936).
3. I. G. Farbenindustrie AG, German Patent 591496 (1932); French Patent 754842 (1933); *Chem. Zbl.* **1934 I**, 2044.
4. I. G. Farbenindustrie AG, German Patent 591496 (1932); French Patent 754842 (1933); *Chem. Zbl.* **1934 I**, 2044.
5. I. G. Farbenindustrie AG, German Patent 644537 (1935); *Chem. Zbl.* **1937 I**, 865.

II—14*

XV. 1.2,4.5,7.8-Tribenzoperinaphthene
(2.3,5.6,8.9-Tribenzoperinaphthene)

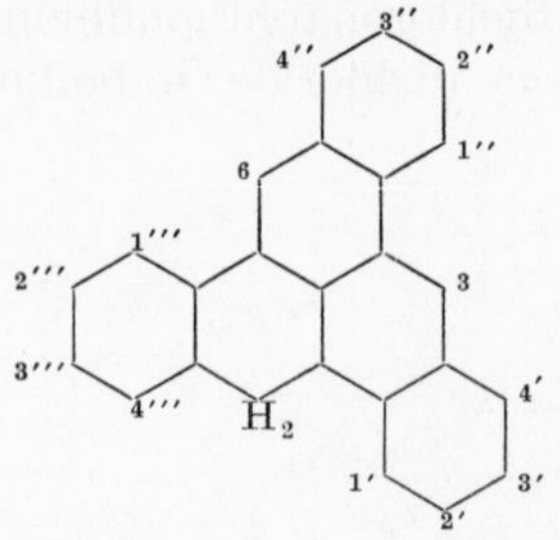

Tetraphenequinone (I) gives 1.2-benzanthrone (II) when reduced with aluminium powder in concentrated sulphuric acid. Its condensation with benzaldehyde in pyridine and piperidine yields the compound (III).

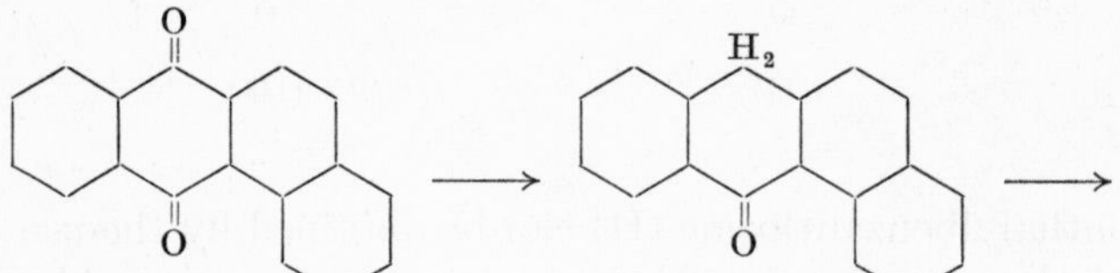

(I) (II)

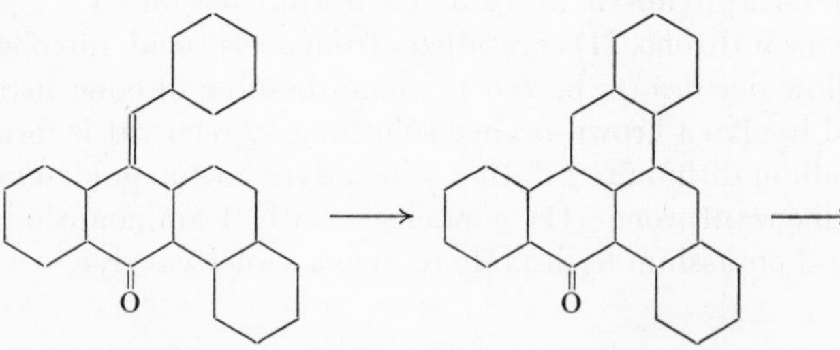

(III) (IV)

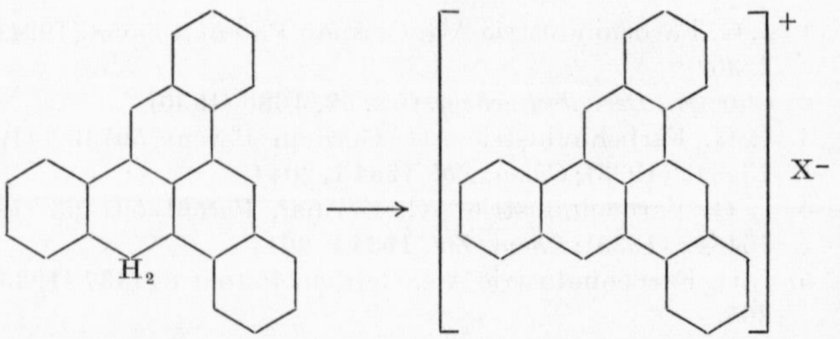

(V) (VI)

Cyclization to (IV) is carried out in boiling benzene with aluminium chloride. Reduction with hydriodic acid and red phosphorus leads to the hydrocarbon (V).

1.2,4.5,7.8-Tribenzoperinaphthene (V) crystallizes from benzene in pale yellow needles (m.p. 253–254°), which show a blue fluorescence in solution and do not dissolve in cold concentrated sulphuric acid; however, a violet-blue solution is obtained on warming. The absorption

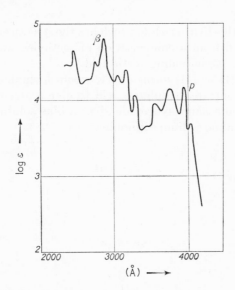

FIG. 228. Absorption spectrum of 1.2,4.5,7.8-tribenzoperinaphthene in ethanol: α, 4020 (3·68); p, 3930 (4·14), 3730 (4·16), 3540 (3·95), 3260 (4·04), 3160 (4·39), 3040 (4·33); β, 2840 (4·79), 2740 (4·50); 2460 (4·66).

spectrum is given in Fig. 228. Prolonged reduction with hydriodic acid and red phosphorus gives a dihydro derivative.

Tribenzoperinaphthene is readily oxidized by air in acidic solution even in acetic acid. Its violet salts have the constitution (VI). The acetate is unstable, but the hydrochloride and the perchlorate are stable and can be obtained in a pure state. These remarkable properties result from the high symmetry which stabilizes the ion (VI). The unstable acetate is readily oxidized by air to the tribenzoperinaphthone (IV).[1]

REFERENCE

1. Clar, E. and Stewart, D. G., *J. chem. Soc.* 23 (1958).

XVI. 7.8-Benzonaphtho-(1″.2″:4.5)-perinaphthene

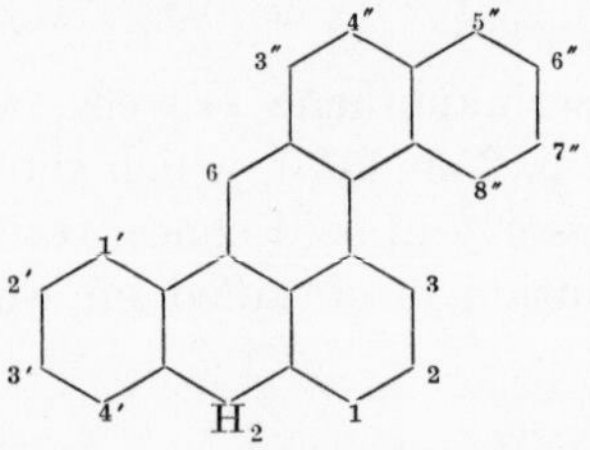

A quinone of this hydrocarbon which has the structure (II), or perhaps (III), is obtained from a condensation of methyleneanthrone (I) with 1,2-naphthoquinone in boiling acetic acid.[1]

The quinone (II or III) forms violet, greenish-shining crystals which dissolve in concentrated sulphuric acid to give a green solution. Alcoholic–aqueous potassium hydroxide gives a blue solution. A red vat is formed with alkaline sodium dithionite.[1]

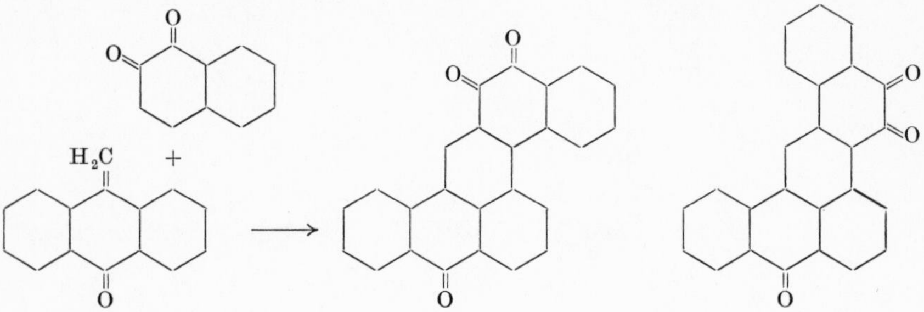

(I)   (II)   (III)

REFERENCE

1. I. G. Farbenindustrie AG, German Patent 591496 (1932); French Patent 75482 (1932); *Chem. Zbl.* **1934 I**, 2044.

XVII. Anthraceno-(2′.3′:7.8)-perinaphthene

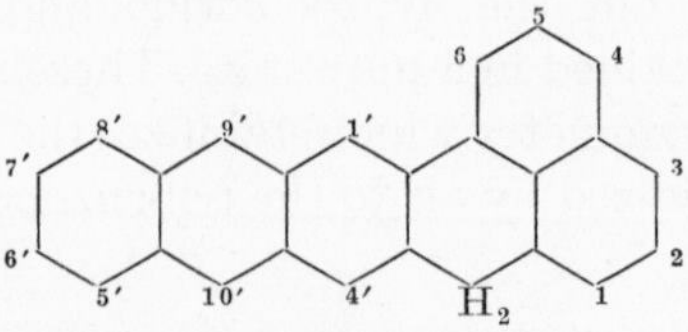

Anthraquinone-carboxylic chloride condenses with naphthalene and aluminium chloride to give the ketone (I), which can be cyclized to (II)

by heating with aluminium chloride. Oxidation of the compound (II) with chromic acid yields pentacene diquinone carboxylic acid (III).[1]

The same phthalylbenzanthrone (II) can be obtained from pentacenediquinone (IV) which, after reduction to (V), condenses with glycerol and sulphuric acid to (II).[2]

Anthraquinono-(2'.3':7.8)-perinaphthone (phthalylbenzanthrone, II) forms dark yellow crystals from nitrobenzene–acetic acid (m.p. 325–326°), which dissolve in concentrated sulphuric acid to give a red solution. The reduction to the hydrocarbon has not yet been reported.

REFERENCES

1. Scholl, R. and Seer, C., *Liebigs Ann.* **394**, 111, 158 (1912); *Mh. Chem.* **33**, 1 (1912).
2. I. G. Farbenindustrie AG, German Patent 579653 (1931); *Chem. Zbl.* **1933 II**, 1933.

XVIII. 7.8-BENZANTHRACENO-(2″.3″:4.5)-PERINAPHTHENE

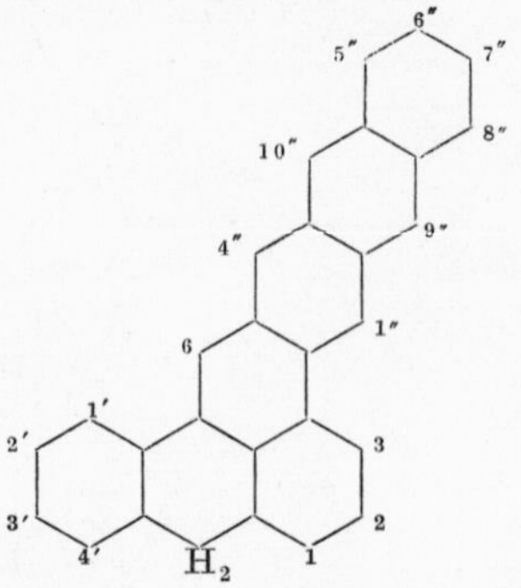

A derivative of this system is obtained if methyleneanthrone (I) is condensed with *endo*-9,10-(*o*-phenylene)-9,10-dihydroanthra-1,4-quinone in boiling xylene. The compound (II) forms red needles (m.p. > 360°), which dissolve in concentrated sulphuric acid to give a brown-orange solution. Alkaline sodium dithionite solution gives a green vat.[1]

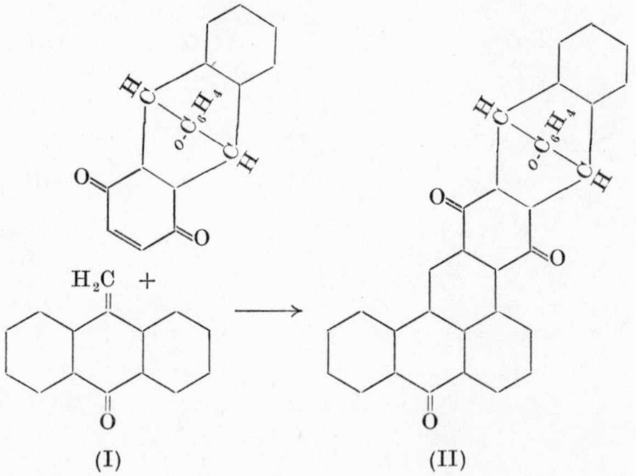

(I)   (II)

REFERENCE

1. Clar, E., *Ber. dtsch. chem. Ges.* **69**, 1686 (1936).

PART IX

peri-Condensed Hydrocarbons consisting of Six-membered Rings in which Two Carbon Atoms Are Linked with Two Hydrogen Atoms

The hydrocarbons described here can be considered dihydro derivatives of hydrocarbons with no Kekulé structures. These are unstable diradicals, or could be formulated only as non-radical structures by the use of *m*-quinoid complexes which have never been found in aromatic compounds. The following hydrocarbons can therefore not be dehydrogenated to aromatic hydrocarbons but to polymers of diradicals.

Hydrocarbons Consisting of Six-membered Rings in which Two Carbon Atoms Are Linked with Two Hydrogen Atoms

I. 4,8-DIHYDROTRIANGULENE

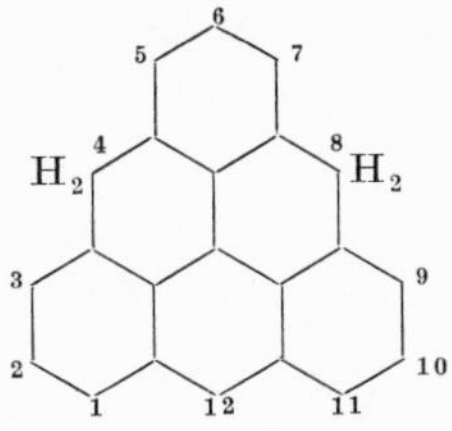

The reaction of o-tolyl magnesium bromide with phthalic anhydride gives di-o-tolylphthalide.[1] However, the main product is di-o-tolyl-benzene.[2] Reduction of the phthalide with sodium amalgam and alkali gives the acid (II), which is oxidized to the tricarboxylic acid (III). Cyclization with sulphuric acid yields the triketone (IV). However this is strongly acidic and must be formulated as 12-hydroxytriangulene-4,8-quinone (IVa).

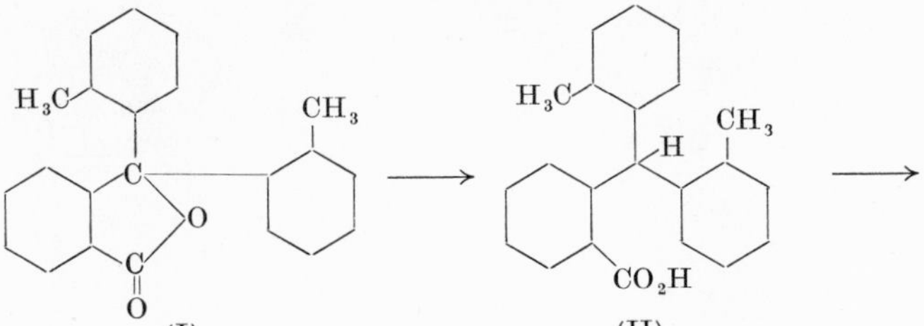

(I)   (II)

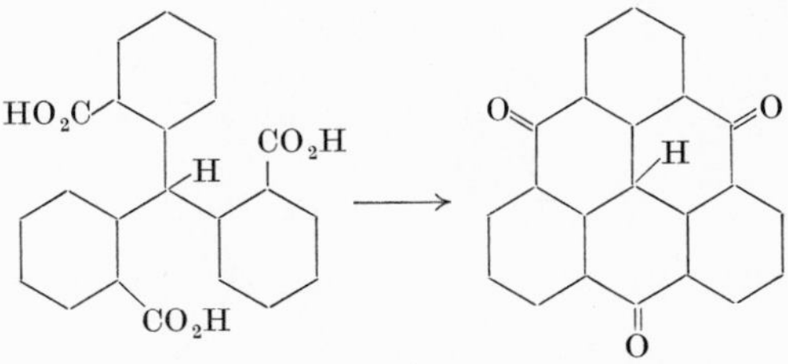

(III)   (IV)

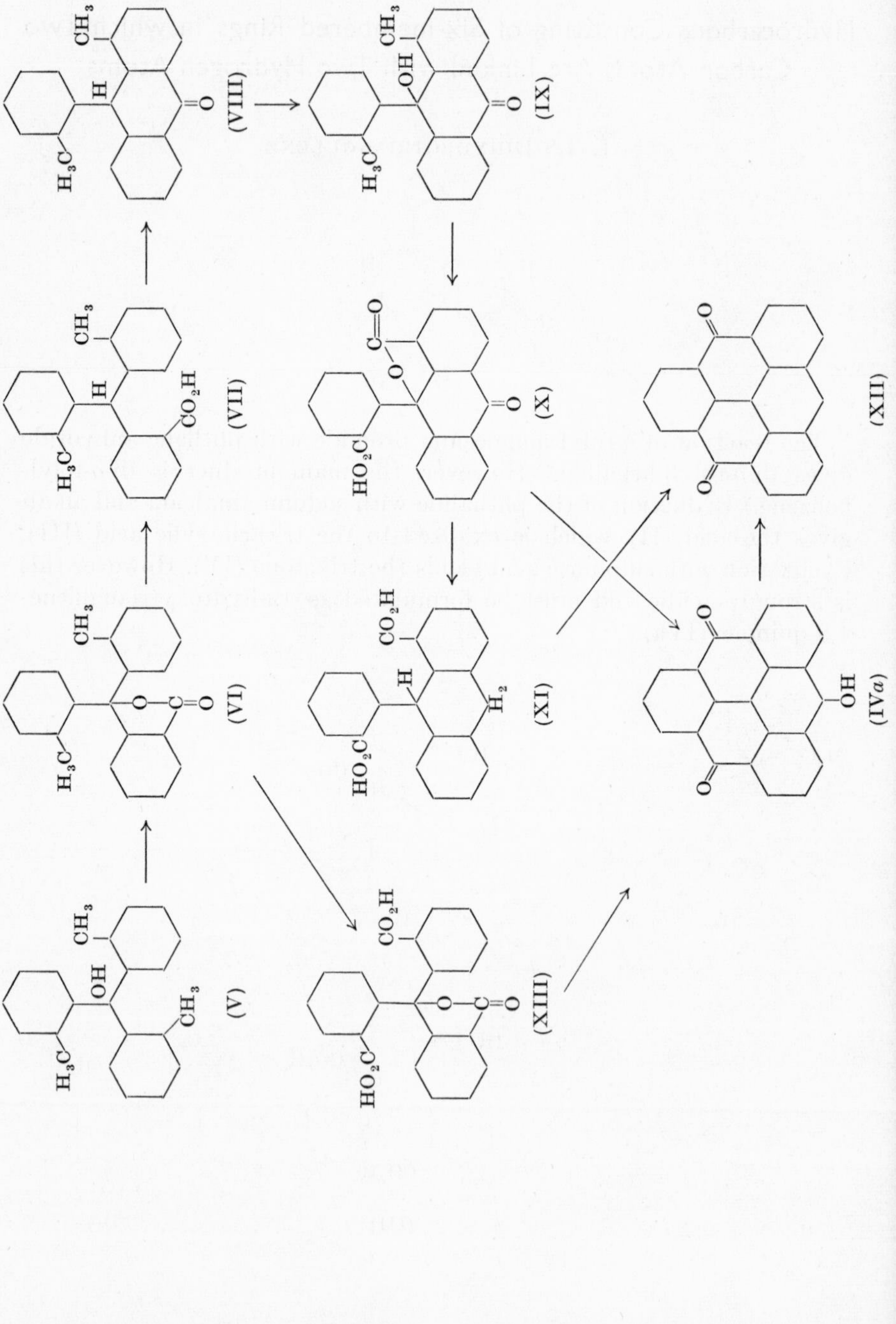
(V)
(VI)
(VII)
(VIII)
(IX)
(X)
(XI)
(XII)
(XIII)
(IVa)

This synthesis gives low yields not only because of the low yields in the Grignard reaction but also because the oxidation is accompanied by re-arrangement which produces mostly benzophenone dicarboxylic anhydride (see Vol. 1, p. 355), which is useless for the above synthesis.

Better results are obtained by starting from o-tolyl chloride, which reacts with o-tolyl lithium to form tritolyl carbinol (V). Oxidation with dilute nitric acid yields the pure phthalide (VI). Reduction with zinc dust and alcoholic potassium hydroxide gives the acid (VII). Cyclization in a melt of zinc chloride and sodium chloride leads to the anthrone

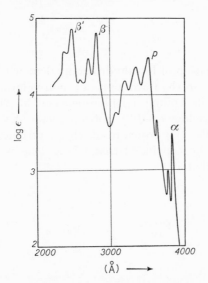

FIG. 229. Absorption spectrum of 1,2,3,5,6,7-hexahydrotriangulene in ethanol: α, 3830 (3·50), 3765 (3·00), 3625 (3·66); p, 3515 (4·48), 3350 (4·32), 3200 (4·16), 3070 (3·77); β, 2815 (4·80), 2700 (4·48), 2590 (4·18); β', 2480 (4·86), 2380 (4·57).

derivative (VIII). Oxidation with dilute nitric acid gives first (IX) and then the lactone acid (X). This is reduced to the dicarboxylic acid (XI) with zinc dust and sodium hydroxide. Cyclization to triangulenequinone (XII) is carried out by warming with concentrated sulphuric acid and m-nitrobenzene sulphonic acid.[3]

Cyclization of the acid (X) with sulphuric acid and copper powder yields the hydroxytriangulenequinone (IVa). It can also be obtained from the acid (XIII), which is formed in small yield by oxidation of the phthalide (VI) with dilute nitric acid at 210°.[3]

The zinc-dust melt of triangulenequinone (XII) or its reduction with hydriodic acid and red phosphorus gives hexahydrotriangulene (XVI).

1,2,3,5,6,7-Hexahydrotriangulene (XVI) crystallizes from petroleum ether or sublimes in long colourless needles (m.p. 176°), which dissolve in concentrated sulphuric acid to a yellowish-green solution. Solutions in organic solvents show a blue fluorescence. The absorption spectrum is given in Fig. 229. This is closely related to the spectrum of pyrene (XIV) and 2,3-trimethylenepyrene (XV).

(XIV)   (XV)   (XVI)

The dehydrogenation of hexahydrotriangulene with palladium–charcoal at 310° results in the formation of a non-volatile polytriangulene. Dehydrogenation in boiling trichlorobenzene at 200° indicates the formation of the yellow 4,8-dihydrotriangulene (XVII), as shown by its spectrum. Finally, the brown insoluble polytriangulene is obtained. It must therefore be concluded that triangulene is a diradical which polymerizes immediately.

(XVII)   (XVIII)   (XIX)

(XX)

4,8-Dihydrotriangulene (XVII) is formed as a by-product in the zinc-dust melt of triangulenequinone. It is a yellow hydrocarbon with absorption bands at 4630 and 4440 Å in benzene solution. Owing to its sensitivity to oxygen it has not been obtained in a pure state. It also decomposes during chromatographic purification. The oxidation product cannot have the structure (XVIII) because it does not give an acetyl derivative, does not react with alcoholic potash and sublimes without decomposition. Its spectrum is closely related to naphthanthrone (XX) and it has therefore the structure (XIX). A vat-like reoxidizable product is formed with alkaline sodium dithionite or with zinc dust in acetic acid. This is also obtained by reduction of triangulenequinone.

Dodecahydrotriangulene (XXI) can be prepared from triangulene-quinone by reduction with hydriodic acid and red phosphorus at 210°. It forms colourless needles (m.p. 162–163°), which dissolve only in warm sulphuric acid and give a crimson solution which on standing becomes yellow with a green fluorescence. This hydrocarbon is also obtained by the decarboxylation of the dicarboxylic acids (XXII) or (XXIII).

(XXII)   (XXI)   (XXIII)

These two acids are formed by the reduction of the corresponding triangulene-dicarboxylic acids with hydriodic acid and red phosphorus. The absorption spectrum of dodecahydrotriangulene shows that it is a naphthalene derivative corresponding to the formula (XXI).

Triangulene-4,8-quinone (XXIV) crystallizes from nitrobenzene or sublimes in deep red needles (m.p. > 300 (dec.)), which dissolve in concentrated sulphuric acid to give a red-violet solution. Triangulenequinone gives a green vat with alkaline sodium dithionite which is not a true vat with the diradical structure (XXV) because the sodium salt of the vat contains only one atom of sodium, so it must be given the structure (XXVII). The hydroxy compound (XXVI) is violet and can also be prepared by reduction of triangulenequinone with zinc dust in acetic acid. Further reduction yields the compound (XXVIII) which rearranges to (XXIX). This is a brown-orange compound which gives a blue Na salt and a monoacetate. Further reduction leads to (XXX) and (XXXI). The latter gives dihydrotriangulene on sublimation, whilst (XXX) yields (XXXIII).

The diacetate (XXXIV) can be obtained by reduction of triangulene-quinone (XXIV) with zinc dust in acetic anhydride. It is a yellow compound which decomposes readily. This shows again that dihydro-triangulene derivatives are unstable and tend to go over into trimethylene derivatives.[4]

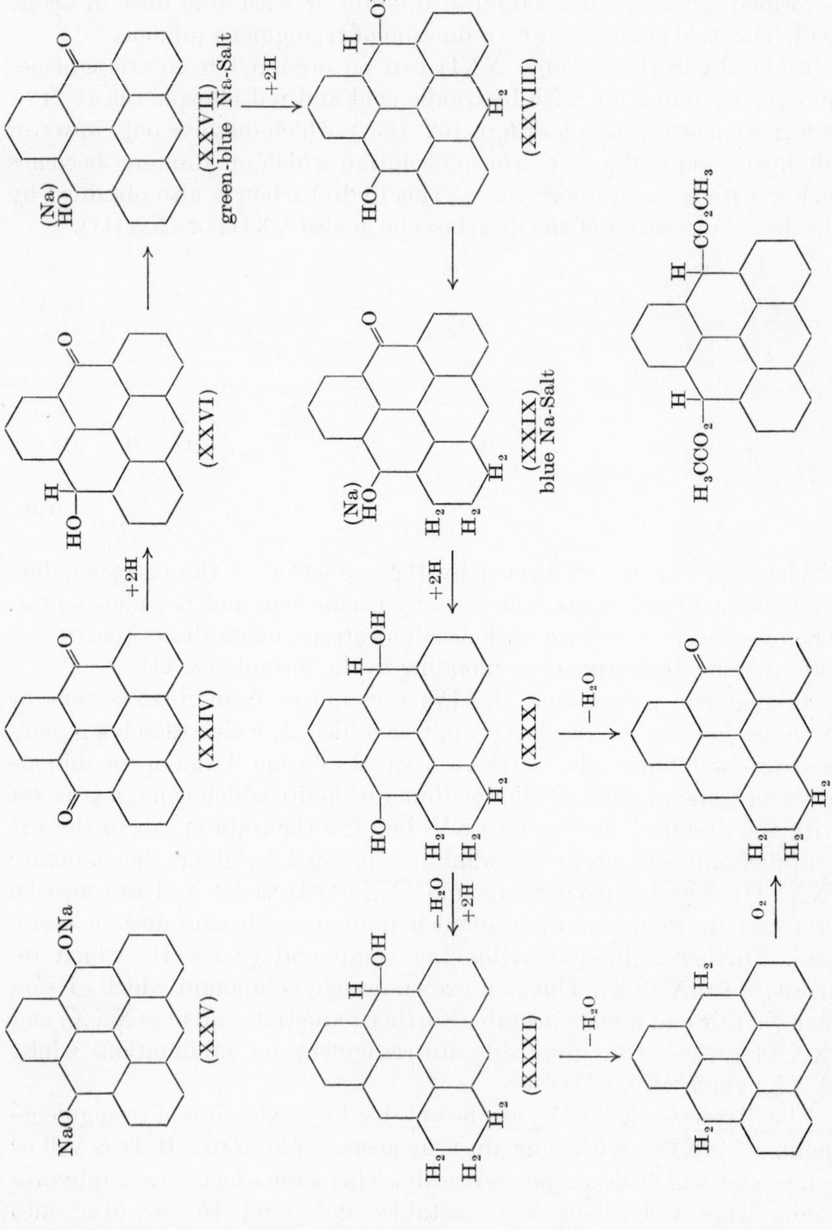
(XXV)
(XXIV)
(XXVI)
(XXVII)
green-blue Na-Salt
(XXVIII)
(XXIX)
blue Na-Salt
(XXX)
(XXXI)
(XXXII)
(XXXIII)
(XXXIV)
+2H
−H₂O
O₂

The triangulenequinone dicarboxylic acids (XXXVI) and (XXXVIII) can be prepared from the two dixylylphthalides (XXXV) and (XXXVII) respectively using the same synthesis as described on p. 434.[5]

(XXXV)   (XXXVI)

(XXXVII)   (XXXVIII)

12-Hydroxytriangulene-4,8-quinone (*IVa*) forms deep blue needles from trichlorobenzene or *o*-toluidine, which dissolve in concentrated sulphuric acid to give a blue solution. They decompose over 450° but can be sublimed in a high vacuum. The compound is so strongly acidic that it forms a greenish-blue sodium salt with sodium acetate solution.[6]

A number of reduction products can be obtained by reduction of hydroxytriangulenequinone.[7] A mono- and a dicarboxylic acid have been prepared by synthesis.[8] The hydroxyquinone gives an acetate with acetic anhydride. Treatment with zinc dust in sodium hydroxide solution gives a vat-like solution which on oxidation with air yields triangulenequinone.[6]

REFERENCES

1. Weisz, R. and Korczyn, J., *Mh. Chem.* **45**, 207 (1924).
2. Clar, E. and Stewart, D. G., *J. chem. Soc.* 3215 (1951).
3. Clar, E. and Stewart, D. G., *J. Amer. chem. Soc.* **75**, 2667 (1953); Amer. Patent 2841597 (1958).
4. Clar, E. and Stewart, D. G., *J. Amer. chem. Soc.* **75**, 2667 (1953); **76**, 3505 (1954).
5. Clar, E. and Stewart, D. G., *J. Amer. chem. Soc.* **76**, 3504 (1954).
6. Clar, E. and Stewart, D. G., *J. Amer. chem. Soc.* **75**, 2667 (1953).
7. Weisz, R. and Müller, Fr., *Mh. Chem.* **65**, 481 (1934).
8. Weisz, R. and Müller, Fr., *Mh. Chem.* **59**, 128 (1932); Weisz, R., Spitzer, A. and Melzer, J. L., *Mh. Chem.* **47**, 307 (1926).

II. 5,6-DIHYDRO-1.12,10.11-DIBENZOTETRACENE

Di-(1-naphthyl)-carbinol (I) is transformed into the chloromethane and condensed with magnesio-malonic ester to give the diester (II). The corresponding dicarboxylic acid, obtained by hydrolysis, is very difficult to cyclize to the quinone (III). Only treatment with phosphorus pentachloride in nitrobenzene gives a condensation product, which probably has the structure (III). It forms red-brown needles (m.p. 270–280° (dec.)), which dissolve in concentrated sulphuric acid to form a red-violet solution. It is also soluble in concentrated hydrochloric acid with a violet colour. It does not form a vat with alkaline sodium dithionite solution.[1]

(I)   (II)   (III)

REFERENCE

1. Clar, E., Kemp, W. and Stewart, D. G., *Tetrahedron* **3**, 325 (1958); Gupte, S. D., Nabar, D. P. and Sunthankar, S. V., *J. Sci. Ind. Research (India)* **19b**, 411 (1960).

III. 3,11-DIHYDRO-1.2,4.5,6.7-TRIBENZOTETRACENE

Methyleneanthrone (I) can be condensed with perinaphthone in boiling nitrobenzene.

The resulting diketone (II) forms orange needles (m.p. 345°), which can be sublimed and which dissolve in concentrated sulphuric acid to give a red solution. The solution in benzene shows a green fluorescence

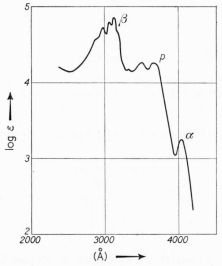

(I)   (II)

and has an absorption band at 4640 Å. Alkaline sodium dithionite solution gives a very short-lived green vat-like solution.[1, 2]

The reduction of the compound (II) with hydriodic acid and red phosphorus gives a pale yellow hydrocarbon which probably has the structure (III).[2]

FIG. 230. Absorption spectrum of tetrahydro-1.2,4.5,6.7-tribenzotetracene (III) in ethanol: α, 4030 (3·24); p, 3700 (4·16), 3520 (4·18), 3360 (4·09); 3170 (4·52); β, 3110 (4·70), 3070 (4·60), 2990 (4·58), 2730 (4·26); 2505 (4·23).

Tetrahydro-1.2,4.5,6.7-tribenzotetracene crystallizes from petroleum ether in pale yellow needles (m.p. 187–188°) which dissolve in concentrated sulphuric acid to form a solution that is first violet and then changes to red. The absorption spectrum is given in Fig. 230. When dehydrogenated with palladium in boiling trichlorobenzene it yields a yellow hydrocarbon (IV) which is immediately oxidized in the presence of air. This oxidation product probably has the structure (V). This result supports the above structure of the condensation product and excludes the possibility of the formation of benzozethrenequinone (see p. 451).[2]

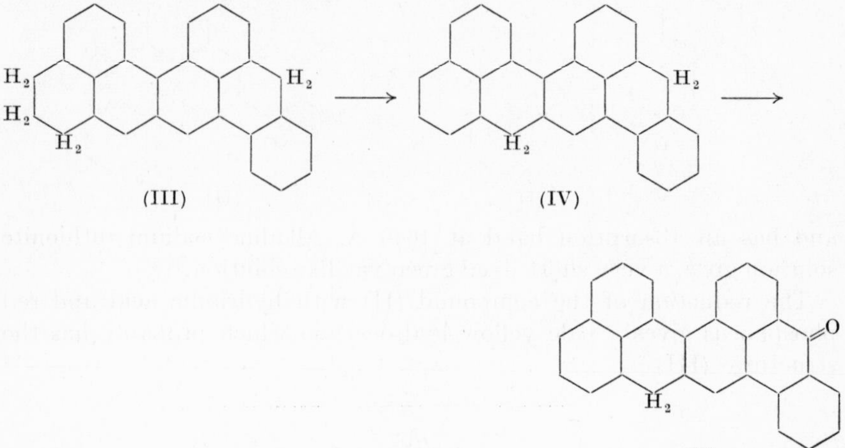

(III)   (IV)

(V)

REFERENCES

1. Vollmann, H., *Liebigs Ann.* **669**, 22 (1963).
2. Clar, E., Macpherson, I. A. and Schulz-Kiesow, H., *Liebigs Ann.* **669**, 44 (1963).

IV. 5,7-DIHYDRO-1.14,11.12-DIBENZOPENTACENE

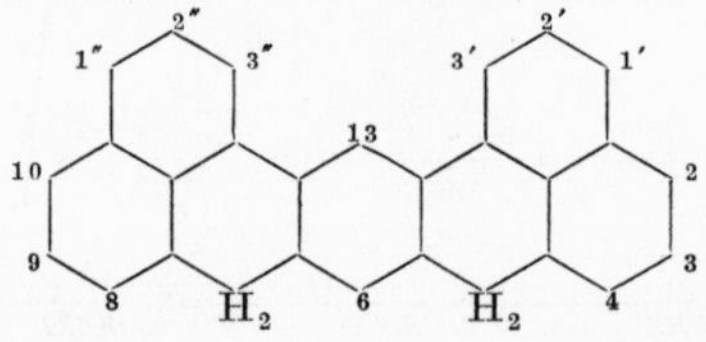

The pentacene derivative (I) which can be prepared from pentacenediquinone (see Vol. 1, p. 428) condenses twice with glycerol and sulphuric acid. The resulting diketone could have two different structures. One is a dibenzo-heptazethrene quinone (see p. 457), the other the diketone (II.)[1]

The following synthesis brings a decision in favour of the structure (II). The reaction of 4,6-dichloroisophthalyl chloride with naphthalene and aluminium chloride gives the diketone (III). Cyclization to the compound (II) is carried out with potassium hydroxide in boiling quinoline.[2, 3] Reduction with zinc dust, pyridine and acetic acid gives the hydrocarbon (IV).[3] Reduction with hydriodic acid and red phosphorus leads to the hydrocarbon (V).[1]

5,7-Dihydro-1.14,11.12-dibenzopentacene (IV) crystallizes from xylene or sublimes in pale yellow needles or prisms (m.p. 346°), which dissolve in concentrated sulphuric acid to give a blue solution with a red fluorescence. The absorption spectrum is given in Fig. 231.

The hydrocarbon cannot be dehydrogenated to dibenzopentacene. It is not attacked by chloranil in boiling benzene. In boiling trichlorobenzene an insoluble, non-sublimable, chlorine-containing condensation product is formed. Palladium–charcoal in trichlorobenzene at 200° very slowly produces a brown solution.[3]

2,3,4,8,9,10-Hexahydro-1.14,11.12-dibenzopentacene (V) forms pale yellow long needles (m.p. 255–256°) which dissolve in concentrated sulphuric acid to give a greenish-blue solution with a red fluorescence. The fluorescence in organic solvent is violet-blue.

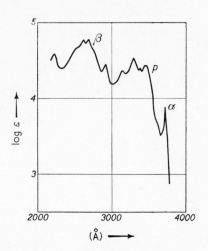

FIG. 231. Absorption spectrum of 5,7-dihydro-1.14,11.12-dibenzopentacene in cyclohexane: α, 3720 (3·88); *p*, 3460 (4·44), 3385 (4·38), 3295 (4·52), 3150 (4·36), 2920 (4·44); β, 2690 (4·77), 2610 (4·76); 2215 (4·58).

1.14,11.12-Dibenzotetracene-5,7-quinone (II) forms yellow, sublimable needles from nitrobenzene (m.p. 435°) which, with concentrated sulphuric acid, give a violet-red solution with a red fluorescence. It does not give a vat with alkaline sodium dithionite solution.

REFERENCES

1. Clar, E., *Ber. dtsch. chem. Ges.* **73**, 409 (1940).
2. Clar, E., Kemp, W. and Stewart, D. G., *Tetrahedron* **3**, 325 (1958).
3. Clar, E. and Macpherson, I. A., *Tetrahedron* **18**, 1411 (1962).

PART X

Hydrocarbons consisting of Six-membered Rings which have Formally Fixed Double Bonds

Hydrocarbons Consisting of Six-membered Rings which Have Formally Fixed Double Bonds

I. ZETHRENE

The synthesis of zethrene starts from chrysene from which chrysene-2,8-dicarboxylic dichloride (I) is obtained via 2,8-dibromochrysene, chrysenedinitrile and chrysene-2,8-dicarboxylic acid.[1]

(I)   (II)   (III)

(IV)   (V)   (VI)

The dichloride (I) is condensed with magnesio-malonic ester to the compound (II). The cyclization with concentrated sulphuric acid yields the dicarboxylic acid (III). Decarboxylation with copper powder in boiling quinoline leads to dihydroxyzethrenequinone (IV). Reduction to hexahydrozethrene (V) is carried out with hydriodic acid and red phosphorus at 200°. The dehydrogenation with palladium–charcoal gives zethrene (VI).[2]

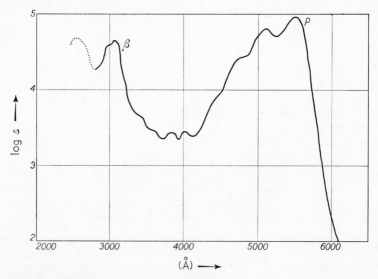

(VII)   (VIII)

Zethrene can also be obtained by pyrolysis of acenaphthene or from acenaphthylene (VIII) or diacenaphthylidene (VII) in a sodium chloride–aluminium chloride melt.[2]

Zethrene (VI) crystallizes from xylene in deep violet needles (m.p. 262°), which dissolve in concentrated sulphuric acid to give a blue

FIG. 232. Absorption spectrum of zethrene in benzene: p, 5500 (4·96), 5100 (4·80), 4750 (4·42); α, 4020 (3·44), 3850 (3·43); β, 3080 (4·64), in dioxane: β', 2550 (4·67).

solution which turns to violet-red on standing. The red solution in benzene or xylene shows an orange fluorescence. The crystals are de-colourized in light and air and react immediately with maleic anhydride to form a colourless adduct. The absorption spectrum is given in Fig. 232. In spite of the fixed double bonds as indicated in formula (VI) the absorption spectrum shows the characteristic bands of an aromatic hydrocarbon.[2]

REFERENCES

1. Funke, K., Müller, E. and Vadasz, L., J. prakt. Chem. (N.F.) **144**, 265 (1936); Funke, K. and Ristic, J., J. prakt. Chem. **145**, 309 (1936); **146**, 151 (1936).
2. Clar, E., Lang, K. F. and Schulz-Kiesow, H., Chem. Ber. **88**, 1520 (1955).

II. 5.6-Benzozethrene

The condensation of chloroperinaphthenone and methyleneanthrone (I) in boiling nitrobenzene gives benzozethrenequinone (II).[1] The re-duction with pyridine, zinc dust and acetic acid yields the tetrahydro-derivative (III), from which benzozethrene (IV) can be obtained by dehydrogenation with palladium–charcoal.[2]

5.6-Benzozethrene is blue and, due to its low melting point, high solubility and sensitivity, is difficult to obtain in a pure state. Small amounts of pure hydrocarbon can be prepared via its green-blue perchlo-rate. The absorption spectrum is given in Fig. 233.[2]

Its tetrahydroderivative (III) forms short needles (m.p. 267–268°) from xylene. They dissolve slowly in concentrated sulphuric acid to give a blue solution. The absorption spectrum is given in Fig. 234.[2]

5.6-Benzozethrene-4,14-quinone (II) crystallizes from nitrobenzene in golden yellow needles (m.p. 334–335°), which dissolve in concen-trated sulphuric acid with a bluish-red colour and a red fluorescence. Alkaline sodium dithionite gives a green vat which changes soon to brown.[1]

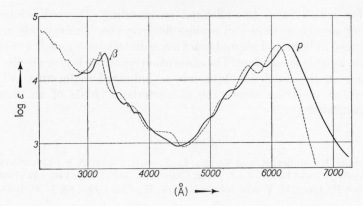

FIG. 233. Absorption spectrum of 5.6-benzozethrene in hexane (broken line): p, 6110 (4·54), 5635 (4·22), 5240 (3·70); 3520 (3·80); β, 3215 (4·44), 3105 (4·34) (log $\epsilon + x$); penta-chloro-5.6-benzozethrene in benzene (full line): p, 6250 (4·56), 5760 (4·27), 5330 (3·84); 3840 (3·48), 3640 (3·64); β, 3290 (4·43), 3160 (4·32), 2940 (4·12).

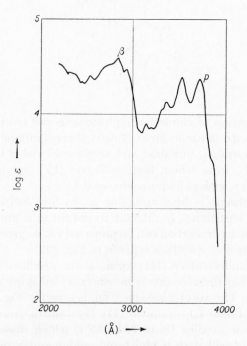

FIG. 234. Absorption spectrum of 4,11,12,13-tetrahydro-5.6-benzozethrene in hexane: p, 3720 (4·37), 3530 (4·38), 3360 (4·12), 3200 (3·85), 3140 (3·90); 2930 (4·46); β, 2840 (4·60); 2530 (4·40); 2420 (4·33); 2320 (4·44).

Halogen derivatives are more stable than benzozethrene itself. A pentachloro derivative can be prepared from the tetrahydro compound (III) with phosphorus pentachloride in boiling chlorobenzene. It crystallizes in small blue crystals. The absorption spectrum is given in Fig. 233.[2]

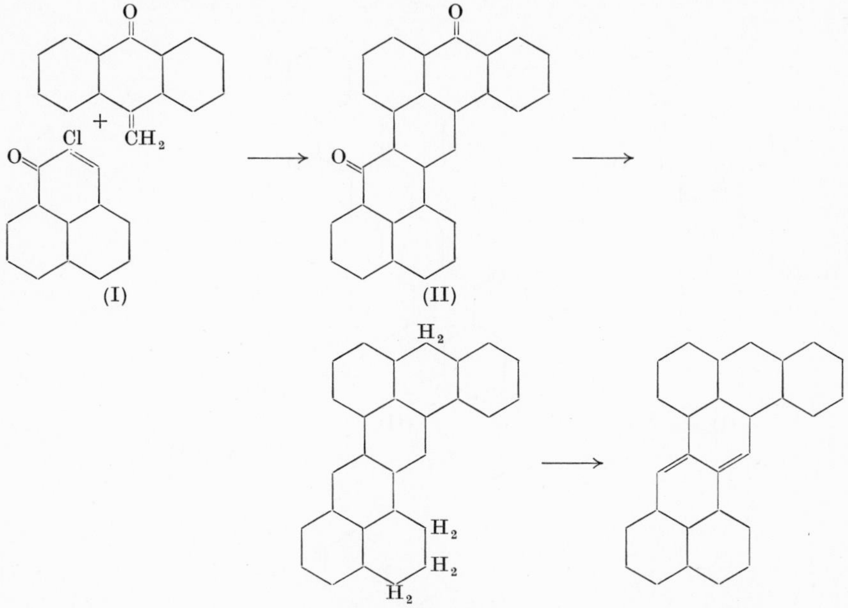

(I) (II) (III) (IV)

REFERENCES

1. Vollmann, H., *Liebigs Ann.* **669**, 22 (1963).
2. Clar, E., Macpherson, I. A. and Schulz-Kiesow, H., *Liebigs Ann.* **669**, 44 (1963).

III. 4.5,11.12-DIBENZOZETHRENE

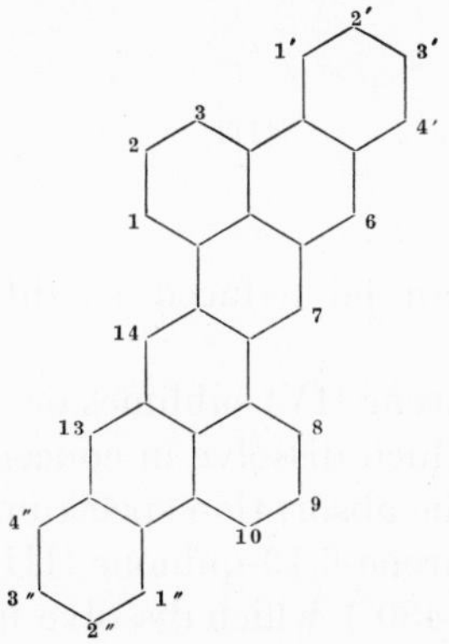

Chrysene-2,8-dicarboxylic dichloride (I) reacts with benzene and aluminium chloride to give the diketone (II). Cyclization to dibenzo-zethrenequinone (III) is carried out in a sodium chloride–aluminium chloride melt at 140–150° in the presence of dry oxygen.[1]

(I)   (II)

(III)   (IV)

The quinone (III) can be reduced to dibenzozethrene (IV) in a zinc-dust melt.[2]

4.5,11.12-Dibenzozethrene (IV) sublimes or crystallizes in deep violet needles (m.p. > 500°), which dissolve in concentrated sulphuric acid to give a violet solution. The absorption spectrum is given in Fig. 235.

4.5,11.12-Dibenzozethrene-6,13-quinone (III) crystallizes or sublimes in brown needles (dec. > 480°), which dissolve in concentrated sulphuric acid to form a violet solution with a red fluorescence. A bluish-green vat, which is unstable, is obtained with alkaline sodium dithionite solution. It dyes cotton yellow. A similar quinone can be prepared if the cyclization is carried out with 2,8-di-(p-chlorobenzoyl)-chrysene.

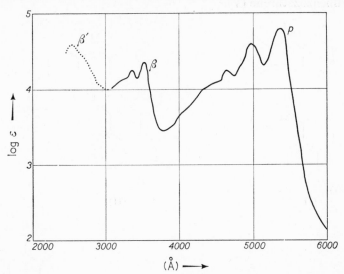

FIG. 235. Absorption spectrum of 4.5,11.12-dibenzozethrene in 1,2,4-trichlorobenzene: p, 5350 (4·80), 4975 (4·60), 4650 (4·25); β, 3525 (4·36), 3360 (4·25); in dioxane: β', 2540 (4·58).

REFERENCES

1. I. G. Farbenindustrie AG, German Patent 691644 (1934); C. **1940, II,** 1947.
2. Clar, E., Macpherson, I. A. and Schulz-Kiesow, H., *Liebigs Ann.* **669,** 44 (1963).

IV. 5.6,12.13-DIBENZOZETHRENE

Benzanthrone-aldehyde (I) condenses with anthrone in pyridine and piperidine to give the compound (II). Cyclization in a sodium chloride–aluminium chloride melt in the presence of oxygen yields dibenzozethrenequinone (III).[1]

The reduction of the quinone (III) in pyridine with zinc dust and acetic acid gives the dihydrodibenzozethrene (IV). This sublimes in ruby-red prisms. The absorption spectrum is given in Fig. 236. Its dehydrogenation with palladium–charcoal or with chloranil leads to the very unstable green dibenzozethrene (V).[2]

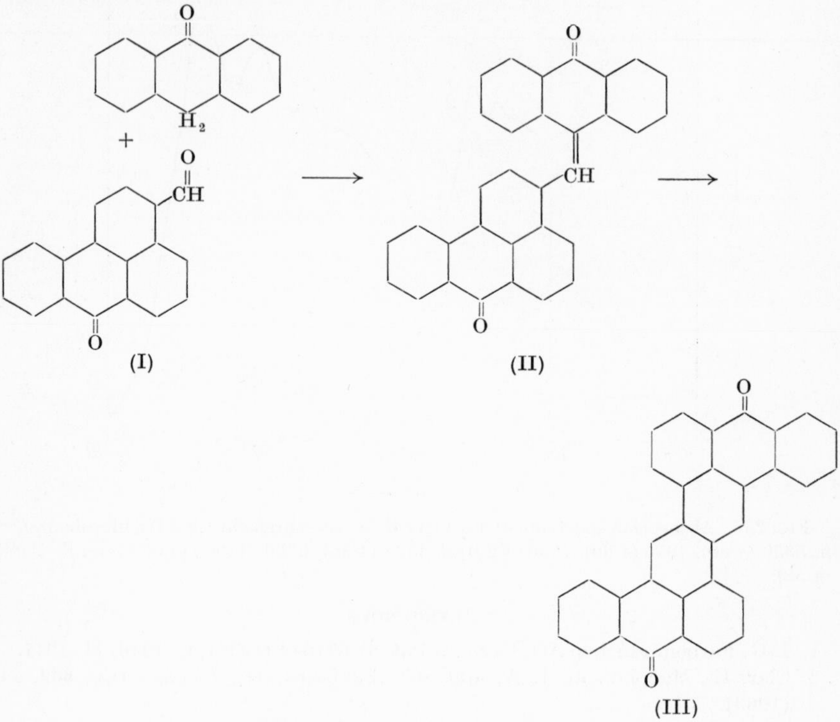

(I)   (II)

(III)

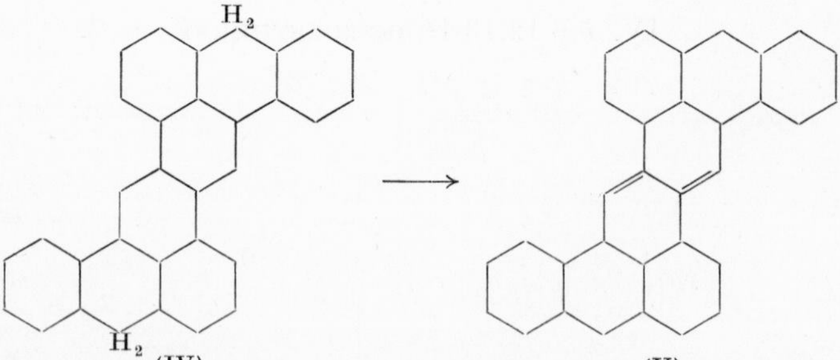

(IV)   (V)

A more stable heptachloro derivative can be obtained from (IV) with phosphorus pentachloride in boiling chlorobenzene. The absorption spectrum is given in Fig. 237.

5.6,12.13-Dibenzozethrene-4,11-quinone (III) crystallizes from nitro-naphthalene or sublimes in yellow-orange needles (dec. > 450°), which dissolve in concentrated sulphuric acid to give a pink solution with a red fluorescence. The pure quinone does not give a vat with alkaline sodium dithionite.[2]

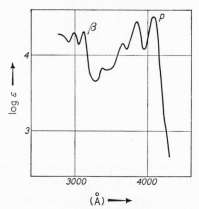

FIG. 236. Absorption spectrum of 4,11-dihydro-5.6,12.13-dibenzozethrene in benzene: p, 4085 (4·50), 3850 (4·44), 3660 (4·16); 3380 (3·82); β, 3210 (4·31), 2985 (4·30).

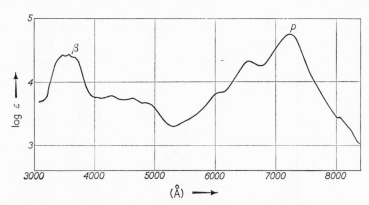

FIG. 237. Absorption spectrum of heptachloro-5.6,12.13-dibenzozethrene in 1,2,4-trichlorobenzene: p, 7220 (4·76), 6540 (4·33), 6070 (3·84); 4630 (3·74), 4270 (3·78); β, 3660 (4·40), 3580 (4·43), 3460 (4·43).

Derivatives of the quinone can be obtained if in the above synthesis anthrone derivatives are used instead of anthrone. Halogen derivatives are prepared by direct halogenation of the quinone.[1]

REFERENCES

1. I. G. Farbenindustrie AG, German Patent 724833 (1938); *Chem. Zbl.* **1943 I**, 98.
2. Clar, E., Macpherson, I. A. and Schulz-Kiesow, H., *Liebigs Ann.* **669**, 44 (1963).

V. HEPTAZETHRENE

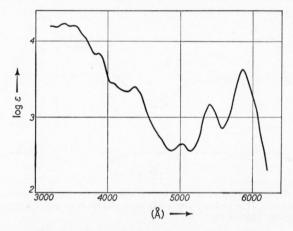

The diketone (I) can be prepared from 2,6-dichloroterephthalyl dichloride, naphthalene and aluminium chloride in methylene chloride solution. Cyclization to heptazethrenequinone (II) takes place in boiling quinoline with the calculated amount of potassium hydroxide. Reduction with zinc dust in pyridine and acetic acid yields dihydro-

FIG. 238. Absorption spectrum of heptazethrene in chlorobenzene: p, 5860 (3·60), 5400 (3·26), 5040 (2·64), 4370 (3·40), 4870 (3·82); β, 3540 (4·20), 3400 (4·24) (log $\epsilon + x$).

heptazethrene (III). Heptazethrene (IV) can be obtained by dehydrogenation with palladium–charcoal, or with chloranil in boiling xylene or trichlorobenzene.

Heptazethrene (IV) is green in the solid state and gives violet solutions with orange fluorescence in xylene or trichlorobenzene. The absorption spectrum is given in Fig. 238. It is a very reactive hydrocarbon which forms a hydrochloride (VI) with hydrochloric acid. This is probably derived from the polar form (V) which contains no fixed double bonds.

Phosphorus pentachloride in boiling xylene solution gives a chloro derivative which has an absorption band at 6230 Å.

Bromine in xylene yields a deep brown precipitate.

(I)   (II)   (III)   (IV)

Dehydrogenation of dihydroheptazethrene (III) with boiling nitrobenzene gives heptazethrene which is quickly oxidized to heptazethrenequinone (II).

(V)   (VI)

Heptazethrene-7,15-quinone (II) crystallizes in yellow needles from nitrobenzene. They melt at about 435° (dec.) and dissolve in concentrated sulphuric acid to give a violet solution with a red fluorescence. No vat can be obtained with alkaline sodium dithionite solution.

7,15-Dihydroheptazethrene (III) forms needles or prisms (m.p. 386°) from xylene, which do not dissolve in concentrated sulphuric acid. It

II—16

reacts quantitatively with boiling maleic anhydride with the formation of a succinic anhydride derivative. The absorption spectrum is given in Fig. 239.[1]

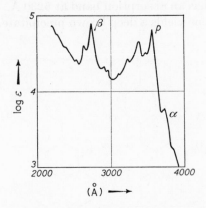

FIG. 239. Absorption spectrum of 7,15-dihydroheptazethrene in cyclohexane: α, 3740 (3·76); p, 3570 (4·82), 3485 (4·50), 3380 (4·65), 3230 (4·42), 3100 (4·22), 2960 (4·27), 2920 (4·30); β, 2740 (4·90), 2640 (4·60), 2530 (4·42), 2380 (4·58), 2270 (4·76).

REFERENCE

1. Clar, E. and Macpherson, I. A., Tetrahedron 18, 1411 (1962

VI. 4.5,12.13-DIBENZOHEPTAZETHRENE

The condensation of terephthalyl dichloride with octahydrophen-anthrene and aluminium chloride gives the diketone (I). Pyrolysis with or without copper powder at 400° yields dihydrodibenzohepta-zethrene (IV), octahydrodibenzoheptazethrene (III) and tetradeca-hydrodibenzoheptazethrene (II). These three hydrocarbons can also be obtained by pyrolysis of the diketone (V). This pyrolysis must involve a complete re-arrangement, which is not unusual if a 1.2,5.6-dibenzanth-racene complex can be formed instead of a 1.2,7.8-complex.

These three hydrocarbons (II), (III) and (IV) give dibenzohepta-zethrene when sublimed over palladium–charcoal at 300°.

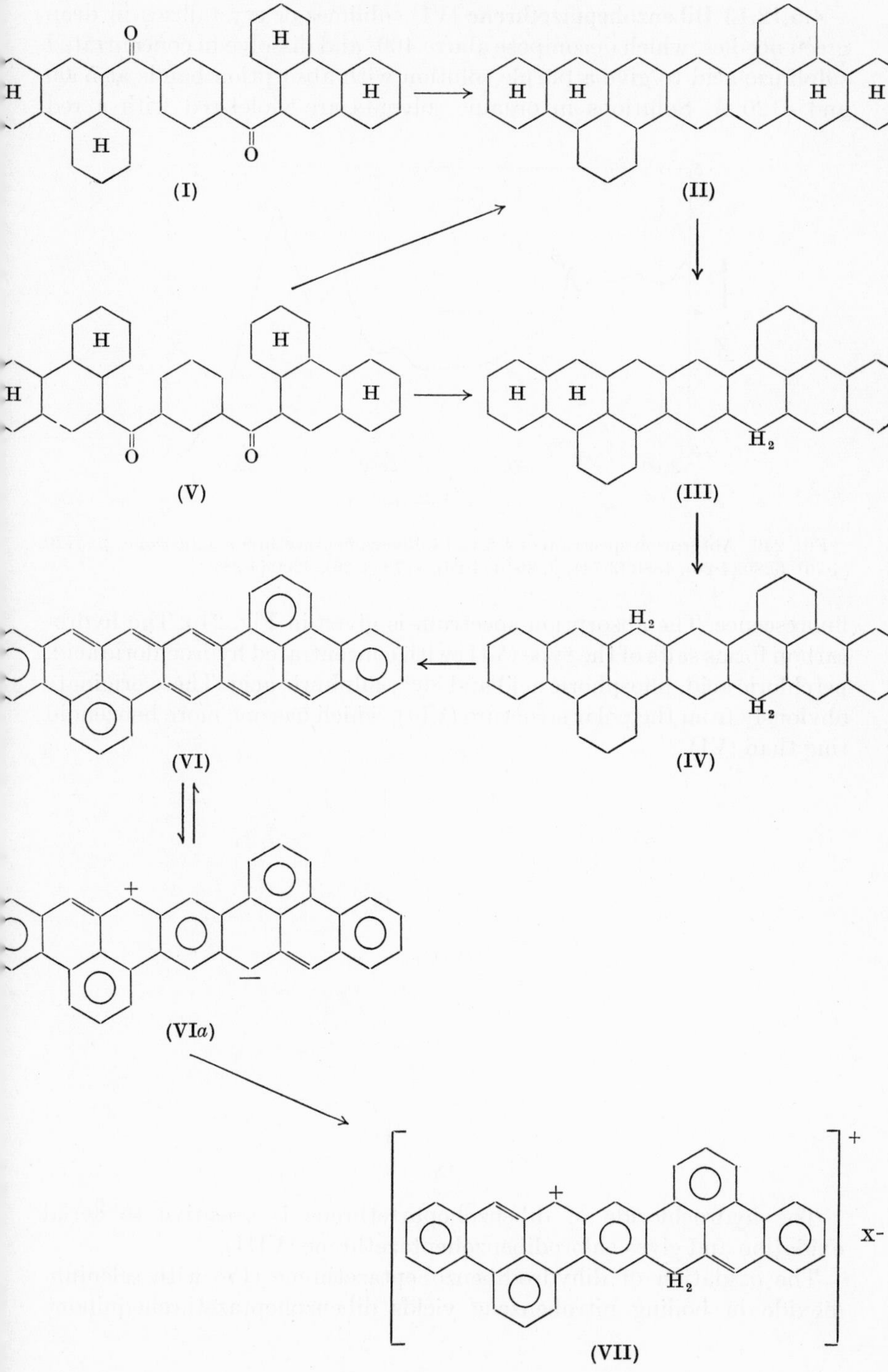
(I)
(II)
(V)
(III)
(VI)
(IV)
(VIa)
(VII)

4.5,12.13-Dibenzoheptazethrene (VI) sublimes or crystallizes in deep green needles, which decompose above 400° and dissolve in concentrated sulphuric acid to give a purple solution with absorption bands at 5500 and 5120 Å. Solutions in organic solvents are violet-red with a red

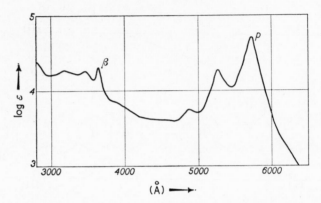

Fig. 240. Absorption spectrum of 4.5,12.13-dibenzoheptazethrene in benzene: p, 5720 (4·70), 5280 (4·26), 4880 (3·74); β, 3640 (4·26), 3470 (4·26), 3200 (4·28).

fluorescence. The absorption spectrum is given in Fig. 240. The hydrocarbon forms salts of the type (VII) with concentrated hydrochloric acid, perchloric acid, phosphoric acid and 80% sulphuric acid. These originate obviously from the polar structure (VIa), which has one more benzenoid ring than (VI).

(VIII)

(IX)

The hydrochloride of dibenzoheptazethrene is sensitive to aerial oxidation and gives chlorodibenzoheptazethrene (VIII).

The oxidation of dihydrodibenzoheptazethrene (IV) with selenium dioxide in boiling nitrobenzene yields dibenzoheptazethrenequinone

(IX). This sublimes in brown needles (m.p. > 450° (dec.)), which dissolve in concentrated sulphuric acid to give a green solution. It does not form a vat with alkaline sodium dithionite solution.[1]

REFERENCE

1. Clar, E., Fell, G. S. and Richmond, M. H., *Tetrahedron* **9**, 96 (1960).

VII. 5.6,13.14-DIBENZOHEPTAZETHRENE

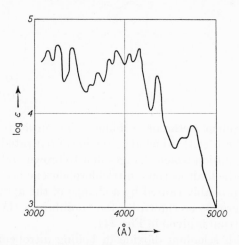

Methyleneanthrone (I) condenses twice with benzoquinone in boiling nitrobenzene to yield the diquinone (II). The formation of the isomeric compound (III) cannot be excluded. However, the hydrocarbon, which is obtained from the quinone by reduction with zinc dust, pyridine and

FIG. 241. Absorption spectrum of dihydrodibenzoheptazethrene in 1,2,4-trichloro-benzene: 4740 (3·88); 4360 (4·40), 4140 (4·69), 4040 (4·64), 3900 (4·66), 3820 (4·58), 3690 (4·42); 3415 (4·70), 3250 (4·74), 3140 (4·66).

acetic acid, can be dehydrogenated with phosphorus pentachloride to a very unstable green product which is probably the dibenzoheptazethrene. Therefore the assumed structure (IV) for the hydrocarbon appears to be correct.

(I)   (II)   (IV)

(IVa)   (V)   (III)

Dihydrodibenzoheptazethrene sublimes *in vacuo* in light brown needles (m.p. 435° (dec.)), which dissolve in concentrated sulphuric acid to give a green solution which changes first to brown and then to violet. The solution of the hydrocarbon in trichlorobenzene becomes yellow on boiling. This is probably caused by a change of the hydrogen atoms of the methylene groups as shown by the equilibrium (IV)⇌(IVa). The absorption spectrum is given in Fig. 241.

Oxidation with selenium dioxide in boiling nitrobenzene gives the quinone (V). This forms brown needles from nitrobenzene or by sublimation which have a m.p. of 480° (dec.). They dissolve in concentrated sulphuric acid with a brown-violet colour. Alkaline sodium dithionite gives no vat.

The diquinone (II) crystallizes from nitrobenzene in silky brown needles, which can be sublimed *in vacuo* and dissolve in concentrated sulphuric acid with a brown-orange colour without fluorescence. Alkaline sodium dithionite forms a green vat.[1]

REFERENCE

1. I. G. Farbenindustrie AG, German Patent 591496 (1932); Clar, E., *Ber. dtsch. chem. Ges.* **69**, 1686 (1936).

PART XI

Hydrocarbons consisting of Five- and Six-membered Rings which Have Formally Fixed Double Bonds

Hydrocarbons Consisting of Six- and Five-membered Rings which Have Formally Fixed Double Bonds

I. INDENO-(2'.1':1.2)-PERINAPHTHENE

Indan-2-one reacts with 1-naphthyl magnesium bromide to yield the carbinol (I). Dehydration gives the compound (II), which can be condensed to (III) with ethyl formate and potassium methoxide. Cyclization with 93% sulphuric acid gives indenoperinaphthene (IV).

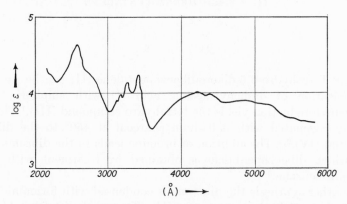

FIG. 242. Absorption spectrum of indeno-(2'.1':1.2)-perinaphthene in cyclohexane: 5700 (3·64), 4840 (3·90), 4420 (3·99), 4200 (4·03), 3440 (4·26), 3290 (4·16), 3200 (3·99), 3150 (3·92), 2620 (4·69) (Aitken, I. M. and Reid, D. H., *J. chem. Soc.* 3487 (1956)).

Indenoperinaphthene (IV) forms red-brown leaflets (m.p. 210–211°) from benzene, which dissolve in concentrated sulphuric acid to a green solution. A black adduct is obtained with trinitrobenzene. Oxidation with chromic acid gives an orange diketone. Indenoperinaphthene is a basic hydrocarbon and dissolves in 60–70% sulphuric acid and aqueous hydrofluoric acid. It is recovered unchanged if these solutions are diluted with water. The hydrocarbon reacts readily with maleic anhydride and benzoquinone. The absorption spectrum is given in Fig. 242.[1]

(I)   (II)

(III)   (IV)

REFERENCE

1. Aitken, I. M. and Reid, D. H., *J. chem. Soc.* 3487 (1956); Reid, D. H., *Tetrahedron* **3**, 339 (1958).

II. 1.2,4.5-DIBENZOPENTALENE

3,6,7,8-Tetrahydro-3,6-diketodibenzopentalene (II) can be prepared by cyclization of diphenylsuccinic acid (I) with sulphuric acid.[1] Clemmensen reduction yields the tetrahydro compound (III).[1] This can be dehydrogenated with palladium–charcoal at 450° to the dihydro compound (IV).[2, 3] The addition of bromine leads to the dibromide (V) from which dibenzopentalene is obtained by treatment with silver acetate in benzene.[3]

In another synthesis the diketone is condensed with formamide and formic acid to yield the compound (VII). Treatment with formaldehyde and formic acid leads to the compound (VIII) and methylation to the compound (IX), which decomposes with alkali to dibenzopentalene (VI).[4]

1.2,4.5-Dibenzopentalene (VI) forms bronze-coloured flakes from benzene. It softens at 275–280° and decomposes at higher temperatures. It dissolves in concentrated sulphuric acid to give a green solution, but does not dissolve in phosphoric acid. It polymerizes very readily, particularly in the presence of acid. It is easily reduced to the dihydro derivative.[4] Ozonolysis yields benzil-2,2'-dicarboxylic acid. The following absorption maxima have been recorded: 4150 (15,000), 3940 (12,000), 3810 (6000), 3700 (6000), 3600 (4000), 2810 (69,000), 2730 (61,000) Å.[5]

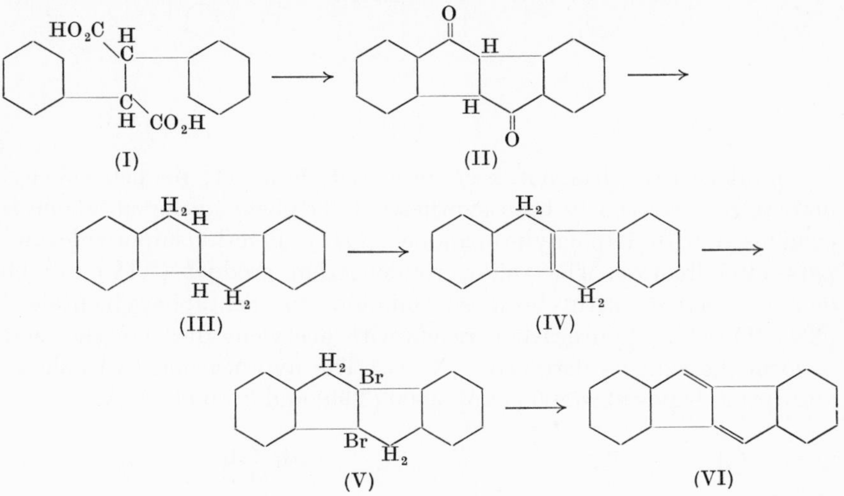

(I)   (II)

(III)   (IV)

(V)   (VI)

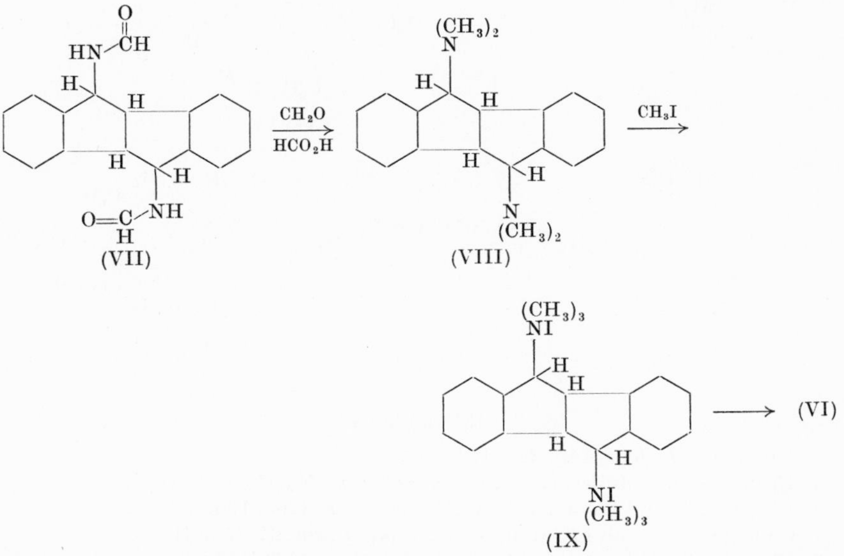

(VII) $\xrightarrow[\text{HCO}_2\text{H}]{\text{CH}_2\text{O}}$ (VIII) $\xrightarrow{\text{CH}_3\text{I}}$

(IX) $\longrightarrow$ (VI)

Dibenzopentalene has two formally fixed double bonds as in formula (X). However, if the double bonds exchange their position the resulting structure (XI) has no benzenoid ring and must be unstable in comparison with (X). This is obviously the reason why 1.2,5.6-dibenzopentalene could not be synthesized.[6] In accordance with this formula (XII) there can be only one benzenoid ring.

3,6-Dichloro-1.2,4.5-dibenzopentalene[7] and the corresponding diphenyl derivative have been synthesized.[8]

(X)   (XI)   (XII)

Pentalene itself has not been prepared; however, its pentaphenyl derivative has recently been synthesized. Triphenylcyclopentadiene is condensed with triphenylpropanone (XIII) dimethylsulphoxide and potassium fluoride. The yellow condensation product (XIV) can be dehydrogenated with bromosuccinimide to pentaphenylpentalene (XV). This blue hydrocarbon reacts with acetylene dicarboxylic ester to form the azulene derivative (XVI).[9] The hydrocarbon (XV) shows absorption bands at: 7200 (1·95), 3800 (3·99) and 3100 (4·52) Å.

(XIII)   (XIV)

(XV)   (XVI)

REFERENCES

1. Roser, W., *Leibigs Ann.* **247**, 153 (1888).
2. Brand, K. and Müller, K. O., *Ber. dtsch. chem. Ges.* **55**, 601 (1922).
3. Blood, C. T. and Linstead, R. P., *J. chem. Soc.* 2263 (1952).
4. Chuen, Chen. C. and Fenton, S. W., *J. org. Chem.* **23**, 1538 (1958).
5. Blood, C. T. and Linstead, R. P., *J. chem. Soc.* 2263 (1952).
6. Baker, W., McOmie, J. F. W., Parfitt, S. D., and Watkins, D. A. M., *J. chem. Soc.* 4026 (1959).
7. Brand, K. and Müller, K. O., *Ber. dtsch. chem. Ges.* **55**, 601 (1922).
8. Brand, K., *Ber. dtsch. chem. Ges.* **45**, 3071 (1912); Brand, K. and Ludwig, H., *Ber. dtsch. chem. Ges.* **53**, 809 (1920); Brand, K. and Hoffmann, F. W., *Ber. dtsch. chem. Ges.* **53**, 915 (1920).
9. le Goff, E., *J. Amer. chem. Soc.* **84**, 3975 (1962).

III. DIANTHRACENO-$(1'.9':1.3)$; $(1''.9'':4.6)$-PENTALENE
(*Aceanthreno-aceanthrene*)

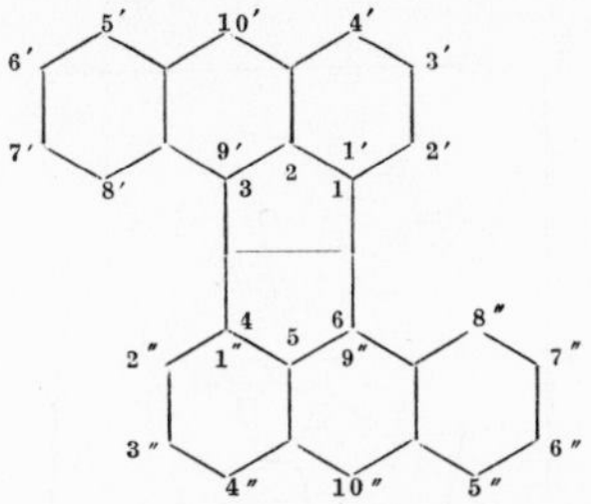

Anthrone can be condensed with glyoxal sulphate[1] or chloral and stannous chloride[2] to the bisanthronylidene-ethane (II). The cyclization to the quinone (III) can be achieved with aluminium chloride[3] or by boiling with benzoyl chloride or other acid chloride in nitrobenzene.[2]

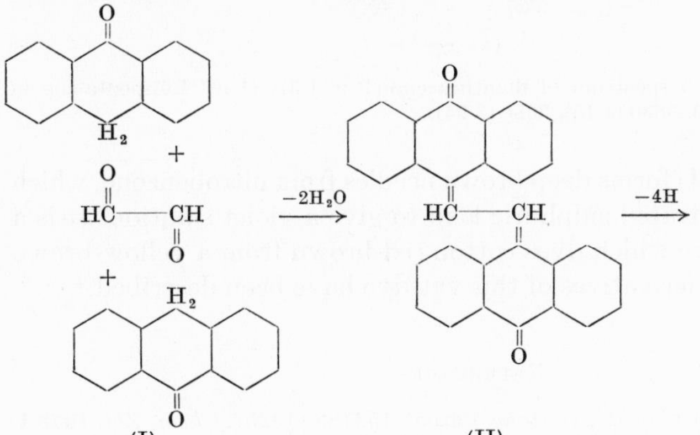

(I)   (II)

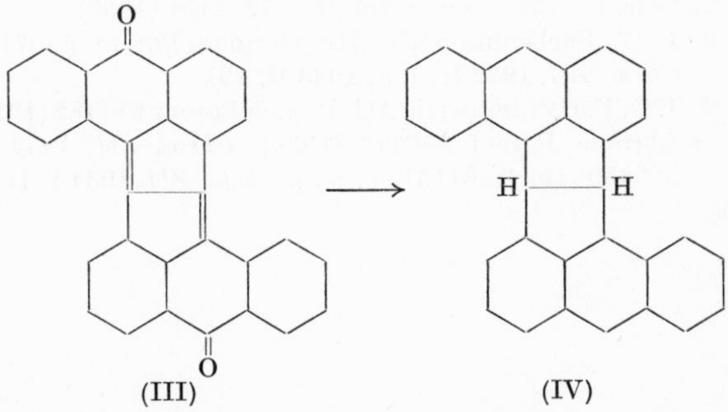

(III)   (IV)

A zinc-dust melt of the quinone (III) gives the dihydroderivative (IV). This forms greenish-yellow needles (m.p. 349°), which dissolve in concentrated sulphuric acid with a yellow colour and a green fluorescence.

The dehydrogenation would lead to the parent hydrocarbon which would have a double bond between the five-membered rings and would therefore be unstable.[2] The absorption spectrum is given in Fig. 243.

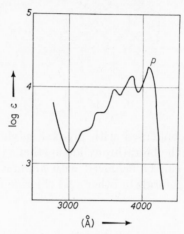

FIG. 243. Absorption spectrum of dianthraceno-(1'.9':1.3); (1".9":4.6)-pentalene in benzene: p, 4060 (4·27), 3830 (4·15), 3680 (3·95).

The quinone (III) forms deep brown needles from nitrobenzene, which dissolve in concentrated sulphuric acid to give a violet solution. It is a commercial vat-dye which dyes cotton red-brown from a yellow-brown vat. A number of derivatives of this vat-dye have been described.[4]

REFERENCES

1. I. G. Farbenindustrie AG, German Patent 453768 (1925); *Chem. Zbl.* **1928 I**, 420.
2. Clar, E., *Ber. dtsch. chem. Ges.* **72**, 2134 (1939).
3. I. G. Farbenindustrie AG, German Patent 550712 (1930); 576466 (1931); *Chem. Zbl.* **1932 II**, 783; **1933 II**, 791.
4. I. G. Farbenindustrie AG, French Patent 644782 (1927); *Chem. Zbl.* **1929 I**, 580; German Patent 550712 (1930); *Chem. Zbl.* **1932 II**, 783; German Patent 589639 (1932); 611512 (1933); *Chem. Zbl.* **1934 I**, 1890; **1935 II**, 282.

Author Index

Numbers in brackets are reference numbers and are included to assist in locating references in which the authors' names are not mentioned in the text. Numbers in italics indicate the page on which the reference is listed.